CGP — the only rational solution...

Edexcel's International GCSE in Maths is quite a handful.
But don't despair — this fantastic CGP book contains all the Maths
know-how you need for the new Grade 9-1 (Spec A) course!

It's full of clear explanations and worked examples, with exam-style practice
questions on every topic, and grade info on the new 9-1 scale.

It even includes a free Online Edition to read on your computer or tablet!

How to get your free Online Edition

Just go to **cgpbooks.co.uk/extras** and enter this code...

0693 6892 9933 5563

By the way, this code only works for one person. If somebody else has used
this book before you, they might have already claimed the Online Edition.

CGP — still the best! ☺

Our sole aim here at CGP is to produce the highest quality books —
carefully written, immaculately presented and dangerously close to being funny.

Then we work our socks off to get them out to you
— at the cheapest possible prices.

Contents

Throughout this book you'll see grade stamps like these:
You can use these to focus your revision on easier or harder work.
But remember — to get a top grade you have to know **everything**, not just the hardest topics.

Published by CGP

Written by Richard Parsons

Updated by: Chris Corrall, Joanna Daniels and Alison Palin

With thanks to Shaun Harrogate for the proofreading

ISBN: 978 1 78294 669 4

Printed by Elanders Ltd, Newcastle upon Tyne.
Clipart from Corel®

Text, design, layout and original illustrations © Richard Parsons 2017

Order of Operations

Ah, the glorious world of maths. OK, maybe it's more like whiffy socks at times, but learn it you must. And there's plenty of it. Here are some nifty exam tricks that could net you quite a few lovely marks.

BODMAS — Brackets, Other, Division, Multiplication, Addition, Subtraction

BODMAS tells you the ORDER in which these operations should be done:
Work out Brackets first, then Other things like squaring, then Divide / Multiply groups of numbers before Adding or Subtracting them.

This set of rules works really well, so remember the word BODMAS.

EXAMPLES:

1. Work out $7 + 9 \div 3$

1) Follow BODMAS — do the division first... $7 + 9 \div 3$
2) ...then the addition: $= 7 + 3$
      $= 10$

If you don't follow BODMAS, you get:
$7 + 9 \div 3$
$= 16 \div 3$
$= 5.333...$ ✗

2. Calculate $15 - 7^2$

1) The square is an 'other' so that's first: $15 - 7^2$
2) Then do the subtraction: $= 15 - 49$
      $= -34$

3. Find $(5 + 3) \times (12 - 3)$

1) Start by working out the brackets: $(5 + 3) \times (12 - 3)$
2) And now the multiplication: $= 8 \times 9$
      $= 72$

4. $e = (f - 7)^2 + \dfrac{4g}{h + 1}$, where f = 4, g = 3, h = -2.
Work out the value of e.

Write down the formula: $e = (f - 7)^2 + \dfrac{4g}{h + 1}$

Put the numbers in: $e = (4 - 7)^2 + \dfrac{4 \times 3}{-2 + 1}$

Then work it out in stages: $= (-3)^2 + \dfrac{12}{-1}$

      $= 9 + \dfrac{12}{-1}$

      $= 9 + -12$

      $= -3$

Putting brackets round the negative number makes it clear that -3 is squared, not just 3.

Work brackets out first.

Around the top and bottom of a fraction there are 'invisible brackets'. You just have to imagine they're there.

Then other stuff — in this case square the first bit.

Then divide.

Finally add or subtract.

What's your BODMAS? About 50 kg, dude...

It's really important to check your working on BODMAS questions. You might be certain you did it right, but it's surprisingly easy to make a slip. Try these Exam Practice Questions and see how you do.

Q1   Find the value of: a) $15 - 12 \div 3$ b) $5 \times 2 + 3 \times 9$ c) $(3 + 5) \div 2 - 1$ [3 marks]

Q2 $d = \dfrac{3a^2 + 2b}{4(c + 3)}$, where a = -2, b = 2 and c = -4. Work out the value of d.   [2 marks]

Calculator Buttons

This page covers some mega-important stuff about using <u>calculators</u>.

Know Your Buttons

Look for these buttons on your calculator — they might be a bit different on yours.

x^{-1} The <u>reciprocal</u> button. The reciprocal of a number is <u>1 divided by it</u>. So the reciprocal of 2 is ½.

Ans This uses your <u>last answer</u> in your current calculation. Super useful.

$\sqrt[3]{\square}$ The <u>cube root</u> button. You might have to press <u>shift</u> first.

S⇔D Flips your answer from a <u>fraction or surd</u> to a <u>decimal</u> and vice versa.

BODMAS on Your Calculator

BODMAS questions can be packed with <u>tricky decimals</u> and maybe a <u>square root</u> and <u>sin/cos/tan</u>. You <u>could</u> do it on your calculator in one go, but that runs the risk of losing precious marks.

EXAMPLE: Work out $\left(\dfrac{64\cos 80°}{0.48+\sqrt{0.79}}\right)^3$.

Write down all the figures on your calculator display.

You <u>MUST</u> write down the numbers <u>as you go</u>. Then if you mess up at the end you'll still get a mark.

$\left(\dfrac{64\cos 80°}{0.48+\sqrt{0.79}}\right)^3$

$=\left(\dfrac{11.11348337}{1.368819442}\right)^3$

$= 8.119027997^3$

$= \underline{535.1950858}$

There are lots of <u>slightly different ways</u> of working out this type of calculation. Here's one:

1) Work out the <u>bottom</u> of the fraction: `0.48` `+` `√` `0.79` `=`

Write the answer down and store it in the <u>memory</u> by pressing: `STO` `M+`

2) Now work out the <u>top</u> of the fraction: `64` `cos` `80` `=`

3) Do the division: `Ans` `÷` `RCL` `M+` `=`
This gets the value of the <u>bottom</u> of the fraction out of the <u>memory</u>.

4) And cube: `Ans` `x▪` `3` `=`

NOTE:
1) On some calculators, a <u>bracket</u> opens when you use a <u>trig function</u> or the square/cube root function. So to enter something like tan 40° + 1, you have to <u>close the bracket</u>: `tan` `40` `)` `+` `1`
2) On some calculators, the cursor stays <u>under the square root bar</u> until you nudge it out by pressing the <u>right arrow</u>.

Check Your Answer Using Brackets (and)

<u>Check your answer</u> to a question like the one above by plugging it into your calculator <u>in fewer steps</u>.

1) To work out $\dfrac{64\cos 80°}{0.48+\sqrt{0.79}}$ you <u>CAN'T</u> just press `64` `cos` `80` `÷` `0.48` `+` `√` `0.79` `=`

2) The calculator follows BODMAS, so it'll think you mean $\dfrac{64\cos 80°}{0.48}+\sqrt{0.79}$.

3) The secret is to <u>OVERRIDE</u> the automatic <u>BODMAS</u> using the <u>BRACKETS BUTTONS</u>.

4) The calculator will do the bits in brackets first. So you'd press:

`(` `64` `cos` `80` `)` `÷` `(` `0.48` `+` `√` `0.79` `)` `=`

(Cube this to check the question above.)

Your calculator might need you to add an extra ")" here. See the note above. And maybe an extra ")" or a <u>right arrow nudge</u> here.

Calculators — only as clever as the button presser...

Different calculators behave differently, so get to know your own. Try everything above on your calculator.

Q1 Work out $\dfrac{\sqrt{8.67-4.94}}{4\tan 87°}$. Write down all the figures on your calculator display. [2 marks]

Types of Number

This section is about numbers, so before we get stuck into the maths, there are a few definitions of different types of number that you need to know.

Integers: (2)

You need to make sure you know the <u>meaning</u> of this word — it'll come up <u>all the time</u> in maths.
An <u>integer</u> is another name for a <u>whole number</u> — either a positive or negative number, or zero.

<u>Examples</u>

Integers:	–365, 0, 1, 17, 989, 1 234 567 890
Not integers:	0.5, $\frac{2}{3}$, $\sqrt{7}$, $13\frac{3}{4}$, –1000.1, 66.66, π

Rational and Irrational Numbers: (5)

All numbers fall into one of these two categories.

<u>Rational numbers</u> can be written as <u>fractions</u>. Most numbers you deal with are rational.

Rational numbers come in 3 different forms:
1) <u>Integers</u> e.g. $4 (= \frac{4}{1})$, $-5 (= \frac{-5}{1})$, $-12 (= \frac{-12}{1})$
2) <u>Fractions</u> p/q, where p and q are (non-zero) integers, e.g. $\frac{1}{4}$, $-\frac{1}{2}$, $\frac{3}{4}$
3) <u>Terminating or recurring decimals</u> e.g. $0.125 (= \frac{1}{8})$, $0.33333333... (= \frac{1}{3})$, $0.143143143... (= \frac{143}{999})$

<u>Irrational numbers</u> are messy. They <u>can't</u> be written as fractions — they're <u>never-ending</u>, <u>non-repeating</u> <u>decimals</u>. <u>Roots</u> of +ve integers are either integers or irrational (e.g. $\sqrt{2}$, $\sqrt{3}$, $\sqrt[3]{2}$ are all irrational, but $\sqrt{4} = 2$ isn't). <u>Surds</u> (see p.36) are numbers or expressions containing irrational roots. π is also irrational.

Square Numbers (2)

1) When you <u>multiply</u> a whole number by <u>itself</u>, you get a <u>square number</u>.

2) You'll save lots of time if you know these <u>by heart</u>:

1^2	2^2	3^2	4^2	5^2	6^2	7^2	8^2	9^2	10^2	11^2	12^2	13^2	14^2	15^2
1	4	9	16	25	36	49	64	81	100	121	144	169	196	225
(1×1)	(2×2)	(3×3)	(4×4)	(5×5)	(6×6)	(7×7)	(8×8)	(9×9)	(10×10)	(11×11)	(12×12)	(13×13)	(14×14)	(15×15)

Cube Numbers (2)

1) When you <u>multiply</u> a whole number by <u>itself</u>, then by itself <u>again</u>, you get a <u>cube number</u>.

2) It's handy to know some cubes <u>by heart</u> too — these are the ones that crop up a lot:

1^3	2^3	3^3	4^3	5^3	10^3
1	8	27	64	125	1000
(1×1×1)	(2×2×2)	(3×3×3)	(4×4×4)	(5×5×5)	(10×10×10)

And there's me thinking numbers were a kind of squiggly shape...

There, that wasn't too bad — a nice, gentle introduction. Now it's time to get stuck into the real maths...

Square Roots and Cube Roots

Take a deep breath, and get ready to tackle this page. Good luck with it, I'll be rootin' for ya...

Square Roots (2)

'Squared' means 'multiplied by itself': $8^2 = 8 \times 8 = 64$

SQUARE ROOT $\sqrt{}$ is the reverse process: $\sqrt{64} = 8$

The best way to think of it is: 'Square Root' means 'What Number <u>Times by Itself</u> gives...'

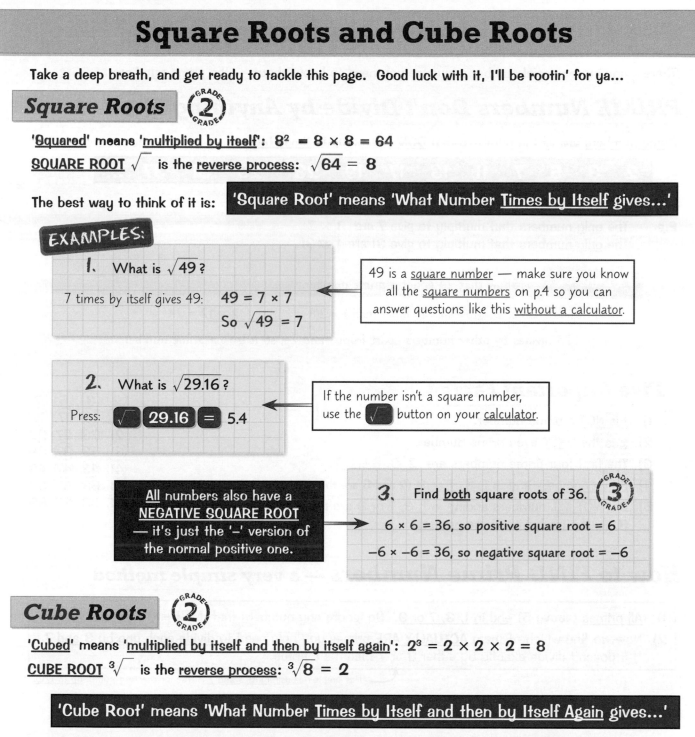

EXAMPLES:

1. What is $\sqrt{49}$?

7 times by itself gives 49: $49 = 7 \times 7$

So $\sqrt{49} = 7$

49 is a <u>square number</u> — make sure you know all the <u>square numbers</u> on p.4 so you can answer questions like this <u>without a calculator</u>.

2. What is $\sqrt{29.16}$?

Press: $\boxed{\sqrt{}}$ $\boxed{29.16}$ $\boxed{=}$ 5.4

If the number isn't a square number, use the $\boxed{\sqrt{}}$ button on your <u>calculator</u>.

All numbers also have a **NEGATIVE SQUARE ROOT** — it's just the '−' version of the normal positive one.

3. Find <u>both</u> square roots of 36. (3)

$6 \times 6 = 36$, so positive square root = 6

$-6 \times -6 = 36$, so negative square root = −6

Cube Roots (2)

'Cubed' means '<u>multiplied by itself and then by itself again</u>': $2^3 = 2 \times 2 \times 2 = 8$

CUBE ROOT $\sqrt[3]{}$ is the <u>reverse process</u>: $\sqrt[3]{8} = 2$

'Cube Root' means 'What Number <u>Times by Itself and then by Itself Again</u> gives...'

Make sure you can write down the cube roots of the <u>cube numbers</u> given on p.4 <u>without</u> using a <u>calculator</u>. To find the cube root of any other number you can use your calculator — press $\boxed{\sqrt[3]{}}$.

EXAMPLES:

1. What is $\sqrt[3]{27}$?

27 is a <u>cube number</u>.

3 times by itself and then by itself again gives 27: $27 = 3 \times 3 \times 3$

So $\sqrt[3]{27} = 3$

2. What is $\sqrt[3]{4913}$?

Press: $\boxed{\sqrt[3]{}}$ $\boxed{4913}$ $\boxed{=}$ 17

"Cue brute", that's what I call Charley when I play him at snooker...

Once you've got the meanings of square root and cube root well and truly sorted, have a go at these:

Q1 Find a) $\sqrt{196}$ and b) $\sqrt{64}$ without using a calculator. c) What is $\sqrt{56.25}$?   [3 marks] (2)

Q2 Find a) $\sqrt[3]{125}$ and b) $\sqrt[3]{1000}$ without using a calculator. c) What is $\sqrt[3]{9261}$?   [3 marks] (2)

Prime Numbers

There's one more special number sequence you need to know about — the prime numbers...

PRIME Numbers Don't Divide by Anything (3) GRADE

Prime numbers are all the numbers that DON'T come up in times tables:

| 2 | 3 | 5 | 7 | 11 | 13 | 17 | 19 | 23 | 29 | 31 | 37 | ... |

The only way to get ANY PRIME NUMBER is: 1 × ITSELF

E.g.   The only numbers that multiply to give 7 are   1 × 7
        The only numbers that multiply to give 31 are   1 × 31

EXAMPLE: Show that 24 is not a prime number.

Just find another way to make 24 other than 1 × 24:   2 × 12 = 24

24 divides by other numbers apart from 1 and 24, so it isn't a prime number.

Five Important Facts

1) 1 is NOT a prime number.

2) 2 is the ONLY even prime number.

3) The first four prime numbers are 2, 3, 5 and 7.

4) Prime numbers end in 1, 3, 7 or 9 (2 and 5 are the only exceptions to this rule).

5) But NOT ALL numbers ending in 1, 3, 7 or 9 are primes, as shown here:
    (Only the circled ones are primes.)

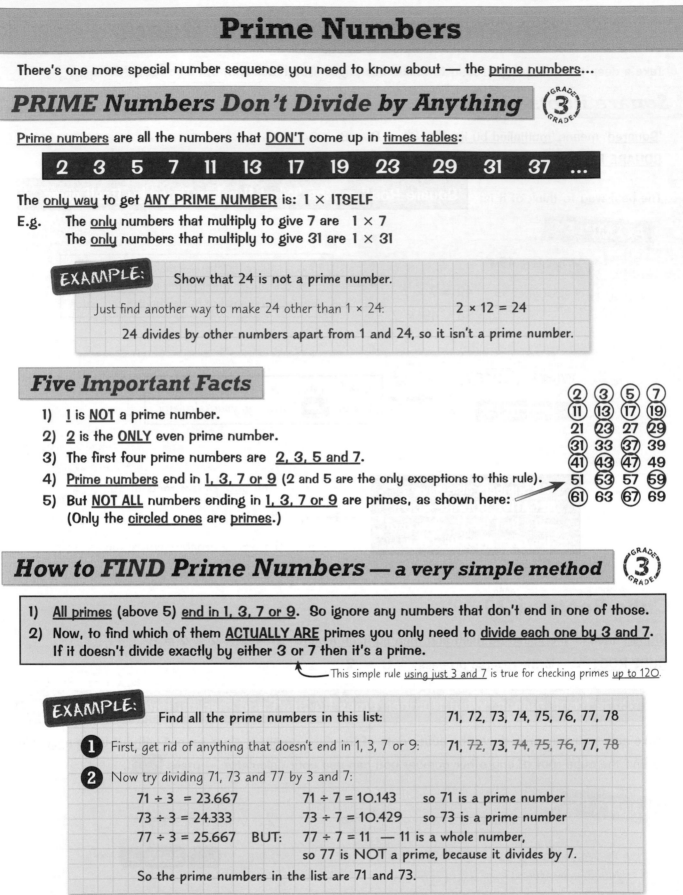

How to FIND Prime Numbers — a very simple method (3) GRADE

1) All primes (above 5) end in 1, 3, 7 or 9. So ignore any numbers that don't end in one of those.

2) Now, to find which of them ACTUALLY ARE primes you only need to divide each one by 3 and 7.
    If it doesn't divide exactly by either 3 or 7 then it's a prime.

This simple rule using just 3 and 7 is true for checking primes up to 120.

EXAMPLE: Find all the prime numbers in this list: 71, 72, 73, 74, 75, 76, 77, 78

1 First, get rid of anything that doesn't end in 1, 3, 7 or 9:   71, 72, 73, 74, 75, 76, 77, 78

2 Now try dividing 71, 73 and 77 by 3 and 7:

71 ÷ 3 = 23.667   71 ÷ 7 = 10.143   so 71 is a prime number

73 ÷ 3 = 24.333   73 ÷ 7 = 10.429   so 73 is a prime number

77 ÷ 3 = 25.667   BUT: 77 ÷ 7 = 11 — 11 is a whole number,
                          so 77 is NOT a prime, because it divides by 7.

So the prime numbers in the list are 71 and 73.

Two is the oddest prime of all — it's the only one that's even...

Learn all three sections above, then cover the page and try this Exam Practice Question without peeking:

Q1   Below is a list of numbers. Write down all the prime numbers from the list.
       39, 51, 46, 35, 61, 53, 42, 47
                                                                    [1 mark] (3) GRADE

Multiples, Factors and Prime Factors

If you think 'factor' is short for 'fat actor', I suggest you give this page a read.
Stop thinking about fat actors now. Stop it...

Multiples and Factors (3)

The MULTIPLES of a number are just its <u>times table</u>.

EXAMPLE: Find the first 8 multiples of 13.
You just need to find the first 8 numbers in the 13 times table:
13 26 39 52 65 78 91 104

The FACTORS of a number are all the numbers that <u>divide into it</u>.

There's a method that guarantees you'll find them all:

1) Start off with 1 × the number itself, then try 2 ×, then 3 × and so on, listing the pairs in rows.
2) Try each one in turn. Cross out the row if it doesn't divide exactly.
3) Eventually, when you get a number <u>repeated</u>, <u>stop</u>.
4) The numbers in the rows you haven't crossed out make up the list of factors.

EXAMPLE: Find all the factors of 24.

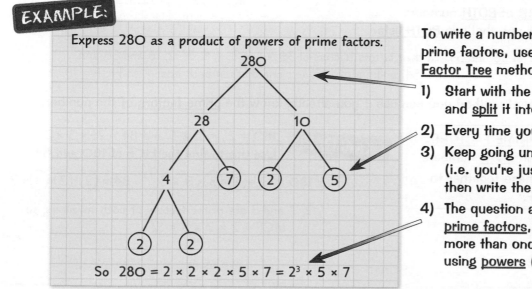

$$1 \times 24$$
$$2 \times 12$$
$$3 \times 8$$
$$4 \times 6$$
$$5 \times$$
$$6 \times 4$$

Increasing by 1 each time

So the <u>factors of 24</u> are: 1, 2, 3, 4, 6, 8, 12, 24

Finding Prime Factors — The Factor Tree (4)

<u>Any number</u> can be broken down into a string of prime numbers all multiplied together — this is called '<u>expressing it as a product of prime factors</u>'.

EXAMPLE:

Express 280 as a product of powers of prime factors.

So 280 = 2 × 2 × 2 × 5 × 7 = $2^3 \times 5 \times 7$

To write a number as a product of its prime factors, use the mildly entertaining <u>Factor Tree</u> method:

1) Start with the number at the top, and <u>split</u> it into <u>factors</u> as shown.
2) Every time you get a prime, <u>ring it</u>.
3) Keep going until you can't go further (i.e. you're just left with primes), then write the primes out <u>in order</u>.
4) The question asks for <u>powers of prime factors</u>, so if a factor appears more than once you need to write it using <u>powers</u> (see p.31).

Takes me back, scrumping prime factors from the orchard...

Make sure you know the factor tree method inside out, then give these Exam Practice Questions a go...

Q1 Express 990 as a product of powers of its prime factors. [3 marks] (4)

Q2 Express 160 as a product of powers of its prime factors. [3 marks] (4)

LCM and HCF

As if the previous page wasn't enough excitement, here's some more factors and multiples fun...

LCM — 'Lowest Common Multiple' (5)

The SMALLEST number that will DIVIDE BY ALL the numbers in question.

If you're given two numbers and asked to find their LCM, just LIST the MULTIPLES of BOTH numbers and find the SMALLEST one that's in BOTH lists.

So, to find the LCM of 12 and 15, list their multiples (multiples of 12 = 12, 24, 36, 48, 60, 72, ... and multiples of 15 = 15, 30, 45, 60, 75, ...) and find the smallest one that's in both lists — so LCM = 60.

However, if you already know the prime factors of the numbers, you can use this method instead:

1) List all the PRIME FACTORS that appear in EITHER number.
2) If a factor appears MORE THAN ONCE in one of the numbers, list it THAT MANY TIMES.
3) MULTIPLY these together to give the LCM.

EXAMPLE: $18 = 2 \times 3^2$ and $30 = 2 \times 3 \times 5$.
Find the LCM of 18 and 30.

$18 = 2 \times 3 \times 3$ $30 = 2 \times 3 \times 5$

So the prime factors that appear in either number are: 2, 3, 3, 5 — List 3 twice as it appears twice in 18.

$LCM = 2 \times 3 \times 3 \times 5 = 90$

HCF — 'Highest Common Factor' (5)

The BIGGEST number that will DIVIDE INTO ALL the numbers in question.

If you're given two numbers and asked to find their HCF, just LIST the FACTORS of BOTH numbers and find the BIGGEST one that's in BOTH lists.

Take care listing the factors — make sure you use the proper method (as shown on the previous page).

So, to find the HCF of 36 and 54, list their factors (factors of 36 = 1, 2, 3, 4, 6, 9, 12, 18 and 36 and factors of 54 = 1, 2, 3, 6, 9, 18, 27 and 54) and find the biggest one that's in both lists — so HCF = 18.

Again, there's a different method you can use if you already know the prime factors of the numbers:

1) List all the PRIME FACTORS that appear in BOTH numbers.
2) MULTIPLY these together to find the HCF.

EXAMPLE: $180 = 2^2 \times 3^2 \times 5$ and $84 = 2^2 \times 3 \times 7$.
Use this to find the HCF of 180 and 84.

$180 = \text{②} \times \text{②} \times \text{③} \times 3 \times 5$ $84 = \text{②} \times \text{②} \times \text{③} \times 7$

2, 2 and 3 are prime factors of both numbers, so
$HCF = 2 \times 2 \times 3 = 12$

LCM and HCF live together — it's a House of Commons...

Method 1 is much simpler in both cases, but make sure you learn Method 2 as well — just in case the exam question specifically tells you to use the prime factors or the numbers are really big.

Q1   Find the Lowest Common Multiple (LCM) of 12, 14 and 21.   [3 marks] (5)

Q2   a) Find the highest common factor (HCF) of 36 and 84.
      b) Given that $150 = 2 \times 3 \times 5^2$ and $60 = 2^2 \times 3 \times 5$, find the HCF of 150 and 60.   [3 marks] (5)

Fractions

These pages show you how to cope with fraction calculations without your <u>beloved calculator</u>.

1) Cancelling down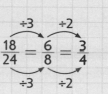

To <u>cancel down</u> or <u>simplify</u> a fraction, <u>divide top and bottom by the same number</u>, till they won't go further:

EXAMPLE: Simplify $\frac{18}{24}$.

Cancel down in a series of <u>easy steps</u> — keep going till the top and bottom don't have <u>any</u> common factors.

$$\frac{18}{24} \overset{\div 3}{\underset{\div 3}{=}} \frac{6}{8} \overset{\div 2}{\underset{\div 2}{=}} \frac{3}{4}$$

> The number on the top of the fraction is the <u>numerator</u>, and the number on the bottom is the <u>denominator</u>.

2) Mixed numbers ③

<u>Mixed numbers</u> are things like $3\frac{1}{3}$, with an integer part and a fraction part. <u>Improper fractions</u> are ones where the top number is larger than the bottom number (they're also sometimes called <u>vulgar fractions</u>). You need to be able to convert between the two.

EXAMPLES:

1. Write $4\frac{2}{3}$ as an improper fraction.

1) Think of the <u>mixed number</u> as an <u>addition</u>:
$$4\frac{2}{3} = 4 + \frac{2}{3}$$

2) Turn the <u>integer part</u> into a <u>fraction</u>:
$$4 + \frac{2}{3} = \frac{12}{3} + \frac{2}{3} = \frac{12 + 2}{3} = \frac{14}{3}$$

2. Write $\frac{31}{4}$ as a mixed number.

<u>Divide</u> the top number by the bottom.
1) The <u>answer</u> gives the <u>whole number part</u>.
2) The <u>remainder</u> goes <u>on top</u> of the fraction.

$31 \div 4 = 7$ remainder 3 so $\frac{31}{4} = 7\frac{3}{4}$

3) Multiplying ③

Multiply top and bottom separately. It usually helps to cancel down first if you can.

EXAMPLE: Find $\frac{8}{15} \times \frac{5}{12}$.

<u>Cancel down</u> by dividing top and bottom by any common factors you find in <u>either</u> fraction:

Now multiply the top and bottom numbers <u>separately</u>:

8 and 12 both divide by 4

15 and 5 both divide by 5

$$\frac{{}^{2}\cancel{8}}{15} \times \frac{5}{{}_{3}\cancel{12}} = \frac{2}{\cancel{15}_{3}} \times \frac{{}^{1}\cancel{5}}{3}$$

$$= \frac{2}{3} \times \frac{1}{3} = \frac{2 \times 1}{3 \times 3} = \frac{2}{9}$$

4) Dividing ③

Turn the 2nd fraction <u>UPSIDE DOWN</u> and then <u>multiply</u>:

> When you're multiplying or dividing with mixed numbers, <u>always</u> turn them into improper fractions first.

EXAMPLE: Find $2\frac{1}{3} \div 3\frac{1}{2}$.

Rewrite the <u>mixed numbers</u> as <u>fractions</u>:
$$2\frac{1}{3} \div 3\frac{1}{2} = \frac{7}{3} \div \frac{7}{2}$$

Turn $\frac{7}{2}$ <u>upside down</u> and <u>multiply</u>:
$$= \frac{7}{3} \times \frac{2}{7}$$

<u>Simplify</u> by cancelling the 7s:
$$= \frac{1}{3} \times \frac{2}{1} = \frac{2}{3}$$

Fractions

5) Common denominators (4)

This comes in handy for <u>ordering fractions</u> by size, and for <u>adding</u> or <u>subtracting</u> fractions.
You need to find a number that <u>all</u> the denominators <u>divide into</u> — this will be your <u>common denominator</u>.
The simplest way is to find the <u>lowest common multiple</u> of the denominators:

EXAMPLE: Put these fractions in ascending order of size: $\frac{8}{3}, \frac{5}{4}, \frac{12}{5}$

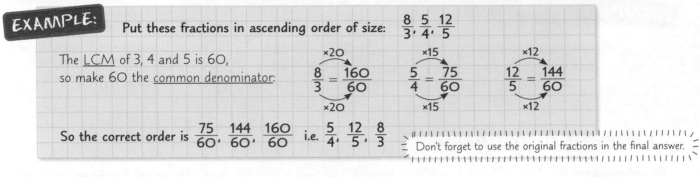

The <u>LCM</u> of 3, 4 and 5 is 60,
so make 60 the <u>common denominator</u>:

$$\frac{8}{3} = \frac{160}{60} \quad (\times 20) \qquad \frac{5}{4} = \frac{75}{60} \quad (\times 15) \qquad \frac{12}{5} = \frac{144}{60} \quad (\times 12)$$

So the correct order is $\frac{75}{60}, \frac{144}{60}, \frac{160}{60}$ i.e. $\frac{5}{4}, \frac{12}{5}, \frac{8}{3}$

Don't forget to use the original fractions in the final answer.

6) Adding, subtracting — sort the denominators first (4)

1) Make sure the denominators are <u>the same</u> (see above).
2) Add (or subtract) the top lines (numerators) <u>only</u>.

If you're adding or subtracting <u>mixed numbers</u>, it usually helps to convert them to improper fractions first.

EXAMPLE: Calculate $2\frac{1}{5} - 1\frac{1}{2}$.

Rewrite the <u>mixed numbers</u> as <u>fractions</u>: $\qquad 2\frac{1}{5} - 1\frac{1}{2} = \frac{11}{5} - \frac{3}{2}$

Find a <u>common denominator</u>: $\qquad\qquad = \frac{22}{10} - \frac{15}{10}$

Combine the <u>top lines</u>: $\qquad\qquad = \frac{22 - 15}{10} = \frac{7}{10}$

People usually find adding and subtracting fractions harder than multiplying and dividing — but it's actually pretty easy as long as you remember to make sure the denominators are the same.

7) Fractions of something

EXAMPLE: What is $\frac{9}{20}$ of £360? (2)

'$\frac{9}{20}$ of' means '$\frac{9}{20} \times$', so <u>multiply</u> the 'something' by the <u>top</u> of the fraction, and <u>divide</u> it by the <u>bottom</u>.

$\frac{9}{20}$ of £360 = (£360 ÷ 20) × 9
= £18 × 9 = £162

It doesn't matter which order you do those two steps in — just start with whatever's easiest.

8) Expressing as a Fraction

EXAMPLE: Write 180 as a fraction of 80.

Just write the first number over the second and <u>cancel down</u>.

$$\frac{180}{80} = \frac{9}{4} \quad (3)$$

No fractions were harmed in the making of these pages...

...although one was slightly frightened for a while, and several were tickled.
When you think you've learnt all this, try all of these Exam Practice Questions without a calculator.

Q1 Calculate: a) $\frac{3}{8} \times 1\frac{5}{12}$ [3 marks] (3) b) $1\frac{7}{9} \div 2\frac{2}{3}$ [3 marks] (3)

c) $4\frac{1}{9} + 2\frac{2}{27}$ [3 marks] (4) d) $5\frac{2}{3} - 9\frac{1}{4}$ [3 marks] (4)

Q2 Dean has baked 550 muffins. $\frac{2}{5}$ of the muffins are chocolate, $\frac{3}{11}$ are lemon and the rest are beetroot. How many beetroot muffins has Dean baked? [4 marks] (3)

Fractions, Decimals and Percentages

The one word that describes all these three is __PROPORTION__. Fractions, decimals and percentages are simply __three different ways__ of expressing a __proportion__ of something — and it's pretty important you should see them as __closely related and completely interchangeable__ with each other. This table shows the really common conversions which you should know straight off without having to work them out:

Fraction	Decimal	Percentage
$\frac{1}{2}$	0.5	50%
$\frac{1}{4}$	0.25	25%
$\frac{3}{4}$	0.75	75%
$\frac{1}{3}$	0.333333...	$33\frac{1}{3}\%$
$\frac{2}{3}$	0.666666...	$66\frac{2}{3}\%$
$\frac{1}{10}$	0.1	10%
$\frac{2}{10}$	0.2	20%
$\frac{1}{5}$	0.2	20%
$\frac{2}{5}$	0.4	40%

The more of those conversions you learn, the better — but for those that you __don't know__, you must __also learn__ how to __convert__ between the three types. These are the methods:

__Fraction__ $\xrightarrow{\text{Divide}}$ __Decimal__ $\xrightarrow{\text{× by 100}}$ __Percentage__

E.g. $\frac{7}{20}$ is 7 ÷ 20 = 0.35 e.g. 0.35 × 100 = 35%

__Fraction__ $\xleftarrow[\text{The awkward one}]{}$ __Decimal__ $\xleftarrow[\text{÷ by 100}]{}$ __Percentage__

__Converting decimals to fractions__ is awkward, because it's different for different types of decimal. There are two different methods you need to learn:

1) __Terminating decimals__ to fractions — this is fairly easy. The digits after the decimal point go on the top, and a __power of 10__ on the bottom — with the same number of zeros as there were decimal places.

$$0.6 = \frac{6}{10} \qquad 0.3 = \frac{3}{10} \qquad 0.7 = \frac{7}{10} \quad \text{etc.}$$

$$0.12 = \frac{12}{100} \qquad 0.78 = \frac{78}{100} \qquad 0.05 = \frac{5}{100} \quad \text{etc.}$$

These can often be __cancelled down__ — see p.9.

$$0.345 = \frac{345}{1000} \qquad 0.908 = \frac{908}{1000} \qquad 0.024 = \frac{24}{1000} \quad \text{etc.}$$

2) __Recurring decimals__ to fractions — this is trickier. See next page...

Eight out of ten cats prefer the perfume Eighty Purr Scent...

Learn the whole of the top table and the 4 conversion processes. Then it's time to break into a mild sweat...

Q1   Turn the following decimals into fractions and reduce them to their simplest form.

a) 0.4   b) 0.02   c) 0.77   d) 0.555   e) 5.6   [5 marks]

Q2   Which is greater: a) 57% or $\frac{5}{9}$, b) 0.2 or $\frac{6}{25}$, c) $\frac{7}{8}$ or 90%?   [3 marks]

Fractions and Recurring Decimals

You might think that a decimal is just a decimal. But oh no — things get a lot more juicy than that...

Recurring or Terminating... (4)

1) <u>Recurring</u> decimals have a <u>pattern</u> of numbers which repeats forever, e.g. $\frac{1}{3}$ is the decimal 0.333333... Note, it doesn't have to be a single digit that repeats. You could have, for instance: 0.143143143...

2) The <u>repeating part</u> is usually marked with <u>dots</u> or a <u>bar</u> on top of the number. If there's one dot, then only one digit is repeated. If there are two dots, then everything from the first dot to the second dot is the repeating bit. E.g. $0.2\dot{5} = 0.2555555...$, $0.\dot{2}\dot{5} = 0.25252525...$, $0.2\dot{5}\dot{5} = 0.255255255...$

3) <u>Terminating</u> decimals are <u>finite</u> (they come to an end), e.g $\frac{1}{20}$ is the decimal 0.05.

> The <u>denominator</u> (bottom number) of a fraction in its simplest form tells you if it converts
> to a <u>recurring</u> or <u>terminating decimal</u>. Fractions where the denominator has <u>prime factors</u>
> of <u>only 2 or 5</u> will give <u>terminating decimals</u>. All <u>other fractions</u> will give <u>recurring decimals</u>.
>
> | | Only prime factors: 2 and 5 | | | | Also other prime factors | | | |
> |---|---|---|---|---|---|---|---|---|
> | **Fraction** | $\frac{1}{5}$ | $\frac{1}{125}$ | $\frac{1}{2}$ | $\frac{1}{20}$ | $\frac{1}{7}$ | $\frac{1}{35}$ | $\frac{1}{3}$ | $\frac{1}{6}$ |
> | **Equivalent Decimal** | 0.2 | 0.008 | 0.5 | 0.05 | $0.\dot{1}4285\dot{7}$ | $0.0\dot{2}8571\dot{4}$ | $0.\dot{3}$ | $0.1\dot{6}$ |
> | | Terminating decimals | | | | Recurring decimals | | | |

For prime factors, see p.7.

Converting <u>terminating decimals</u> into fractions was covered on the previous page.
Converting <u>recurring decimals</u> is quite a bit harder — but you'll be OK once you've learnt the method...

Recurring Decimals into Fractions

1) Basic Ones (7)

Turning a recurring decimal into a fraction uses a really clever trick. Just watch this...

EXAMPLE: Write $0.2\dot{3}\dot{4}$ as a fraction.

1) Name your decimal — I've called it <u>r</u>.

2) Multiply r by a <u>power of ten</u> to move it past the decimal point by <u>one full repeated lump</u> — here that's 1000:

3) Now you can <u>subtract</u> to <u>get rid</u> of the decimal part:

4) Then just <u>divide</u> to leave r, and <u>cancel</u> if possible:

Let $r = 0.2\dot{3}\dot{4}$

$1000r = 234.2\dot{3}\dot{4}$

$$1000r = 234.2\dot{3}\dot{4}$$
$$- \quad r = 0.2\dot{3}\dot{4}$$
$$999r = 234$$

$$r = \frac{234}{999} = \frac{26}{111}$$

The 'Just Learning the Result' Method:

1) For converting recurring decimals to fractions, you <u>could</u> just learn the result that the fraction always has the <u>repeating unit</u> on the top and <u>the same number of nines</u> on the bottom...

2) <u>BUT</u> this <u>only</u> works if the repeating bit starts <u>straight after</u> the decimal point (see the next page for an example where it doesn't).

3) <u>AND</u> some exam questions will ask you to '<u>show that</u>' or '<u>prove</u>' that a fraction and a recurring decimal are equivalent — and that means you have to use the <u>proper method</u>.

Fractions and Recurring Decimals

2) The Trickier Type (GRADE 7)

If the recurring bit doesn't come right after the decimal point, things are slightly trickier — but only slightly.

EXAMPLE:

Write $0.1\dot{6}$ as a fraction.

1)	Name your decimal.	Let r = $0.1\dot{6}$
2)	Multiply r by a <u>power of ten</u> to move the <u>non-repeating part</u> past the decimal point.	10r = $1.\dot{6}$
3)	Now multiply again to move <u>one full repeated lump</u> past the decimal point.	100r = $16.\dot{6}$
4)	<u>Subtract</u> to <u>get rid</u> of the decimal part:	$\begin{array}{r} 100r = 16.\dot{6} \\ -\quad 10r = 1.\dot{6} \\ \hline 90r = 15 \end{array}$
5)	<u>Divide</u> to leave r, and <u>cancel</u> if possible:	$r = \dfrac{15}{90} = \dfrac{1}{6}$

Fractions into Recurring Decimals (GRADE 5)

You might find this cropping up in your exam too...

EXAMPLE:

Write $\dfrac{8}{33}$ as a recurring decimal.

There are <u>two ways</u> you can do this:

1 Find an equivalent fraction with <u>all nines</u> on the bottom. The number on the top will tell you the <u>recurring part</u>.

$\overset{\times 3}{\dfrac{8}{33}} = \dfrac{24}{99} \quad \times 3$

Watch out — the <u>number of nines</u> on the bottom tells you the <u>number of digits</u> in the recurring part. E.g. $\dfrac{24}{99} = 0.\dot{2}\dot{4}$, but $\dfrac{24}{999} = 0.\dot{0}2\dot{4}$

$\dfrac{24}{99} = 0.\dot{2}\dot{4}$

2 Remember, $\dfrac{8}{33}$ means $8 \div 33$, so you could just <u>do the division</u> on your calculator:

$8 \div 33 = 0.24242424...$

$\dfrac{8}{33} = 0.\dot{2}\dot{4}$

Oh, what's recurrin'?...

Learn how to tell whether a fraction will be a terminating or recurring decimal, and all the methods above. Then turn over and write it all down. Now, try to answer these beauties...

Q1   Express $0.\dot{1}2\dot{6}$ as a fraction in its simplest form.   [2 marks] (GRADE 7)

Q2   Show that $0.\dot{0}\dot{7} = \dfrac{7}{99}$ [3 marks] (GRADE 7)

Q3   Without using a calculator, convert $\dfrac{5}{111}$ to a recurring decimal.   [2 marks] (GRADE 5)

Percentages

You shouldn't have any trouble with the <u>simple types</u> of percentage question.
Watch out for the <u>trickier types</u> and make sure you know the <u>proper method</u> for each of them.

Three Simple Question Types

Type 1 — "Find x% of y"   (GRADE 3)

Turn the percentage into a <u>decimal</u>, then <u>multiply</u>.

EXAMPLE: Find 15% of £46.

1) Write 15% as a <u>decimal</u>: $15\% = 15 \div 100 = 0.15$
2) <u>Multiply</u> £46 by 0.15: $0.15 \times £46 = £6.90$

Type 2 — "Find the new amount after a % increase/decrease"   (GRADE 3)

Turn the percentage into a <u>decimal</u>, then <u>multiply</u>. Add this on (or subtract from) the original value.

EXAMPLE: A toaster is reduced in price by 40% in the sales.
It originally cost £68. What is the new price of the toaster?

1) Write 40% as a <u>decimal</u>: $40\% = 40 \div 100 = 0.4$
2) <u>Multiply</u> to find 40% <u>of</u> £68: $0.4 \times £68 = £27.20$
3) It's a decrease, so subtract from the original: $£68 - £27.20 = £40.80$

> If you prefer, you can use the <u>multiplier</u> method:
> multiplier $= 1 - 0.4$
> $= 0.6$
> $68 \times 0.6 = £40.80$

Type 3 — "Express x as a percentage of y"   (GRADE 3)

<u>Divide</u> x by y, then multiply by <u>100</u>.

EXAMPLE: Give 40p as a percentage of £3.34.

1) Make sure both amounts are in the <u>same units</u> — convert £3.34 to pence: $£3.34 = 334p$
2) <u>Divide</u> 40p by 334p, <u>then multiply</u> by 100: $(40 \div 334) \times 100 = 12.0\%$ (1 d.p.)

Three Trickier Question Types

Type 1 — Finding the percentage change   (GRADE 4)

1) This is the formula for giving a <u>change in value</u> as a <u>percentage</u> — **LEARN IT, AND USE IT:**

$$\text{PERCENTAGE 'CHANGE'} = \frac{\text{'CHANGE'}}{\text{ORIGINAL}} \times 100$$

2) This is similar to Type 3 above, because you end up with a <u>percentage</u> rather than an amount.

3) Typical questions will ask 'Find the percentage <u>increase</u>/<u>profit</u>/<u>error</u>' or 'Calculate the percentage <u>decrease</u>/<u>loss</u>/<u>discount</u>', etc.

EXAMPLE: A trader buys watches for £5 and sells them for £7. Find his profit as a percentage.

1) Here the 'change' is <u>profit</u>, so the formula looks like this: percentage profit $= \dfrac{\text{profit}}{\text{original}} \times 100$
2) Work out the <u>actual value</u> of the profit: profit $= £7 - £5 = £2$
3) Calculate the <u>percentage</u> profit: percentage profit $= \dfrac{2}{5} \times 100 = 40\%$

Percentages

Type 2 — Finding the original value (GRADE 4)

This is the type that <u>most people get wrong</u> — but only because they <u>don't recognise</u> it as this type and don't apply this simple method:

1) Write the amount in the question as a <u>percentage of the original value</u>.
2) <u>Divide</u> to find <u>1%</u> of the original value.
3) <u>Multiply by 100</u> to give the original value (= 100%).

EXAMPLE: A house increases in value by 20% to £72 000. Find what it was worth before the rise.

Note: The <u>new</u>, not the original value is given.

1) An <u>increase</u> of 20% means £72 000 represents <u>120% of the original</u> value.

2) Divide by 120 to find <u>1%</u> of the original value.

3) Then multiply by 100.

£72 000 = 120%
÷120 ⟶ £600 = 1%
×100 ⟶ £60 000 = 100%

If it was a <u>decrease</u> of 20%, then you'd put '£72 000 = <u>80%</u>' and divide by 80 instead of 120.

So the original value was £60 000

Always set them out <u>exactly like this example</u>. The trickiest bit is deciding the top % figure on the right-hand side — the 2nd and 3rd rows are <u>always</u> 1% and 100%.

Type 3 — Simple Interest vs Compound Interest (GRADE 3)

1) There are two types of <u>interest</u> you could get asked about — <u>simple</u> and <u>compound</u>. Funnily enough, <u>simple interest</u> is the simpler of the two.

Compound interest is covered on the next page.

2) Simple interest means a certain percentage of the <u>original amount only</u> is paid at regular intervals (usually once a year). So the amount of interest is <u>the same every time</u> it's paid.

EXAMPLE: Regina invests £380 in an account which pays 3% simple interest per annum. How much interest will she earn in 4 years?

'Per annum' just means 'each year'.

1) Work out the amount of interest earned <u>in one year</u>:

$$3\% = 3 \div 100 = 0.03$$
$$3\% \text{ of } £380 = 0.03 \times £380 = £11.40$$

2) Multiply by 4 to get the <u>total interest</u> for <u>4 years</u>:

$$4 \times £11.40 = £45.60$$

Fact: 70% of people understand percentages, the other 40% don't...

Learn the details for each type of percentage question, then turn over and write it all down. Then try these Exam Practice Questions:

Q1 A normal bottle of Kenny's Kiwi Juice contains 450 ml of juice. A special offer bottle contains 22% extra. How much juice is in the special offer bottle? **[2 marks]** (GRADE 3)

Q2 Jenny bought a llama for £4500. She later sold it for £3285. Calculate Jenny's percentage loss. **[3 marks]** (GRADE 4)

Q3 A car is reduced in price by £6150 in a 30% off sale. What did it cost before the sale? **[3 marks]** (GRADE 4)

Q4 Benny invests £1900 for 5 years in an account which pays simple interest at a rate of 2.2% per annum. How much interest will Benny earn in total? **[3 marks]** (GRADE 3)

Compound Interest and Depreciation

One more sneaky % type for you... Unlike <u>simple interest</u>, in <u>compound interest</u> the amount added on (or taken away) <u>changes</u> each time — it's a percentage of the <u>new amount</u>, rather than the <u>original amount</u>.

The Formula (5)

This topic is simple if you <u>LEARN THIS FORMULA</u>. If you don't, it's pretty well impossible:

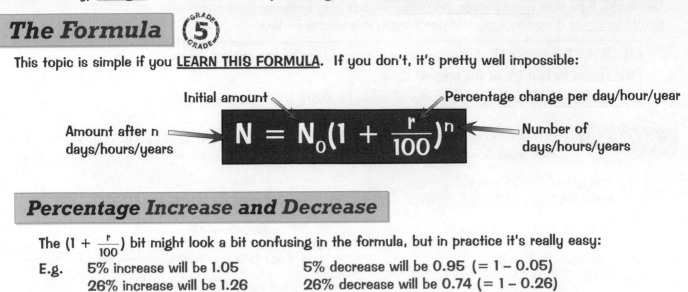

Initial amount

Percentage change per day/hour/year

Amount after n days/hours/years

$$N = N_0\left(1 + \frac{r}{100}\right)^n$$

Number of days/hours/years

Percentage Increase and Decrease

The $\left(1 + \frac{r}{100}\right)$ bit might look a bit confusing in the formula, but in practice it's really easy:

E.g.   5% increase will be 1.05   5% decrease will be 0.95 (= 1 − 0.05)
       26% increase will be 1.26   26% decrease will be 0.74 (= 1 − 0.26)

Two Examples to show you how EASY it is: (5)

The most popular context for these is <u>compound interest</u>. Compound interest means the interest is <u>added on each time</u>, and the next lot of interest is calculated using the <u>new total</u> rather than the original amount.

EXAMPLE: A man invests £1000 in a savings account which pays 8% compound interest per annum. How much will there be after 6 years?

'Per annum' just means 'each year'.

Use the formula: Amount = 1000(1.08)⁶ = £1586.87

initial amount   8% increase   6 years

<u>Depreciation</u> questions are about things (e.g. cars) which <u>decrease in value</u> over time.

EXAMPLE: Susan has just bought a car for £6500. If the car depreciates by 9% each year, how much will it be worth in 3 years' time?

Just use the formula again: Value = 6500(0.91)³ = £4898.21

initial value   9% decrease   3 years

Oh man, that last joke has still got me increases...

Bleurgh. What a horrible looking formula. Make sure you learn it... learn it real good. Oh, and try these:

Q1   Josie's savings account pays 5% compound interest.
      If she invests £400, how much will she have in the account after 4 years?   [3 marks] (5)

Q2   The value of Naveen's favourite painting has been depreciating by 11% per year.
      6 years ago, the painting was worth £200 000. What is it worth now?   [3 marks] (5)

Ratios

Ratios can be a grisly subject, no doubt about it — but work your way through the examples on the next two pages, and the whole murky business should become crystal clear...

Reducing Ratios to Their Simplest Form (2)

To reduce a ratio to a <u>simpler form</u>, divide <u>all the numbers</u> in the ratio by the <u>same thing</u> (a bit like simplifying a fraction). It's in its <u>simplest form</u> when there's nothing left you can divide by.

EXAMPLE: Write the ratio 15:18 in its simplest form.

For the ratio 15:18, both numbers have a <u>factor</u> of 3, so <u>divide them by 3</u>.

We can't reduce this any further. So the simplest form of 15:18 is **5:6**.

$$\div 3 \left(\begin{array}{c} 15:18 \\ = \quad 5:6 \end{array} \right) \div 3$$

A handy trick — use the fraction button

If you enter a fraction with the ⊞ or a b/c button, the calculator automatically cancels it down when you press ▣.

So for the ratio 8:12, just enter $\frac{8}{12}$ as a fraction, and you'll get the reduced fraction $\frac{2}{3}$.

Now you just change it back to ratio form, i.e. <u>2 : 3</u>. Ace.

The More Awkward Cases: (3)

1) If the ratio contains decimals or fractions — multiply

EXAMPLES: **1.** Simplify the ratio 2.4:3.6 as far as possible.

1) <u>Multiply both sides by 10</u> to get rid of the decimal parts.
2) Now <u>divide</u> to reduce the ratio to its simplest form.

$$\begin{array}{c} \times 10 \left(\begin{array}{c} 2.4:3.6 \\ 24:36 \end{array} \right) \times 10 \\ \div 12 \left(\begin{array}{c} \\ 2:3 \end{array} \right) \div 12 \end{array}$$

2. Give the ratio $\frac{5}{4} : \frac{7}{2}$ in its simplest form.

1) Put the fractions over a <u>common denominator</u> (see p.10).
2) Multiply <u>both sides</u> by 4 to get rid of the fractions.
3) This ratio won't cancel further, so we're done.

$$\frac{5}{4} : \frac{7}{2}$$
$$= \frac{5}{4} : \frac{14}{4}$$
$$\times 4 \left(\frac{5}{4} : \frac{14}{4} \right) \times 4$$
$$5:14$$

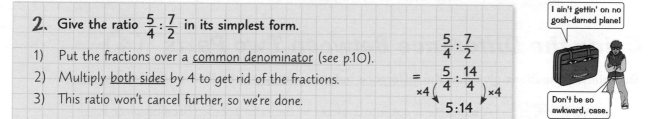
I ain't gettin' on no gosh-darned plane!

Don't be so awkward, case.

2) If the ratio has mixed units — convert to the smaller unit

EXAMPLE: Reduce the ratio 24 mm : 7.2 cm to its simplest form.

1) <u>Convert</u> 7.2 cm to millimetres.
2) <u>Simplify</u> the resulting ratio. Once the units on both sides are the same, <u>get rid of them</u> for the final answer.

$$24 \text{ mm}:7.2 \text{ cm}$$
$$= 24 \text{ mm}:72 \text{ mm}$$
$$\div 24 \left(\begin{array}{c} \\ 1:3 \end{array} \right) \div 24$$

3) To get the form 1 : n or n : 1 — just divide

EXAMPLE: Reduce 3:56 to the form 1:n.

Divide both sides by 3:

$$\div 3 \left(\begin{array}{c} 3:56 \\ 1:\frac{56}{3} \end{array} \right) \div 3$$
$$= 1:18\frac{2}{3} \text{ (or } 1:18.\dot{6})$$

This form is often the <u>most useful</u>, since it shows the ratio very clearly.

Ratios

There's just so much <u>great stuff</u> to say about ratios. I couldn't possibly fit it onto only one page...

Scaling Up Ratios (3)

If you know the <u>ratio between parts</u> and the actual size of <u>one part</u>,
you can <u>scale the ratio up</u> to find the other parts.

> **EXAMPLE:**
> Mrs Miggins owns tabby cats and ginger cats in the ratio 3:5.
> All her cats are either tabby or ginger, and she has 12 tabby cats.
> How many cats does Mrs Miggins have in total?
>
>
>
> Multiply <u>both sides</u> by 4 to go from 3 to 12 on the LHS:
>
> tabby : ginger
> $= \quad ×4 \left(\begin{array}{c} 3:5 \\ 12:20 \end{array} \right) ×4$
>
> So Mrs Miggins has <u>12 tabby cats</u> and <u>20 ginger cats</u>.
> So in total she has **12 + 20 = 32 cats**

Proportional Division (4)

In a <u>proportional division</u> question a **TOTAL AMOUNT** is split into parts <u>in a certain ratio</u>.
The key word here is **PARTS** — concentrate on 'parts' and it all becomes quite painless:

> **EXAMPLE:**
> Jess, Mo and Greg share £9100 in the ratio 2:4:7. How much does Mo get?
>
> 1) **ADD UP THE PARTS:**
>   The ratio 2:4:7 means there will be a total of 13 <u>parts</u>:   2 + 4 + 7 = 13 parts
>
> 2) **DIVIDE TO FIND ONE "PART":**
>   Just divide the <u>total amount</u> by the number of <u>parts</u>:   £9100 ÷ 13 = £700   (= 1 part)
>
> 3) **MULTIPLY TO FIND THE AMOUNTS:**
>   We want to know <u>Mo's share</u>, which is <u>4 parts</u>:   4 parts = 4 × £700 = £2800

Using the Difference Between Two Parts (4)

Sometimes questions give you the <u>difference between two parts</u> instead of the <u>total amount</u>.

> **EXAMPLE:**
> A baguette is cut into 3 pieces in the ratio 1:2:5. The first piece is
> 28 cm smaller than the third piece. How long is the second piece?
>
> 1) Work out <u>how many parts</u> 28 cm makes up.
> 28 cm = 3rd piece − 1st piece
> = 5 parts − 1 part = 4 parts
>
> 2) <u>Divide</u> to find <u>one part</u>.
> 28 cm ÷ 4 = 7 cm
>
> 3) <u>Multiply</u> to find the length of the <u>2nd piece</u>.
> 2nd piece = 2 parts = 2 × 7 cm = 14 cm

Ratio Nelson — he proportionally divided the French at Trafalgar...

Learn the rules for simplifying, how to scale ratios up and the three steps for proportional division.

Q1   Simplify: a) 25:35   b) 3.4:5.1   c) $\dfrac{9}{4} : \dfrac{15}{2}$ [4 marks] (3)

Q2   Porridge and ice cream are mixed in the ratio 7:4.
How much porridge should go with 12 bowls of ice cream?   [1 mark] (3)

Q3   The ages of Ben, Graham and Pam are in the ratio 3:7:8.
Pam is 25 years older than Ben. How old is Graham?   [3 marks] (4)

Proportion

Proportion problems all involve amounts that increase or decrease together. Awww.

Learn the Golden Rule for Proportion Questions

There are lots of exam questions which at first sight seem completely different but in fact they can all be done using the GOLDEN RULE...

DIVIDE FOR ONE, THEN TIMES FOR ALL

EXAMPLE: 5 pints of milk cost £1.30. How much will 3 pints cost?

The GOLDEN RULE says: **DIVIDE FOR ONE, THEN TIMES FOR ALL**

which means: Divide the price by 5 to find how much FOR ONE PINT, then multiply by 3 to find how much FOR 3 PINTS.

So for 1 pint: £1.30 ÷ 5 = 0.26 = 26p
For 3 pints: 26p × 3 = 78p

My favourite cereal is muesli.

Use the Golden Rule to Scale Recipes Up or Down

EXAMPLE: A fruit punch uses the recipe shown on the right.

Judy wants to make enough fruit punch to serve 20 people. How much grape juice will she need?

Use the GOLDEN RULE again:

DIVIDE FOR ONE, THEN TIMES FOR ALL

Fruit Punch (serves 8)
800 ml orange juice
600 ml grape juice
200 ml cherry juice
140 g fresh pineapple

which means: Divide the amount of grape juice by 8 to find how much FOR ONE PERSON, then multiply by 20 to find how much FOR 20 PEOPLE.

So for 1 person you need: And for 20 people you need:

600 ml ÷ 8 = 75 ml grape juice ⇒ 20 × 75 ml = 1500 ml grape juice

You'll need to do something a bit different for some proportion questions.

EXAMPLE: Using the recipe above, Arthur makes enough fruit punch for all the guests at a party. He uses 4 litres of orange juice. How many guests were at the party?

First, convert litres into millilitres. 4 l = (4 × 1000) ml = 4000 ml.

Divide the amount of orange juice in the recipe by 8 to find how much FOR ONE PERSON.

For 1 person: 800 ml ÷ 8 = 100 ml orange juice.

To find the number of guests, just divide the amount of orange juice Arthur uses by the amount needed for one person.

4000 ml ÷ 100 ml = 40 people

Divide for one, but DON'T multiply for all because you already know the 'all' (4 litres of juice). Instead, divide to find the missing number of people.

The Three Mathsketeers say "divide for one, then times for all"...

It's a simple rule — the trick is knowing when to use it. Learning the examples above will help.

Q1 If seven pencils cost 98p, how much will 4 pencils cost? [3 marks]

Q2 To make 4 servings of leek and liquorice soup, you need 600 g of leeks and 80 g of liquorice.
 a) What quantity of leeks do you need for 6 servings of soup? [3 marks]
 b) How much liquorice do you need for 9 servings? [3 marks]

Rounding Numbers

There are <u>two different ways</u> of specifying <u>where</u> a number should be <u>rounded</u>.
They are: 'Decimal Places' and 'Significant Figures'.
We'll do decimal places first, but the basic method is the same for both...

Decimal Places (d.p.) — ②

To round to a given number of <u>decimal places</u>:

1) <u>Identify</u> the position of the '<u>last digit</u>' from the number of decimal places.

'<u>Last digit</u>' = last one in the <u>rounded version</u>, not the original number.

2) Then look at the next digit to the <u>right</u> — called <u>the decider</u>.

3) If the <u>decider</u> is <u>5 or more</u>, then <u>round up</u> the <u>last digit</u>.
If the <u>decider</u> is <u>4 or less</u>, then leave the <u>last digit</u> as it is.

4) There must be <u>no more digits</u> after the last digit (not even zeros).

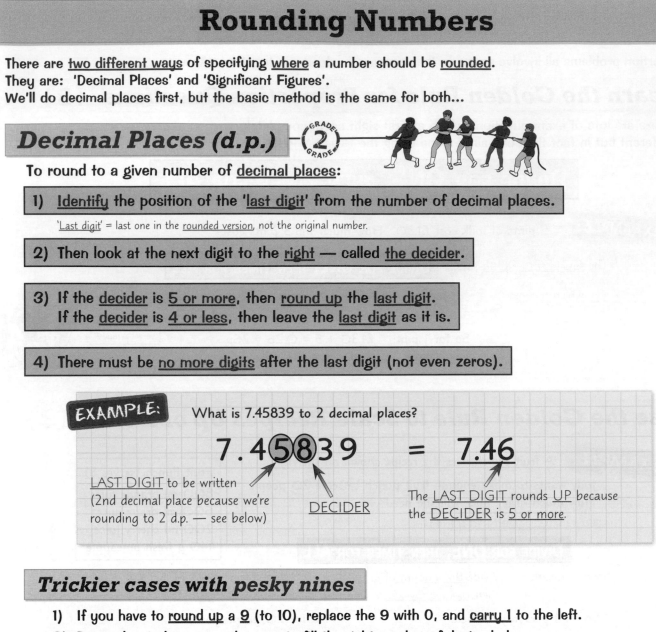

EXAMPLE: What is 7.45839 to 2 decimal places?

$$7.4\,\textcircled{5}\,\textcircled{8}\,39 \quad = \quad \underline{7.46}$$

LAST DIGIT to be written
(2nd decimal place because we're
rounding to 2 d.p. — see below)

DECIDER

The <u>LAST DIGIT</u> rounds <u>UP</u> because
the <u>DECIDER</u> is <u>5 or more</u>.

Trickier cases with pesky nines

1) If you have to <u>round up</u> a <u>9</u> (to 10), replace the 9 with 0, and <u>carry 1</u> to the left.

2) Remember to keep enough <u>zeros</u> to fill the right number of decimal places.

EXAMPLES:

1. Round 45.699 to 2 d.p.

$$45.6\overset{\text{decider}}{9}9 \longrightarrow 45.6\overset{7\,0}{9}9 \longrightarrow 45.70 \text{ to 2 d.p.}$$

last digit — round up

> 45.7 has the <u>same value</u> as 45.70,
> but 45.7 <u>isn't</u> rounded to <u>2 d.p.</u> so
> it would be marked <u>wrong</u>.

2. Round 64.996 to 2 d.p.

$$64.9\overset{\text{decider}}{9}6 \longrightarrow 64.9\overset{5\,0\,0}{9}6 \longrightarrow 65.00 \text{ to 2 d.p.}$$

last digit

When you carry the 1, this 9 rounds up
to 10 too, so carry 1 to the left again.

It's official — this is the most exciting page of revision ever...

OK, maybe not, but it is important stuff, so learn the steps of the basic method, and make
sure you know what to do with those cheeky nines. Then have a crack at these:

Q1   a) Round 3.5743 to 2 decimal places.   b) Give 0.0481 to 2 decimal places.
     c) Express 12.9096 to 3 d.p.   d) Express 3546.054 to 1 d.p.   [4 marks] ②

Rounding Numbers

The method for significant figures is <u>identical</u> to that for decimal places except that locating the <u>last digit</u> is more difficult — it wouldn't be so bad, but for the <u>zeros</u>...

Significant Figures (s.f.)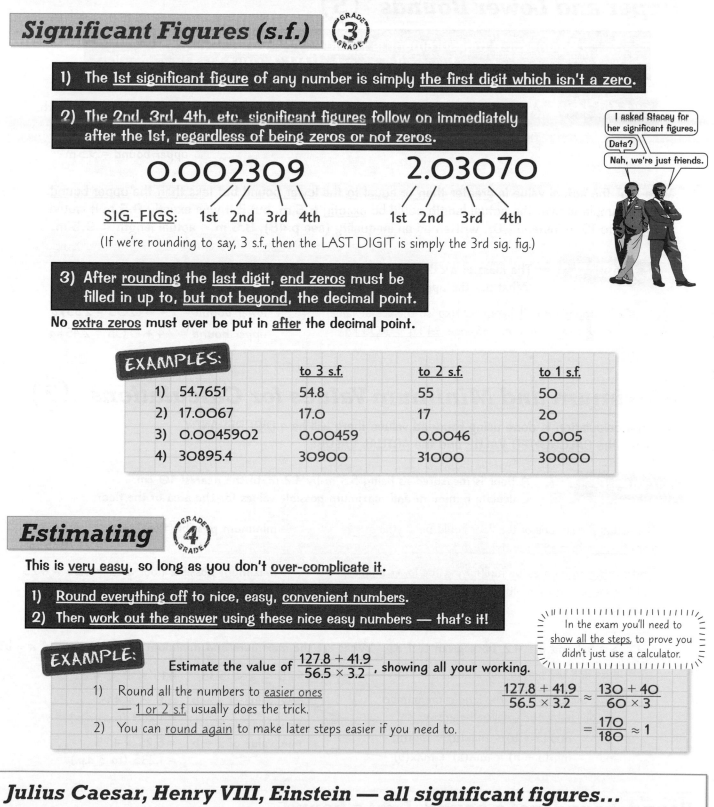

1) The <u>1st significant figure</u> of any number is simply <u>the first digit which isn't a zero.</u>

2) The <u>2nd, 3rd, 4th,</u> etc. <u>significant figures</u> follow on immediately after the 1st, <u>regardless of being zeros or not zeros.</u>

0.002309   2.03070

SIG. FIGS: 1st 2nd 3rd 4th   1st 2nd 3rd 4th

(If we're rounding to say, 3 s.f., then the LAST DIGIT is simply the 3rd sig. fig.)

I asked Stacey for her significant figures.
Data?
Nah, we're just friends.

3) After <u>rounding</u> the <u>last digit</u>, <u>end zeros</u> must be filled in up to, <u>but not beyond,</u> the decimal point.

No <u>extra zeros</u> must ever be put in <u>after</u> the decimal point.

EXAMPLES:

		to 3 s.f.	to 2 s.f.	to 1 s.f.
1)	54.7651	54.8	55	50
2)	17.0067	17.0	17	20
3)	0.0045902	0.00459	0.0046	0.005
4)	30895.4	30900	31000	30000

Estimating

This is <u>very easy</u>, so long as you don't <u>over-complicate it.</u>

1) <u>Round everything off</u> to nice, easy, <u>convenient numbers.</u>
2) Then <u>work out the answer</u> using these nice easy numbers — that's it!

EXAMPLE: Estimate the value of $\dfrac{127.8 + 41.9}{56.5 \times 3.2}$, showing all your working.

1) Round all the numbers to <u>easier ones</u> — <u>1 or 2 s.f.</u> usually does the trick.

2) You can <u>round again</u> to make later steps easier if you need to.

$$\frac{127.8 + 41.9}{56.5 \times 3.2} \approx \frac{130 + 40}{60 \times 3}$$
$$= \frac{170}{180} \approx 1$$

In the exam you'll need to <u>show all the steps</u>, to prove you didn't just use a calculator.

Julius Caesar, Henry VIII, Einstein — all significant figures...

If a question says 'give your answer to an appropriate degree of accuracy', work out how many significant figures the numbers in the question are rounded to, and use the same number of s.f. in your answer.

Now, learn the whole of this page, turn over and write down everything you've learned. And for pudding...

Q1   Round these to 3 s.f. :   a) 567.78   b) 23445   c) 0.04563   d) 0.90876   [4 marks]

Q2   Estimate the value of $\dfrac{4.23 \times 11.8}{7.7}$ [2 marks]

Bounds

Rounding and bounds go hand in hand, and not just because they sort of rhyme...

Upper and Lower Bounds $\boxed{5}$ GRADE

Whenever a measurement is rounded to a given UNIT, the actual measurement can be anything up to HALF A UNIT bigger or smaller.

EXAMPLE: A room is 9 m long to the nearest metre. Find upper and lower bounds for its length.

The actual length could be half a metre either side of 9 m.
lower bound = 8.5 m
upper bound = 9.5 m

Note that the actual value is greater than or equal to the lower bound but less than the upper bound. In the example above, the actual length could be exactly 8.5 m, but if it was exactly 9.5 m it would round up to 10 m instead. Or, written as an inequality (see p.48), 8.5 m ≤ actual length < 9.5 m.

EXAMPLE: The mass of a cake is given as 2.4 kg to the nearest 0.1 kg.
What are the upper and lower bounds for the actual mass of the cake?

The rounding unit here is 0.1 kg, so the actual value could be anything in the range 2.4 kg ± 0.05 kg.
lower bound = 2.4 − 0.05 = 2.35 kg
upper bound = 2.4 + 0.05 = 2.45 kg

Maximum and Minimum Values for Calculations $\boxed{7}$ GRADE

When a calculation is done using rounded values there will be a **DISCREPANCY** between the **CALCULATED VALUE** and the **ACTUAL VALUE**:

EXAMPLES:

1. A floor is measured as being 5.3 m by 4.2 m, to the nearest 10 cm.
Calculate minimum and maximum possible values for the area of the floor.

The actual dimensions of the floor could be anything from 5.25 m to 5.35 m and 4.15 m to 4.25 m.

Find the minimum area by multiplying the lower bounds, and the maximum by multiplying the upper bounds.

$$\text{minimum possible floor area} = 5.25 \times 4.15$$
$$= 21.7875 \text{ m}^2$$

$$\text{maximum possible floor area} = 5.35 \times 4.25$$
$$= 22.7375 \text{ m}^2$$

2. $a = 5.3$ and $b = 4.2$, both given to 1 d.p. What are the maximum and minimum possible values of $a \div b$?

First find the bounds for a and b. $\longrightarrow$ $5.25 \leq a < 5.35$, $\quad 4.15 \leq b < 4.25$

Now the tricky bit... The bigger the number you divide by, the smaller the answer, so:

$$\max(a \div b) = \max(a) \div \min(b)$$
and $$\min(a \div b) = \min(a) \div \max(b)$$

$$\text{max. value of } a \div b = 5.35 \div 4.15$$
$$= 1.289 \text{ (to 3 d.p.)}$$

$$\text{min. value of } a \div b = 5.25 \div 4.25$$
$$= 1.235 \text{ (to 3 d.p.)}$$

Bound, bound, get a bound, I get a bound...

This is bound to come up in the exam — or at least, it's not beyond the bounds of possibility that it could. When you think you know this page, try an Exam Practice Question:

Q1 x, y and z are measured as 2.32 m, 0.45 m and 1.15 m, all to the nearest 0.01 m.

a) Find the upper and lower bounds of x, y and z. [3 marks] $\boxed{5}$ GRADE

b) If $w = \dfrac{3(z - y)}{x}$, find the maximum possible value of w. [2 marks] $\boxed{8}$ GRADE

Standard Form

Standard form (or 'standard index form') is useful for writing <u>VERY BIG</u> or <u>VERY SMALL</u> numbers in a more convenient way, e.g.

$56\,000\,000\,000$ would be 5.6×10^{10} in standard form.

$0.000\,000\,003\,45$ would be 3.45×10^{-9} in standard form.

But <u>ANY NUMBER</u> can be written in standard form and you need to know how to do it:

What it Actually is:

A number written in standard form must <u>always</u> be in <u>exactly</u> this form:

This <u>number</u> must <u>always</u> be <u>between 1 and 10</u>.

(The fancy way of saying this is $1 \le A < 10$)

$$A \times 10^n$$

This number is just the <u>number of places</u> the <u>decimal point</u> moves.

Learn the Three Rules:

1) The <u>front number</u> must always be <u>between 1 and 10</u>.
2) The power of 10, n, is <u>how far the decimal point moves</u>.
3) n is <u>positive for BIG numbers</u>, n is <u>negative for SMALL numbers</u>.

(This is much better than rules based on which way the decimal point moves.)

Four Important Examples:

1 Express 35 600 in standard form.

1) <u>Move the decimal point</u> until 35 600 becomes 3.56 ($1 \le A < 10$)
2) The decimal point has moved <u>4 places</u> so n = 4, giving: 10^4
3) 35 600 is a <u>big number</u> so n is +4, not −4

$$3\,5\,6\,0\,0.0$$
$$= 3.56 \times 10^4$$

2 Express 0.0000623 in standard form.

1) The decimal point must move <u>5 places</u> to give 6.23 ($1 \le A < 10$). So the power of 10 is 5.
2) Since 0.0000623 is a <u>small number</u> it must be 10^{-5} not 10^{+5}

$$0.0\,0\,0\,0\,6\,2\,3$$
$$= 6.23 \times 10^{-5}$$

3 Express 4.95×10^{-3} as an ordinary number.

1) The power of 10 is <u>negative</u>, so it's a <u>small number</u> — the answer will be less than 1.
2) The power is −3, so the decimal point moves <u>3 places</u>.

$$0\,0\,0\,4.9\,5 \times 10^{-3}$$
$$= 0.00495$$

4 What is 146.3 million in standard form?

Too many people get this type of question <u>wrong</u>. Just take your time and do it in <u>two stages</u>:

146.3 million
$= 146\,300\,000$
$= 1.463 \times 10^8$

The two favourite <u>wrong answers</u> for this are:

146.3×10^6 — which is kind of right but it's not in <u>standard form</u> because 146.3 is not between 1 and 10

1.463×10^6 — this one <u>is</u> in standard form but it's <u>not big enough</u>

Standard Form

Calculations with Standard Form (5)

These are really popular <u>exam questions</u> — you might be asked to add, subtract, multiply or divide using numbers written in <u>standard form</u>.

Multiplying and Dividing — not too bad

> 1) Rearrange to put the <u>front numbers</u> and the <u>powers of 10 together</u>.
> 2) Multiply or divide the front numbers, and use the <u>power rules</u> (see p.31) to multiply or divide the powers of 10.
> 3) Make sure your answer is still in <u>standard form</u>.

EXAMPLES:

1. Find $(2.24 \times 10^3) \times (6.75 \times 10^5)$. Give your answer in standard form.

Multiply front numbers and powers separately

$$(2.24 \times 10^3) \times (6.75 \times 10^5)$$
$$= (2.24 \times 6.75) \times (10^3 \times 10^5)$$
$$= 15.12 \times 10^{3+5}$$ — Add the powers (see p.31)
$$= 15.12 \times 10^8$$

Not in standard form — convert it
$$= 1.512 \times 10 \times 10^8$$
$$= 1.512 \times 10^9$$

2. Calculate $189\,000 \div (5.4 \times 10^{10})$. Give your answer in standard form.

Convert 189 000 to standard form

$$189\,000 \div (5.4 \times 10^{10})$$
$$= \frac{1.89 \times 10^5}{5.4 \times 10^{10}} = \frac{1.89}{5.4} \times \frac{10^5}{10^{10}}$$

Divide front numbers and powers separately
$$= 0.35 \times 10^{5-10}$$ — Subtract the powers (see p.31)
$$= 0.35 \times 10^{-5}$$

Not in standard form — convert it
$$= 3.5 \times 10^{-1} \times 10^{-5}$$
$$= 3.5 \times 10^{-6}$$

Adding and Subtracting — a bit trickier

> 1) Make sure the <u>powers of 10</u> are <u>the same</u> — you'll probably need to rewrite one of them.
> 2) Add or subtract the <u>front numbers</u>.
> 3) Convert the answer to <u>standard form</u> if necessary.

EXAMPLE: Calculate $(9.8 \times 10^4) + (6.6 \times 10^3)$. Give your answer in standard form.

$$(9.8 \times 10^4) + (6.6 \times 10^3)$$

1) <u>Rewrite one number</u> so both powers of 10 are equal: $= (9.8 \times 10^4) + (0.66 \times 10^4)$

2) Now add the <u>front numbers</u>: $= (9.8 + 0.66) \times 10^4$

3) 10.46×10^4 isn't in standard form, so <u>convert it</u>: $= 10.46 \times 10^4 = 1.046 \times 10^5$

To put standard form numbers into your <u>calculator</u>, use the **EXP** or the **×10ˣ** button. E.g. enter 2.67×10^{15} by pressing **2.67** **EXP** **15** **=** or **2.67** **×10ˣ** **15** **=** .

Your calculator might <u>display</u> an answer such as 7.986×10^{15} as $\boxed{7.986 \quad ^{15}}$. If so, <u>don't forget</u> to add in the "×10" bit when you write it down. Some calculators do display a little "×10" so check what yours does.

Or for just £25, you can upgrade to luxury form...

Make sure you understand all the examples on these pages. Then try these Exam Practice Questions:

Q1 Express 0.854 million and 0.00018 in standard form. [2 marks] (4)

Q2 Express 4.56×10^{-3} and 2.7×10^5 as ordinary numbers. [2 marks] (4)

Q3 Work out the following. Give your answers in standard form.
   a) $(3.2 \times 10^7) \div (1.6 \times 10^{-4})$ [2 marks] b) $(6.7 \times 10^{10}) + (5.8 \times 10^{11})$ [2 marks] (5)

Sets

Sets come with some pretty weird notation, but a <u>set</u> is just a maths word for a <u>collection of things</u>.

Learn How to Use Set Notation (GRADE 4)

1) You can describe a set by listing everything in it, e.g. {2, 4, 6}, ← *The <u>curly brackets</u> tell you that this is a set.*
   or by giving a rule, e.g. {things that are red} or {odd numbers}.

2) Each object in a set is called a <u>member</u> or <u>element</u>. There's some special notation for this:

   | ∈ ...IS A MEMBER OF... | | ∉ ...IS NOT A MEMBER OF... |

   E.g. strawberry ∈ {things that are red}, *2* ∉ {odd numbers}

3) You can use a <u>capital letter</u> to stand for <u>a set</u>, e.g. A = {numbers that are multiples of four},
   and a <u>lower case letter</u> to stand for <u>a member</u> of a set, e.g. x ∉ A.

Two important sets have their own symbols:

| {} or ∅ THE EMPTY SET | If a set has <u>no members</u> at all, it's called <u>the empty set</u>.
E.g. if set B = {negative numbers between 1 and 10} then set B = ∅. |

| ξ THE UNIVERSAL SET | The <u>universal set</u> is the group of things that the members of a set are selected from. |

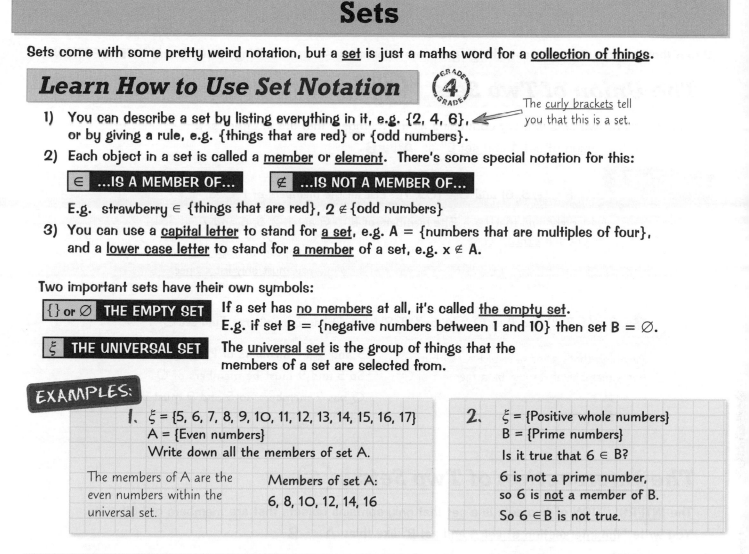

EXAMPLES:

1. ξ = {5, 6, 7, 8, 9, 10, 11, 12, 13, 14, 15, 16, 17}
   A = {Even numbers}
   Write down all the members of set A.

   The members of A are the even numbers within the universal set.

   Members of set A:
   6, 8, 10, 12, 14, 16

2. ξ = {Positive whole numbers}
   B = {Prime numbers}

   Is it true that 6 ∈ B?

   6 is not a prime number, so 6 is <u>not</u> a member of B.

   So 6 ∈ B is not true.

You Can Describe Sets Using Numbers and Symbols (GRADE 6)

If a set is described using numbers and symbols, work out what the description <u>means in words</u> before you start working with the set.

The <u>colon</u> means 'such that'.

{x: x < 0} ← This is <u>the set of numbers, x, such that x is less than 0</u>, i.e. the set of negative numbers.

{(x, y): y = 2x + 2} ← This is <u>the set of all the points (x, y) such that y = 2x + 2</u>, i.e. the set of coordinates that lie on the line y = 2x + 2.

See p.48 for more on the inequality symbols > and <.

EXAMPLE: ξ = {Negative integers}, P = { x : x > −6 }. List all the members of set P.

1) Check what the <u>universal set</u> is. The universal set is the negative whole numbers.

2) Combine this with the <u>definition</u> of set P to find the <u>members</u> of P.
   So, P is the set of whole numbers that are bigger than −6 but less than 0.
   The members of P are −5, −4, −3, −2 and −1.

Collect similar things to make sets — this reminds me of Monopoly...

Make sure you know what all the set notation means, and then have a go at these questions:

Q1 ξ = {Members of a sports club}, K = {People who play badminton}.
    Peter is a member of the sports club and Peter ∉ K. What does this tell you about Peter? [1 mark] (GRADE 4)

Q2 ξ = {Odd numbers}, L = {x: 2 < x < 10}. Write down all the members of set L. [2 marks] (GRADE 6)

Sets

When there's more than one set, things get more interesting — we're talking UNIONS and INTERSECTIONS.

The Union of Two Sets (4)

The UNION of two sets is a set containing all the members that are in either set.
You write "the union of set A and set B" as $A \cup B$.

EXAMPLES:

1. F = {2, 5, 6} and G = {1, 5, 7}. List all the members of F ∪ G.

List everything that appears in either F or G.

The members of F ∪ G are 1, 2, 5, 6 and 7.

5 appears in both sets but you must only list it once.

2. P = {4, 7, 8} and P ∪ Q = {4, 5, 7, 8, 9}. Set Q has 2 members. Find set Q.

Anything that's a member of P ∪ Q but not a member of P must be a member of Q.

5 and 9 are members of P ∪ Q but not members of P.
So 5 and 9 must be members of Q.
Q has 2 members, so 5 and 9 must be its only members.
So Q = {5, 9}

The Intersection of Two Sets (4)

The INTERSECTION of two sets is a set that only contains objects that are members of both sets.
You write "the intersection of set A and set B" like this: $A \cap B$

EXAMPLE:

ξ = {9, 10, 11, 12, 13, 14, 15, 16, 17, 18}, J = {Odd numbers}, K = {Multiples of 3}
List all the members of J ∩ K.

1) Find the members of J and K:
2) Members of J ∩ K are members of both J and K.

Members of J: 9, 11, 13, 15, 17
Members of K: 9, 12, 15, 18
Members of J ∩ K: 9, 15

n(A) — the Number of Members (6)

n(A) is shorthand for the number of members of set A. n(A) = 12 means "Set A has 12 members".

EXAMPLE:

ξ = {Positive integers}, L = { $x : 3 < x < 8$ }. What is n(L)?

1) Find the members of L:
2) Count the number of members:

Members of L: 4, 5, 6, 7
n(L) = 4

I wish the union of sets would call a strike...

You can find the union or intersection of more than two sets — we'll see this on page 29.

Q1 ξ = {1, 2, 3, 4, 5, 6}, A = {Even numbers}, B = {Prime numbers}.
a) Find A ∪ B. b) What is n(A ∪ B)? [2 marks] (6)
Q2 C = {Trees}, D = {Things over 3 m tall}. Describe the members of C ∩ D. [1 mark] (4)

Sets

Oh joy, there are some more sets definitions and symbols coming your way...

The Complement of a Set (5)

The **COMPLEMENT** of a set is all the members of the <u>universal set</u> that <u>aren't</u> in the set. "The <u>complement of set A</u>" is written as A'.

EXAMPLES:

1. ξ = {1, 2, 3, 4, 5, 6, 7, 8, 9, 10}, F = {Multiples of 3}
List the members of F'.

1)	First find the members of F.	The members of F are 3, 6 and 9.
2)	The members of F' are the <u>members of the universal set</u> that <u>aren't members of</u> F:	So the members of F' are 1, 2, 4, 5, 7, 8 and 10.

2. ξ = {1, 2, 3, 4, 5, 6, 7, 8}, G = {$x : 2 \le x \le 7$}, H = {Factors of 12}
a) Find G ∩ H'.

1)	Write G and H in terms of their <u>members</u>.	G = {2, 3, 4, 5, 6, 7}
2)	Find H'.	H = {1, 2, 3, 4, 6} so H' = {5, 7, 8}
3)	Find G ∩ H' — 5 and 7 are the only <u>members of both G and H'</u>.	G ∩ H' = {5, 7}

b) Find (G ∩ H)'.
First find G ∩ H, then find its complement.

G ∩ H = {2, 3, 4 6}
(G ∩ H)' = {1, 5, 7, 8}

> Watch out for brackets — G ∩ H' means the intersection of G and H', but (G ∩ H)' means the complement of G ∩ H.

Subsets are Sets Within Sets (6)

1) A **SUBSET** is a set that is entirely contained <u>within</u> another set.
This means that <u>all</u> the members of the <u>first set</u> are <u>also in the second set</u>.

2) There's another handy symbol for this: $\subset$ **...IS A SUBSET OF...**
E.g. if A = {5, 7, 11} and B = {prime numbers}, you can write "A $\subset$ B".

3) And, of course, there's a symbol meaning the opposite too: $\not\subset$ **...IS NOT A SUBSET OF...**
E.g. if set A = {4, 8, 12} and set B = {prime numbers}, you can write "A $\not\subset$ B".

EXAMPLE:

ξ = {Positive integers less than 10},
S = {$x : 5 \le x \le 9$}, T = {Odd numbers}, U = {Prime numbers}
Is (S ∩ T) $\subset$ U a true statement?

1)	Write S, T and U in terms of their <u>members</u>.	S = {5, 6, 7, 8, 9}, T = {1, 3, 5, 7, 9}, U = {2, 3, 5, 7}
2)	Find S ∩ T.	S ∩ T = {5, 7, 9}
3)	If S ∩ T is a <u>subset</u> of U, every member of S ∩ T must also be a member of U. Decide whether this is true.	9 is a member of S ∩ T but not a member of U. So, (S ∩ T) $\not\subset$ U and the statement is false.

{me, you} — a subset of people who are glad this page is over...

Learn the definitions of the complement and a subset, and then give these Exam Practice Questions a try:

Q1 ξ = {Positive integers less than 8}, P = {Odd numbers}, Q = {Factors of 6}. Find P' $\cup$ Q.
[2 marks] (5)

Q2 ξ = {2, 3, 4, 5, 6, 7, 8, 9}, X = {Prime numbers}, Y = {Factors of 24}, Z = {Even numbers}
Is (X' ∩ Y) $\subset$ Z a true statement?
[3 marks] (6)

Venn Diagrams

Venn diagrams look a bit odd, but they're actually pretty handy for showing the <u>relationships between sets</u>.

Venn Diagrams Use Circles to Represent Sets ⑤

1) Each set is represented by a <u>circle</u> — the space inside the circle represents everything in the set.

2) Each circle is labelled with a <u>letter</u> — this tells you which set each circle represents.

3) There might be a <u>number</u> inside the circle — this tells you the <u>number of members</u> of the set.

E.g. T = {People called Tim in my class}   T

3

This tells you there are 3 people called Tim in my class — so n(T) = 3.

Venn diagrams can also show the <u>actual elements</u> of the sets, not just the numbers of elements.

4) The universal set is shown as a <u>rectangle</u> that goes <u>around</u> <u>all of the circles</u>, like this:

ξ   A   B

This rectangle is the universal set.

Venn Diagrams Show Intersections and Unions ⑤

The <u>intersection</u> of sets is where the circles <u>overlap</u>. If two sets have no shared members then their circles won't overlap at all.

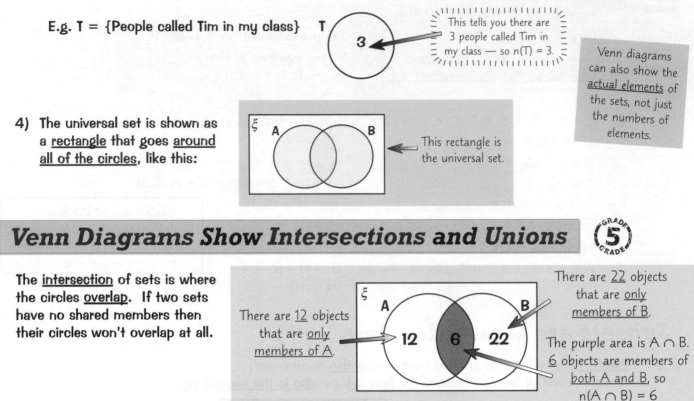

There are <u>12</u> objects that are <u>only</u> <u>members of A</u>.

There are <u>22</u> objects that are <u>only</u> <u>members of B</u>.

The purple area is A ∩ B. <u>6</u> objects are members of <u>both A and B</u>, so n(A ∩ B) = 6

The <u>union</u> of sets is all the space covered by the circles representing those sets.

You can find n(A ∪ B) by <u>adding</u> the number of members in each part of A ∪ B.
So here: n(A ∪ B) = 12 + 6 + 22 = 40

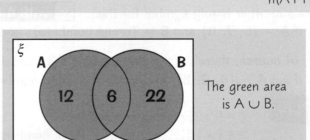

ξ   A   B
12   6   22

The green area is A ∪ B.

They Can Also Show Subsets and Complements

On a Venn diagram, the <u>complement</u> of a set is everything outside the circle representing that set.

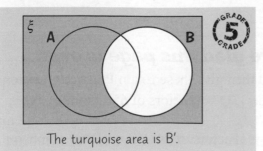

ξ   A   B

The turquoise area is B'.

If set A is a <u>subset</u> of set B then on a Venn diagram the circle representing set A lies <u>completely inside</u> the circle representing set B.

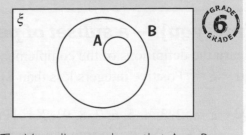

ξ   A   B

The Venn diagram shows that A ⊂ B.

Venn Diagrams

Thought you'd missed out on some lovely examples? We wouldn't want that...

Using the Numbers (7)

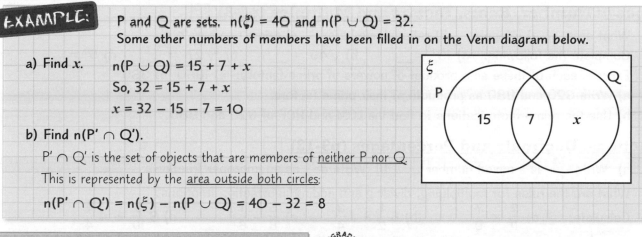

EXAMPLE: P and Q are sets. $n(\xi) = 40$ and $n(P \cup Q) = 32$.
Some other numbers of members have been filled in on the Venn diagram below.

a) Find x.

$n(P \cup Q) = 15 + 7 + x$

So, $32 = 15 + 7 + x$

$x = 32 - 15 - 7 = 10$

b) Find $n(P' \cap Q')$.

$P' \cap Q'$ is the set of objects that are members of <u>neither P nor Q</u>.

This is represented by the <u>area outside both circles</u>:

$n(P' \cap Q') = n(\xi) - n(P \cup Q) = 40 - 32 = 8$

Drawing a Venn Diagram (7)

To draw a Venn diagram you need to work out whether the <u>intersections</u> of each pair of sets have any members — this will tell you if the circles should overlap. Look out for any <u>subsets</u> too.

EXAMPLE: ξ = {Positive integers less than 20},
A = {Odd numbers}, B = {Multiples of 3}, C = {Multiples of 6}
Draw a Venn Diagram representing the relationships between A, B and C.

A = {1, 3, 5, 7, 9, 11, 13, 15, 17, 19},

B = {3, 6, 9, 12, 15, 18},

C = {6, 12, 18}

$A \cap B = \{3, 9, 15\}$, so circles A and B overlap.

C is a subset of B, so circle C is completely inside circle B.

$A \cap C = \varnothing$, so circles A and C do not overlap.

Venn Diagrams with Three Intersecting Sets (8)

Venn diagrams can show <u>three intersecting sets</u>.
For sets A, B and C, the area where <u>all three circles overlap</u> represents $A \cap B \cap C$.
This is the set containing the objects that are <u>members of all three sets</u>.

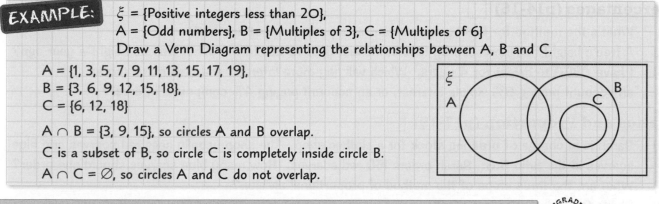

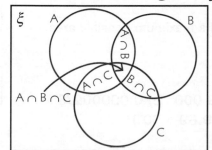

EXAMPLE: Using set notation, describe the yellow area of the Venn diagram below.

Everything in the yellow area is a member of Z, but not a member of X and not a member of Y.

So, they're members of Z <u>and</u> X' <u>and</u> Y'.

So the set is $X' \cap Y' \cap Z$. ◄——$(X \cup Y)' \cap Z$ would also be correct here.

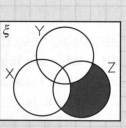

Be prepared — sets will appear Venn you least expect them...

You've almost made it through the final page on sets. Just give this practice question a go to finish off...

Q1 For the example at the top of the page, find: a) n(P)   b) n(Q') [2 marks] (7)

Q2 ξ = {10, 11, 12, 13, 14, 15, 16, 17, 18, 19}
J = {Odd numbers}, K = {Even numbers}, L = {Prime numbers}
Draw a Venn diagram representing the relationships between these sets. [2 marks] (8)

Revision Questions for Section One

Well, that wraps up <u>Section One</u> — time to put yourself to the test and find out <u>how much you really know</u>.
- Try these questions and <u>tick off each one</u> when you <u>get it right</u>.
- When you've done <u>all the questions</u> for a topic and are <u>completely happy</u> with it, tick off the topic.

Types of Number, Roots, Factors and Multiples (p4-8) ☑

1) What are: a) integers b) rational numbers c) prime numbers?
2) Complete the following: a) 13^2 = __ b) $\sqrt{49}$ = __ c) $\sqrt[3]{27}$ = __ d) 5^3 = __
3) Express each of these as a product of powers of prime factors: a) 1050 b) 360
4) a) Write 320 and 880 as products of their prime factors.
    b) Use the prime factorisations to find the LCM and HCF of 320 and 880.

Fractions, Decimals and Percentages (p9-13) ☑

5) a) Write $\frac{74}{9}$ as a mixed number b) Write $4\frac{5}{7}$ as an improper fraction
6) What are the rules for multiplying, dividing and adding/subtracting fractions?
7) Calculate: a) $\frac{2}{11} \times \frac{7}{9}$ b) $5\frac{1}{2} \div 1\frac{3}{4}$ c) $\frac{5}{8} - \frac{1}{6}$ d) $3\frac{3}{10} + 4\frac{1}{4}$
8) How do you convert: a) a fraction to a decimal? b) a terminating decimal to a fraction?
9) Write: a) 0.04 as: (i) a fraction (ii) a percentage b) 65% as: (i) a fraction (ii) a decimal
10) Show that $0.5\dot{1} = \frac{17}{33}$

Percentages (p14-16) ☑

11) What's the method for finding one amount as a percentage of another?
12) A tree's height has increased by 15% in the last year to 20.24 m. What was its height a year ago?
13) I have £850 to invest for 4 years. Which will pay more interest, and how much more:
    an account paying 6% simple interest, or an account paying 4% compound interest?

Ratios and Proportion (p17-19) ☑

14) Sarah is in charge of ordering stock for a clothes shop. The shop usually sells red scarves and blue
    scarves in the ratio 5:8. Sarah orders 150 red scarves. How many blue scarves should she order?
15) What are the three steps of the method of proportional division?
16) Divide 3000 in the ratio 5:8:12.
17) Rick ordered 5 pints of milk from the milkman. His bill was £2.35. How much would 3 pints cost?

Rounding and Bounds (p20-22) ☑

18) Round 427.963 to: a) 2 d.p. b) 1 d.p. c) 2 s.f. d) 4 s.f.
19) Estimate the value of $(124.6 + 87.1) \div 9.4$
20) A rectangle measures 15.6 m by 8.4 m, to the nearest 0.1 m. Find its maximum possible area.

Standard Form (p23-24) ☑

21) What are the three rules for writing numbers in standard form?
22) Write these numbers in standard form: a) 970 000 b) 3 560 000 000 c) 0.00000275
23) Calculate: a) $(2.54 \times 10^6) \div (1.6 \times 10^3)$ b) $(1.75 \times 10^{12}) + (9.89 \times 10^{11})$
    Give your answers in standard form.

Sets and Venn Diagrams (p25-29) ☑

24) ξ = {Positive integers less than 16}, A = {Multiples of 5}, B = {x: x ≤ 10}
    a) List the members of A ∩ B.
    b) Fill in the boxes in the Venn diagram on the right to show
        the number of members in each part of the diagram.
    c) Find n(A ∪ B).

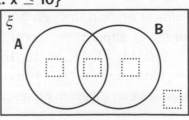

Powers and Roots

Powers are a very useful **shorthand**: $2 \times 2 \times 2 \times 2 \times 2 \times 2 \times 2 = 2^7$ ('two to the power 7')

That bit is easy to remember. Unfortunately, there are also **ten special rules** for powers that you need to learn.

Learn these Eight Rules (5)

Warning: Rules 1 & 2 don't work for things like $2^3 \times 3^7$, only for powers of the same number.

1) When **MULTIPLYING**, you **ADD THE POWERS**. e.g. $3^4 \times 3^6 = 3^{4+6} = 3^{10}$, $a^2 \times a^7 = a^{2+7} = a^9$

2) When **DIVIDING**, you **SUBTRACT THE POWERS**. e.g. $5^4 \div 5^2 = 5^{4-2} = 5^2$, $b^8 \div b^5 = b^{8-5} = b^3$

3) When **RAISING** one power to another, you **MULTIPLY THEM**. e.g. $(3^2)^4 = 3^{2 \times 4} = 3^8$, $(c^3)^6 = c^{3 \times 6} = c^{18}$

4) $x^1 = x$, **ANYTHING** to the **POWER 1** is just **ITSELF**. e.g. $3^1 = 3$, $d \times d^3 = d^1 \times d^3 = d^{1+3} = d^4$

5) $x^0 = 1$, **ANYTHING** to the **POWER 0** is just **1**. e.g. $5^0 = 1$, $67^0 = 1$, $e^0 = 1$

6) $1^x = 1$, **1 TO ANY POWER** is **STILL JUST 1**. e.g. $1^{23} = 1$, $1^{89} = 1$, $1^2 = 1$

7) **FRACTIONS** — Apply the power to **both TOP and BOTTOM**. e.g. $\left(1\frac{3}{5}\right)^3 = \left(\frac{8}{5}\right)^3 = \frac{8^3}{5^3} = \frac{512}{125}$, $\left(\frac{u}{v}\right)^5 = \frac{u^5}{v^5}$

8) **NEGATIVE Powers** — Turn it Upside Down.
   People have real difficulty remembering this — whenever you see a negative power you need to immediately think: "Aha, that means turn it the other way up and make the power positive".

   e.g. $7^{-2} = \frac{1}{7^2} = \frac{1}{49}$, $a^{-4} = \frac{1}{a^4}$, $\left(\frac{3}{5}\right)^{-2} = \left(\frac{5}{3}\right)^{+2} = \frac{5^2}{3^2} = \frac{25}{9}$

These Two Rules are a bit more Tricky (7)

9) **FRACTIONAL POWERS**

The power $\frac{1}{2}$ means **Square Root**, The power $\frac{1}{3}$ means **Cube Root**, The power $\frac{1}{4}$ means **Fourth Root** etc.

e.g. $25^{\frac{1}{2}} = \sqrt{25} = 5$
$64^{\frac{1}{3}} = \sqrt[3]{64} = 4$
$81^{\frac{1}{4}} = \sqrt[4]{81} = 3$
$z^{\frac{1}{5}} = \sqrt[5]{z}$

The one to really watch is when you get a negative fraction like $49^{-1/2}$ — people get mixed up and think that the minus is the square root, and forget to turn it upside down as well.

10) **TWO-STAGE FRACTIONAL POWERS**

With fractional powers like $64^{\frac{5}{6}}$ always **split the fraction** into a **root** and a **power**, and do them in that order: **root** first, then **power**: $(64)^{\frac{1}{6} \times 5} = \left(64^{\frac{1}{6}}\right)^5 = (2)^5 = 32$.

EXAMPLE: Simplify $28p^5q^3 \div 14p^3q^3$

Just deal with each bit separately:
$$= (28 \div 14)(p^5 \div p^3)(q^3 \div q^3)$$
$$= (28 \div 14)p^{5-3}q^{3-3}$$
$$= 2p^2$$

$q^{3-3} = q^0 = 1$

You simplify algebraic fractions using the power rules (though you might not realise it).

So if you had to simplify e.g. $\frac{p^3 q^6}{p^2 q^3}$, you'd just cancel using the power rules to get $p^{3-2}q^{6-3} = pq^3$.

Don't let the power go to your head...

Learn all ten exciting rules on this page, then have a go at these Exam Practice Questions:

Q1 Simplify: a) $e^4 \times e^7$ [1 mark]   b) $f^9 \div f^5$ [1 mark] (4)

Q2 Simplify: a) $(g^6)^{\frac{1}{2}}$ [1 mark]   b) $2h^5 j^{-2} \times 3h^2 j^4$ [2 marks] (5)

Q3 Evaluate: a) $625^{\frac{3}{4}}$ [2 marks]   b) $25^{-\frac{1}{2}}$ [2 marks]   c) $\left(\frac{27}{216}\right)^{-\frac{1}{3}}$ [2 marks] (7)

Algebra Basics

Before you can really get your teeth into <u>algebra</u>, there are some basics you need to get your head around.

Negative Numbers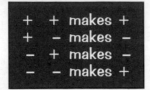

Negative numbers crop up everywhere so you need to learn these rules for dealing with them:

+	+	makes	+
+	−	makes	−
−	+	makes	−
−	−	makes	+

Use these rules when:

1) <u>Multiplying or dividing</u>.
   e.g. $-2 \times 3 = -6$, $-8 \div -2 = +4$, $-4p \times -2 = +8p$

2) <u>Two signs are together</u>.
   e.g. $5 - 4 = 5 + 4 = 9$, $x + -y - -z = x - y + z$

Letters Multiplied Together ③

Watch out for these combinations of letters in algebra that regularly catch people out:

1) abc means $a \times b \times c$. The ×'s are often left out to make it clearer.

2) gn^2 means $g \times n \times n$. Note that only the n is squared, not the g as well — e.g. πr^2 means $\pi \times r \times r$.

3) $(gn)^2$ means $g \times g \times n \times n$. The brackets mean that <u>BOTH</u> letters are squared.

4) $p(q-r)^3$ means $p \times (q-r) \times (q-r) \times (q-r)$. Only the brackets get cubed.

5) -3^2 is a bit ambiguous. It should either be written $(-3)^2 = 9$, or $-(3^2) = -9$ (you'd usually take -3^2 to be -9).

Terms ②

Before you can do anything else with algebra, you must understand what a term is:

> **A TERM IS A COLLECTION OF NUMBERS, LETTERS AND BRACKETS, ALL MULTIPLIED/DIVIDED TOGETHER**

Terms are separated by <u>+ and − signs</u>. Every term has a + or − attached to the <u>front of it</u>.

If there's no sign in front of the first term, it means there's an invisible + sign.

$$4xy \quad + \quad 5x^2 \quad - \quad 2y \quad + \quad 6y^2 \quad + \quad 4$$

'xy' term   'x²' term   'y' term   'y²' term   'number' term

Simplifying or 'Collecting Like Terms' ②

To <u>simplify</u> an algebraic expression, you combine '<u>like terms</u>' — terms that have the <u>same combination of letters</u> (e.g. all the x terms, all the y terms, all the number terms etc.).

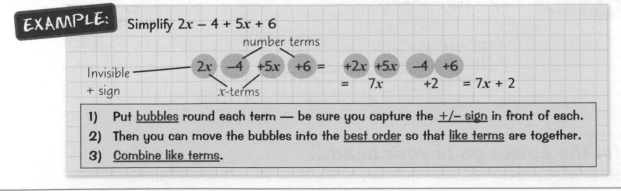

EXAMPLE: Simplify $2x - 4 + 5x + 6$

    number terms

Invisible + sign $2x \quad -4 \quad +5x \quad +6 =$ $+2x \quad +5x \quad -4 \quad +6$

    x-terms $= \quad 7x \quad\quad +2 \quad = 7x + 2$

1) Put <u>bubbles</u> round each term — be sure you capture the <u>+/− sign</u> in front of each.
2) Then you can move the bubbles into the <u>best order</u> so that <u>like terms</u> are together.
3) <u>Combine like terms</u>.

Ahhh algebra, it's as easy as abc, or 2(ab) + c, or something like that...

Nothing too tricky on this page — but simplifying questions do come up in the exam so here's some practice:

Q1   Simplify $5x + y - 2x + 7y$ [2 marks] ②

Making Formulas from Words

Before we get started, there are a few <u>definitions</u> you need to know:

> 1) EXPRESSION — a <u>collection</u> of <u>terms</u> (see p.32). Expressions <u>DON'T</u> have an = sign in them.
> 2) EQUATION — an expression with an = sign in it (so you can solve it).
> 3) FORMULA — a <u>rule</u> that helps you work something out (it will also have an = sign in it).

Making a Formula from Given Information

Making <u>formulas</u> from <u>words</u> can be a bit confusing as you're given a lot of <u>information</u> in one go.
You just have to go through it slowly and carefully and <u>extract the maths</u> from it.

EXAMPLE: Tiana is x years old. Leah is 5 years younger than Tiana. Martin is 4 times as old as Tiana.

a) Write an expression for Leah's age in terms of x.

Tiana's age is x
So Leah's age is $x - 5$ Leah is 5 years younger, so subtract 5

b) Write an expression for Martin's age in terms of x.

Tiana's age is x <u>4 times</u> older
So Martin's age is $4 \times x = 4x$

EXAMPLE: Windsurfing lessons cost £15 per hour, plus a fixed fee of £20 for equipment hire.
h hours of lessons cost £W. Write a formula for W in terms of h.

$$W = 15h + 20$$

One hour costs 15, so h hours will cost $15 \times h$

Don't forget to add on the fixed fee (20)

> Because you're asked for a formula, you must include the 'W = ' bit to get full marks (i.e. don't just put 15h + 20).

EXAMPLE: In rugby union, tries score 5 points and conversions score 2 points.
In a game, Morgan scores a total of M points, made up of t tries and c conversions.
Write a formula for M in terms of t and c.

Tries score 5 points —— t tries will score $5 \times t = 5t$ points
Conversions score 2 points —— c conversions will score $2 \times c = 2c$ points
So total points scored are $M = 5t + 2c$

> Penalties and drop-goals score 3 points (in case you thought I'd forgotten) — but he doesn't score any of these.

Using Your Formula to Solve Equations

Sometimes, you might be asked to <u>use</u> a formula to <u>solve an equation</u>.

EXAMPLE: A decorator uses the formula $C = 200r + 150$, where C is the cost in £ and r is the number of rooms. Gabrielle spends £950. How many rooms does she have decorated?

$C = 200r + 150$ —— Write down the formula first.
$950 = 200r + 150$ —— Replace C with the value given in the question (£950).
(-150) $950 - 150 = 200r + 150 - 150$ —— Now solve the equation.
$800 = 200r$
$(\div 200)$ $800 \div 200 = 200r \div 200$
$4 = r$ So Gabrielle has 4 rooms decorated

In h hours of windsurfing, I fell off 8h times...

You know the drill — learn this page and have a go at this Exam Practice Question (then have a cup of tea).

Q1   The cost of hiring a wallpaper-stripper is £12 per day, plus a deposit of £18.
If the cost for hiring it for d days is £C, find an expression for C in terms of d.   [3 marks]

Multiplying Out Brackets

I usually use brackets to make witty comments (I'm very witty), but in algebra they're useful for simplifying things. First of all, you need to know how to expand brackets (multiply them out).

Single Brackets (3)

The main thing to remember when multiplying out brackets is that the thing <u>outside</u> the bracket multiplies <u>each separate term</u> inside the bracket.

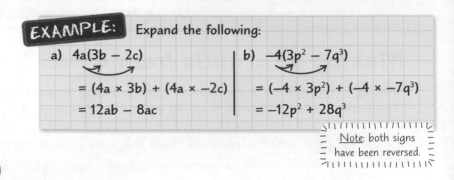

EXAMPLE: Expand the following:

a) $4a(3b - 2c)$

$= (4a \times 3b) + (4a \times -2c)$
$= 12ab - 8ac$

b) $-4(3p^2 - 7q^3)$

$= (-4 \times 3p^2) + (-4 \times -7q^3)$
$= -12p^2 + 28q^3$

<u>Note</u>: both signs have been reversed.

Double Brackets (4)

<u>Double</u> brackets are trickier than single brackets — this time, you have to multiply <u>everything</u> in the <u>first bracket</u> by <u>everything</u> in the <u>second bracket</u>. You'll get <u>4 terms</u>, and usually 2 of them will combine to leave <u>3 terms</u>. There's a handy way to multiply out double brackets — it's called the <u>FOIL method</u>:

First — multiply the first term in each bracket together

Outside — multiply the outside terms (i.e. the first term in the first bracket by the second term in the second bracket)

Inside — multiply the inside terms (i.e. the second term in the first bracket by the first term in the second bracket)

Last — multiply the second term in each bracket together

EXAMPLE: Expand and simplify $(2p - 4)(3p + 1)$

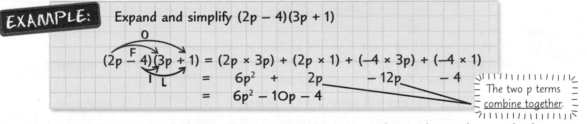

$(2p - 4)(3p + 1) = (2p \times 3p) + (2p \times 1) + (-4 \times 3p) + (-4 \times 1)$
$= 6p^2 + 2p - 12p - 4$
$= 6p^2 - 10p - 4$

The two p terms <u>combine together</u>.

Always write out <u>SQUARED BRACKETS</u> as <u>TWO BRACKETS</u> (to avoid mistakes), then multiply out as above.
So $(3x + 5)^2 = (3x + 5)(3x + 5) = 9x^2 + 15x + 15x + 25 = 9x^2 + 30x + 25$.
(DON'T make the mistake of thinking that $(3x + 5)^2 = 9x^2 + 25$ — this is <u>wrong wrong wrong</u>.)

Triple Brackets (7)

1) For <u>three</u> brackets, just multiply <u>two</u> together as above, then multiply the result by the remaining bracket.

It doesn't matter which pair of brackets you multiply together first.

2) If you end up with <u>three terms</u> in one bracket, you <u>won't</u> be able to use FOIL. Instead, you can reduce it to a <u>series</u> of <u>single bracket multiplications</u> — like in the example below.

EXAMPLE: Expand and simplify $(x + 2)(x + 3)(2x - 1)$

$(x + 2)(x + 3)(2x - 1) = (x + 2)(2x^2 + 5x - 3) = x(2x^2 + 5x - 3) + 2(2x^2 + 5x - 3)$
$= (2x^3 + 5x^2 - 3x) + (4x^2 + 10x - 6)$
$= 2x^3 + 9x^2 + 7x - 6$

Go forth and multiply out brackets...

You can expand cubed brackets by writing them out as three brackets and expanding as above.

Q1 Expand and simplify: a) $(y + 4)(y - 5)$ [2 marks] b) $(2p - 3)^2$ [2 marks] (4)

Q2 Expand and simplify: a) $(2t + \sqrt{2})(t - 3\sqrt{2})$ [3 marks] b) $(x - 2)^3$ [3 marks] (7)

Factorising

Right, now you know how to expand brackets, it's time to put them back in. This is known as <u>factorising</u>.

Factorising — Putting Brackets In (4)

This is the <u>exact reverse</u> of multiplying out brackets. Here's the method to follow:

1) Take out the <u>biggest number</u> that goes into all the terms.

2) <u>For each letter in turn</u>, take out the <u>highest power</u> (e.g. x, x^2 etc.) that will go into EVERY term.

3) Open the brackets and fill in all the bits needed to <u>reproduce each term</u>.

4) <u>Check</u> your answer by <u>multiplying out</u> the brackets and making sure it matches the original expression.

EXAMPLES:

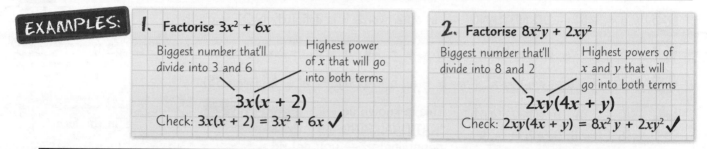

1. Factorise $3x^2 + 6x$

Biggest number that'll divide into 3 and 6

Highest power of x that will go into both terms

$$3x(x + 2)$$

Check: $3x(x + 2) = 3x^2 + 6x$ ✔

2. Factorise $8x^2y + 2xy^2$

Biggest number that'll divide into 8 and 2

Highest powers of x and y that will go into both terms

$$2xy(4x + y)$$

Check: $2xy(4x + y) = 8x^2y + 2xy^2$ ✔

> <u>REMEMBER</u>: The bits <u>taken out</u> and put at the front are the <u>common factors</u>. The bits <u>inside the brackets</u> are what's needed to get back to the <u>original terms</u> if you multiply the brackets out again.

D.O.T.S. — The Difference Of Two Squares (6)

The 'difference of two squares' (D.O.T.S. for short) is where you have 'one thing squared' <u>take away</u> 'another thing squared'. There's a quick and easy way to factorise it — just use the rule below:

$$a^2 - b^2 = (a + b)(a - b)$$

EXAMPLE:

Factorise: a) $x^2 - 1$ Answer: $x^2 - 1 = (x + 1)(x - 1)$
Don't forget that 1 is a square number (it's 1^2).

b) $9p^2 - 16q^2$ Answer: $9p^2 - 16q^2 = (3p + 4q)(3p - 4q)$
Here you had to spot that 9 and 16 are square numbers.

c) $3x^2 - 75y^2$ Answer: $3x^2 - 75y^2 = 3(x^2 - 25y^2) = 3(x + 5y)(x - 5y)$
This time, you had to take out a factor of 3 first.

Watch out — the difference of two squares can creep into other algebra questions. A popular <u>exam question</u> is to put a difference of two squares on the top or bottom of a <u>fraction</u> and ask you to simplify it. There's more on algebraic fractions on p.47.

EXAMPLE:

Simplify $\dfrac{x^2 - 36}{5x + 30}$

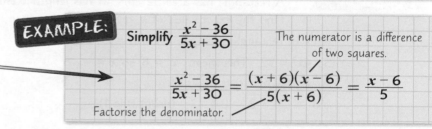

The numerator is a difference of two squares.

$$\frac{x^2 - 36}{5x + 30} = \frac{(x + 6)(x - 6)}{5(x + 6)} = \frac{x - 6}{5}$$

Factorise the denominator.

■ ■ *Well, one's green and one's yellow...*

As factorising is the reverse process of expanding brackets, you <u>must check</u> your answer by multiplying out the brackets. Make sure you can spot differences of two squares as well — they can be a bit sneaky.

Q1   Factorise $7x - 14$ [2 marks] (4)

Q2   Factorise $6xy + 15y^2$ [2 marks] (5)

Q3   Factorise $8x^2 - 2y^2$ [2 marks] (6)

Q4   Simplify $\dfrac{6x - 42}{x^2 - 49}$ [3 marks] (7)

Manipulating Surds

Surds are expressions with <u>irrational square roots</u> in them (remember from p.4 that irrational numbers are ones which <u>can't</u> be written as <u>fractions</u>, such as most square roots, cube roots and π).

Manipulating Surds — 6 Rules to Learn (7)

There are 6 rules you need to learn for dealing with surds...

1 $\sqrt{a} \times \sqrt{b} = \sqrt{a \times b}$ e.g. $\sqrt{2} \times \sqrt{3} = \sqrt{2 \times 3} = \sqrt{6}$ — also $(\sqrt{b})^2 = \sqrt{b} \times \sqrt{b} = b$, fairly obviously

2 $\dfrac{\sqrt{a}}{\sqrt{b}} = \sqrt{\dfrac{a}{b}}$ e.g. $\dfrac{\sqrt{8}}{\sqrt{2}} = \sqrt{\dfrac{8}{2}} = \sqrt{4} = 2$

3 $\sqrt{a} + \sqrt{b}$ — <u>DO NOTHING</u> — in other words it is definitely <u>NOT</u> $\sqrt{a+b}$

4 $(a + \sqrt{b})^2 = (a + \sqrt{b})(a + \sqrt{b}) = a^2 + 2a\sqrt{b} + b$ — <u>NOT</u> just $a^2 + (\sqrt{b})^2$ (see p.34)

5 $(a + \sqrt{b})(a - \sqrt{b}) = a^2 + a\sqrt{b} - a\sqrt{b} - (\sqrt{b})^2 = a^2 - b$ (see p.35).

6 $\dfrac{a}{\sqrt{b}} = \dfrac{a}{\sqrt{b}} \times \dfrac{\sqrt{b}}{\sqrt{b}} = \dfrac{a\sqrt{b}}{b}$

This is known as 'RATIONALISING the denominator' — you get rid of the $\sqrt{}$ on the bottom.

EXAMPLE: Write $\dfrac{3}{\sqrt{5}}$ in the form $\dfrac{a\sqrt{5}}{b}$, where a and b are whole numbers.

You have to rationalise the denominator — so multiply top and bottom by $\sqrt{5}$:

$\dfrac{3\sqrt{5}}{\sqrt{5}\sqrt{5}} = \dfrac{3\sqrt{5}}{5}$ — so a = 3 and b = 5

For denominators of the form $a \pm \sqrt{b}$, you always multiply by the denominator but <u>change the sign</u> in front of the root (see the example below).

EXAMPLE: Write $\dfrac{3}{2 + \sqrt{5}}$ in the form $a + b\sqrt{5}$, where a and b are integers. (9)

To rationalise the denominator, multiply top and bottom by $2 - \sqrt{5}$:

$$\dfrac{3}{2 + \sqrt{5}} = \dfrac{3(2 - \sqrt{5})}{(2 + \sqrt{5})(2 - \sqrt{5})} = \dfrac{6 - 3\sqrt{5}}{2^2 - 2\sqrt{5} + 2\sqrt{5} - (\sqrt{5})^2} = \dfrac{6 - 3\sqrt{5}}{4 - 5} = \dfrac{6 - 3\sqrt{5}}{-1} = -6 + 3\sqrt{5}$$

Leave Surds in Exact Answers (7)

If a question asks for an <u>exact answer</u>, just <u>leave</u> the surds in your answer. The same goes for calculations involving π — if you're asked for an <u>exact</u> answer, leave π in instead of using your π calculator button.

EXAMPLES:

1. A rectangle has area 32 cm². It has length x cm and width $4x$ cm. Find the exact value of x, giving your answer in its simplest form.

Area of rectangle = length × width = $x \times 4x = 4x^2$

So $4x^2 = 32$. This means $x^2 = 8$, so $x = \pm\sqrt{8}$ (8)

Now get $\sqrt{8}$ into its simplest form:

$\sqrt{8} = \sqrt{4 \times 2} = \sqrt{4}\sqrt{2}$ (using rule 1)
$= 2\sqrt{2}$ So $x = 2\sqrt{2}$

You can ignore the negative square root (see p.38) as length must be positive.

2. Find the exact area of a circle with radius 4 cm.

Area = $\pi r^2 = \pi \times 4^2$
$= 16\pi$ cm²

Rationalise the denominator? How absurd...

Learn the 6 rules for manipulating surds, then give these Exam Practice Questions a go...

Q1 Simplify: a) $(1 + \sqrt{2})(4 - \sqrt{2})$ [2 marks] b) $(2 - \sqrt{5})^2$ [2 marks] (7)

Q2 Write $\dfrac{2}{2 + \sqrt{3}}$ in the form $a + b\sqrt{3}$, where a and b are integers. [3 marks] (9)

Solving Equations

The basic idea of <u>solving equations</u> is very simple — keep <u>rearranging</u> until you end up with x = number. The two most common methods for <u>rearranging</u> equations are: 1) '<u>same to both sides</u>' and 2) do the <u>opposite</u> when you cross the '<u>=</u>'. We'll use the 'same to both sides' method on these pages.

Rearrange Until You Have x = Number ③

The easiest ones to solve are where you just have a <u>mixture</u> of x's and numbers.

1) First, <u>rearrange</u> the equation so that all the <u>x's</u> are on one side and the <u>numbers</u> are on the other. <u>Combine</u> terms where you can.

2) Then <u>divide</u> both sides by the <u>number multiplying x</u> to find the value of x.

EXAMPLE:

Solve $5x + 4 = 8x - 5$

This means 'add 5 to both sides'.

$(+5)$ $5x + 4 + 5 = 8x - 5 + 5$
$5x + 9 = 8x$
$(-5x)$ $5x + 9 - 5x = 8x - 5x$ — Numbers on left, x's on right.
$9 = 3x$
$(\div 3)$ $9 \div 3 = 3x \div 3$ — Divide by number multiplying x.
$3 = x$

Once you're happy with the method, you don't have to write everything out in full — your working might be:

$5x + 9 = 8x$
$9 = 3x$
$3 = x$

Multiply Out Brackets First

If your equation has <u>brackets</u> in it... ④

1) <u>Multiply</u> them out <u>before rearranging</u>.

2) <u>Solve it</u> in the same way as above.

EXAMPLE:

Solve $3(3x - 2) = 5x + 10$

$9x - 6 = 5x + 10$
$(-5x)$ $9x - 6 - 5x = 5x + 10 - 5x$
$4x - 6 = 10$
$(+6)$ $4x - 6 + 6 = 10 + 6$
$4x = 16$
$(\div 4)$ $4x \div 4 = 16 \div 4$
$x = 4$

Get Rid of Fractions (before they take over the world) ⑤

1) <u>Fractions</u> make everything more complicated — so you need to get rid of them <u>before doing anything else</u> (yep, even before multiplying out brackets).

2) To get rid of fractions, multiply <u>every term</u> of the equation by whatever's on the <u>bottom</u> of the fraction. If there are <u>two</u> fractions, multiply by <u>both</u> denominators (or by a <u>common multiple</u> of them).

EXAMPLES:

1. Solve $\dfrac{x + 2}{4} = 4x - 7$

$(\times 4)$ $\dfrac{4(x + 2)}{4} = 4(4x) - 4(7)$

Multiply every term by 4 to get rid of the fraction.

$x + 2 = 16x - 28$
$30 = 15x$ — And solve.
$2 = x$

2. Solve $\dfrac{3x + 5}{2} = \dfrac{4x + 10}{3}$ *Multiply everything by 2 then by 3.*

$(\times 2), (\times 3)$ $\dfrac{2 \times 3 \times (3x + 5)}{2} = \dfrac{2 \times 3 \times (4x + 10)}{3}$

$3(3x + 5) = 2(4x + 10)$
And solve. $9x + 15 = 8x + 20$
$x = 5$

Solving equations — more fun than greasing a seal...

Here's a handy final tip — you can always check your answer by sticking it in both sides of the original equation. They should both give the same number. Now practise what you've learned on these beauts:

Q1   Solve $2x + 5 = 17 - 4x$ [2 marks] ③

Q2   Solve $4(y + 3) = 3y + 16$ [3 marks] ④

Q3   Solve $\dfrac{3x + 2}{5} = \dfrac{5x + 6}{9}$ [3 marks] ⑤

Solving Equations

Now you know the basics of solving equations, it's time to put it all together into a handy step-by-step method.

Solving Equations Using the 6-Step Method (5)

Here's the method to follow (just ignore any steps that don't apply to your equation):

> 1) Get rid of any <u>fractions</u>.
> 2) <u>Multiply out</u> any brackets.
> 3) Collect all the <u>x-terms</u> on one side and all <u>number terms</u> on the other.
> 4) Reduce it to the form '<u>Ax = B</u>' (by <u>combining like terms</u>).
> 5) Finally <u>divide both sides by A</u> to give 'x =   ', and that's your answer.
> 6) If you had 'x^2 =   ' instead, <u>square root</u> both sides to end up with 'x = ±   '.

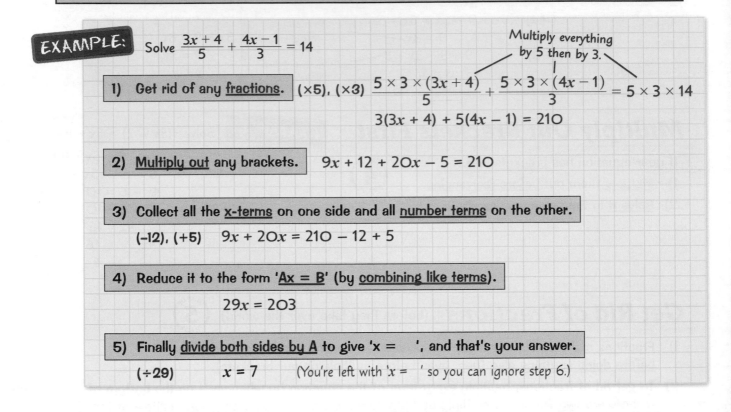

EXAMPLE: Solve $\dfrac{3x+4}{5} + \dfrac{4x-1}{3} = 14$

Multiply everything by 5 then by 3.

1) **Get rid of any <u>fractions</u>.** (×5), (×3) $\dfrac{5 \times 3 \times (3x+4)}{5} + \dfrac{5 \times 3 \times (4x-1)}{3} = 5 \times 3 \times 14$

$3(3x+4) + 5(4x-1) = 210$

2) **<u>Multiply out</u> any brackets.** $9x + 12 + 20x - 5 = 210$

3) **Collect all the <u>x-terms</u> on one side and all <u>number terms</u> on the other.**

(−12), (+5) $\quad 9x + 20x = 210 - 12 + 5$

4) **Reduce it to the form '<u>Ax = B</u>' (by <u>combining like terms</u>).**

$29x = 203$

5) **Finally <u>divide both sides by A</u> to give 'x =   ', and that's your answer.**

(÷29) $\quad x = 7 \quad$ (You're left with '$x = $' so you can ignore step 6.)

Dealing with Squares (5)

If you're unlucky, you might get an $\underline{x^2}$ in an equation. If this happens, you'll end up with '$x^2 = ...$' at step 5, and then step 6 is to take <u>square roots</u>. There's one very important thing to remember: whenever you take the square root of a number, the answer can be <u>positive</u> or <u>negative</u>...

EXAMPLE: Solve $3x^2 = 75$.

(÷3) $\quad x^2 = 25$

($\sqrt{}$) $\quad x = \pm 5$

You always get a <u>+ve</u> and <u>−ve</u> version of the <u>same number</u> (your calculator only gives the +ve answer). This shows why:
$5^2 = 5 \times 5 = 25$ but also
$(-5)^2 = (-5) \times (-5) = 25$.

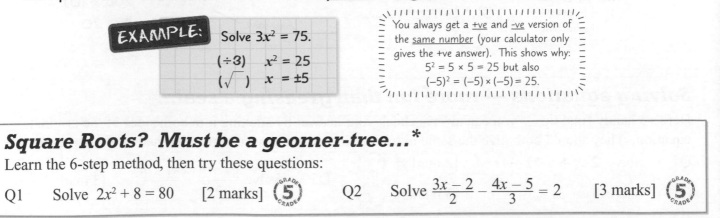

Square Roots? Must be a geomer-tree...*

Learn the 6-step method, then try these questions:

Q1   Solve $2x^2 + 8 = 80$ [2 marks] (5)   Q2   Solve $\dfrac{3x-2}{2} - \dfrac{4x-5}{3} = 2$ [3 marks] (5)

    *winner of Best Maths Gag in a Supporting Role, International Algebra Awards 2016

Rearranging Formulas

Rearranging formulas means making one letter the subject, e.g. getting 'y = ' from '2x + z = 3(y + 2p)'
— you have to get the subject on its own.

Use the Solving Equations Method to Rearrange Formulas

Rearranging formulas is remarkably similar to solving equations. The method below is identical to the method for solving equations, except that I've added an extra step at the start.

1) Get rid of any square root signs by squaring both sides.

2) Get rid of any fractions.

3) Multiply out any brackets.

4) Collect all the subject terms on one side and all non-subject terms on the other.

5) Reduce it to the form 'Ax = B' (by combining like terms). You might have to do some factorising here too.

6) Divide both sides by A to give 'x = '.

7) If you're left with 'x² = ', square root both sides to get 'x = ± ' (don't forget the ±).

x is the subject term here. A and B could be numbers or letters (or a mix of both).

What to Do If...

...the Subject Appears in a Fraction

You won't always need to use all 7 steps in the method above — just ignore the ones that don't apply.

EXAMPLE: Make b the subject of the formula $a = \dfrac{5b + 3}{4}$.

There aren't any square roots, so ignore step 1.

2) Get rid of any fractions. (by multiplying every term by 4, the denominator)

$(\times 4) \quad 4a = \dfrac{4(5b + 3)}{4}$

$4a = 5b + 3$

There aren't any brackets, so ignore step 3.

4) Collect all the subject terms on one side and all non-subject terms on the other.

(remember that you're trying to make b the subject)

$(-3) \quad 5b = 4a - 3$

5) It's now in the form Ax = B. (where A = 5 and B = 4a − 3)

6) Divide both sides by 5 to give 'b = '.

$(\div 5) \quad b = \dfrac{4a - 3}{5}$

b isn't squared, so you don't need step 7.

If I could rearrange my subjects, I'd have maths all day every day...

Learn the 7 steps for rearranging formulas. Then get rearrangin' with these snazzy Exam Practice Questions:

Q1   Make q the subject of the formula $p = \dfrac{q}{7} + 2r$ [2 marks]

Q2   Make z the subject of the formula $x = \dfrac{y + 2z}{3}$ [3 marks]

Rearranging Formulas

Carrying straight on from the previous page, now it's time for what to do if...

...there's a Square or Square Root Involved (5)

If the subject appears as a <u>square</u> or in a <u>square root</u>, you'll have to use steps 1 and 7 (not necessarily both).

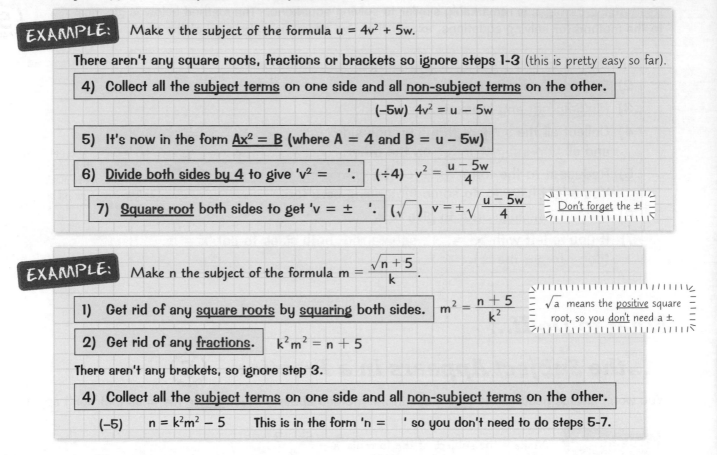

EXAMPLE: Make v the subject of the formula $u = 4v^2 + 5w$.

There aren't any square roots, fractions or brackets so ignore steps 1-3 (this is pretty easy so far).

4) Collect all the <u>subject terms</u> on one side and all <u>non-subject terms</u> on the other.

$(-5w)$ $\quad 4v^2 = u - 5w$

5) It's now in the form $\underline{Ax^2 = B}$ (where A = 4 and B = u – 5w)

6) <u>Divide both sides by 4</u> to give '$v^2 =$ '. $\quad (\div 4) \quad v^2 = \dfrac{u - 5w}{4}$

7) <u>Square root</u> both sides to get '$v = \pm$ '. $\quad (\sqrt{\ }) \quad v = \pm\sqrt{\dfrac{u - 5w}{4}}$ $\quad$ <u>Don't forget</u> the ±!

EXAMPLE: Make n the subject of the formula $m = \dfrac{\sqrt{n + 5}}{k}$.

1) Get rid of any <u>square roots</u> by <u>squaring</u> both sides. $\quad m^2 = \dfrac{n + 5}{k^2}$ $\quad$ $\sqrt{a}$ means the <u>positive</u> square root, so you <u>don't</u> need a ±.

2) Get rid of any <u>fractions</u>. $\quad k^2m^2 = n + 5$

There aren't any brackets, so ignore step 3.

4) Collect all the <u>subject terms</u> on one side and all <u>non-subject terms</u> on the other.

$(-5) \quad n = k^2m^2 - 5 \quad$ This is in the form 'n = ' so you don't need to do steps 5-7.

...the Subject Appears Twice (6)

Go home and cry. No, not really — you'll just have to do some <u>factorising</u>, usually in step 5.

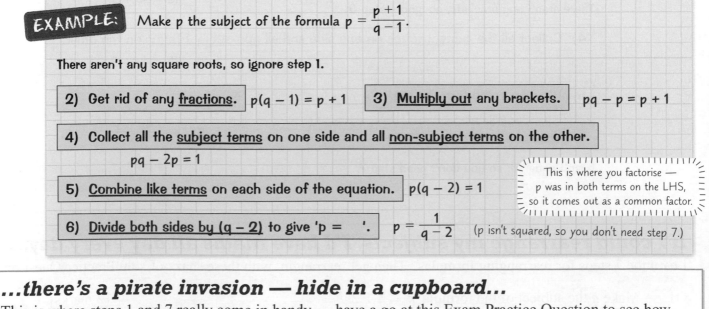

EXAMPLE: Make p the subject of the formula $p = \dfrac{p + 1}{q - 1}$.

There aren't any square roots, so ignore step 1.

2) Get rid of any <u>fractions</u>. $\quad p(q - 1) = p + 1$ $\qquad$ 3) <u>Multiply out</u> any brackets. $\quad pq - p = p + 1$

4) Collect all the <u>subject terms</u> on one side and all <u>non-subject terms</u> on the other.

$pq - 2p = 1$

5) <u>Combine like terms</u> on each side of the equation. $\quad p(q - 2) = 1$ $\quad$ This is where you factorise — p was in both terms on the LHS, so it comes out as a common factor.

6) <u>Divide both sides by (q – 2)</u> to give '$p =$ '. $\quad p = \dfrac{1}{q - 2}$ $\quad$ (p isn't squared, so you don't need step 7.)

...there's a pirate invasion — hide in a cupboard...

This is where steps 1 and 7 really come in handy — have a go at this Exam Practice Question to see how...

Q1 $\quad$ Make y the subject of: $\quad$ a) $x = \dfrac{y^2}{4}$ $\quad$ [2 marks] (5) $\qquad$ b) $x = \dfrac{y}{y - z}$ $\quad$ [4 marks] (6)

Factorising Quadratics

There are several ways of solving a quadratic equation, as detailed on the following pages.
You need to know all the methods as they sometimes ask for specific ones in the exam.

Factorising a Quadratic

1) 'Factorising a quadratic' means 'putting it into 2 brackets'.

2) The standard format for quadratic equations is: $ax^2 + bx + c = 0$.

3) Most exam questions have $\underline{a = 1}$, making them much easier. E.g. $x^2 + 3x + 2 = 0$

See next page for when 'a' is not 1.

4) As well as factorising a quadratic, you might be asked to solve it.
This just means finding the values of x that make each bracket $\underline{0}$ (see example below).

Factorising Method when a = 1

1) **ALWAYS** rearrange into the **STANDARD FORMAT**: $ax^2 + bx + c = 0$.

2) Write down the **TWO BRACKETS** with the x's in: $(x\ \ \ )(x\ \ \ ) = 0$.

3) Then find 2 numbers that **MULTIPLY to give 'c'** (the end number) but also **ADD/SUBTRACT to give 'b'** (the coefficient of x).

Ignore any minus signs at this stage.

4) Fill in the +/− signs and make sure they work out properly.

5) As an **ESSENTIAL CHECK**, expand the brackets to make sure they give the original equation.

6) Finally, **SOLVE THE EQUATION** by setting each bracket equal to 0.

You only need to do step 6) if the question asks you to solve the quadratic
— if it just tells you to factorise, you can stop at step 5).

EXAMPLE: Solve $x^2 - x = 12$.

1) $x^2 - x - 12 = 0$ 1) Rearrange into the standard format.

2) $(x\ \ \ )(x\ \ \ ) = 0$ 2) Write down the initial brackets.

3)
	Add/subtract to give:	
1×12	Add/subtract to give:	13 or 11
2×6	Add/subtract to give:	8 or 4
3×4	Add/subtract to give:	7 or ①

3) Find the right pairs of numbers that multiply to give c (= 12), and add or subtract to give b (= 1) (remember, we're ignoring the +/− signs for now).

$(x\ \ \ 3)(x\ \ \ 4) = 0$ This is what we want.

4) $(x + 3)(x - 4) = 0$ 4) Now fill in the +/− signs so that 3 and 4 add/subtract to give −1 (= b).

5) Check:
$(x + 3)(x - 4) = x^2 - 4x + 3x - 12$
$= x^2 - x - 12$ ✓

5) **ESSENTIAL** check — **EXPAND the brackets** to make sure they give the original equation.

But we're not finished yet — we've only factorised it, we still need to...

6) $(x + 3) = 0 \Rightarrow x = -3$
$(x - 4) = 0 \Rightarrow x = 4$

6) **SOLVE THE EQUATION** by setting each bracket equal to 0.

Bring me a biscuit or I'll factorise your quadratic...

Handy tip: to help you work out which signs you need, look at c. If c is positive, the signs will be the same (both positive or both negative), but if c is negative the signs will be different (one positive and one negative).

Q1   Factorise $x^2 + 2x - 15$ [2 marks]   Q2   Solve $x^2 - 9x + 20 = 0$ [3 marks]

Factorising Quadratics

So far so good. It gets a bit more complicated when 'a' isn't 1, but it's all good fun, right? Right?
Well, I think it's fun anyway.

When 'a' is Not 1 (GRADE 7)

The basic method is still the same but it's <u>a bit messier</u> — the initial brackets are <u>different</u> as the first terms in
each bracket have to multiply to give '<u>a</u>'. This means finding the <u>other</u> numbers to go in the brackets is harder
as there are more <u>combinations</u> to try. The best way to get to grips with it is to have a look at an <u>example</u>.

EXAMPLE: Solve $3x^2 + 7x - 6 = 0$.

1) $3x^2 + 7x - 6 = 0$

2) $(3x \quad)(x \quad) = 0$

3) Number pairs: 1×6 and 2×3

$(3x \quad 1)(x \quad 6)$ multiplies to give <u>18x and 1x</u>
which <u>add/subtract</u> to give <u>17x or 19x</u>

$(3x \quad 6)(x \quad 1)$ multiplies to give <u>3x and 6x</u>
which <u>add/subtract</u> to give <u>9x or 3x</u>

$(3x \quad 3)(x \quad 2)$ multiplies to give <u>6x and 3x</u>
which <u>add/subtract</u> to give <u>9x or 3x</u>

$(3x \quad 2)(x \quad 3)$ multiplies to give <u>9x and 2x</u>
which <u>add/subtract</u> to give <u>11x or (7x)</u> ✓

$(3x \quad 2)(x \quad 3)$

4) $(3x - 2)(x + 3)$

5) $(3x - 2)(x + 3) = 3x^2 + 9x - 2x - 6$
$\qquad\qquad\qquad\quad = 3x^2 + 7x - 6$ ✓

6) $(3x - 2) = 0 \Rightarrow x = \frac{2}{3}$
$\quad (x + 3) = 0 \Rightarrow x = -3$

1) <u>Rearrange</u> into the standard format.

2) Write down the <u>initial brackets</u> — this time,
one of the brackets will have a <u>3x</u> in it.

3) The <u>tricky part</u>: first, find <u>pairs of numbers</u>
that <u>multiply to give c</u> (= 6), ignoring the
minus sign for now.

Then, <u>try out</u> the number pairs you just
found in the brackets until you find one
that gives 7x. But remember, each pair
of numbers has to be tried in <u>2 positions</u>
(as the brackets are different — one has
3x in it).

4) <u>Now fill in the +/− signs</u> so that 9 and 2
add/subtract to give +7 (= b).

5) <u>ESSENTIAL check</u> — <u>EXPAND the brackets</u>.

6) <u>SOLVE THE EQUATION</u> by setting each
bracket <u>equal to 0</u> (if a isn't 1, one of your
answers will be a <u>fraction</u>).

EXAMPLE: Solve $2x^2 - 9x = 5$.

1) Put in standard form: $2x^2 - 9x - 5 = 0$

2) Initial brackets: $(2x \quad)(x \quad) = 0$

3) Number pairs: 1×5

$(2x \quad 5)(x \quad 1)$ multiplies to give <u>2x and 5x</u>
which <u>add/subtract</u> to give <u>3x or 7x</u>

$(2x \quad 1)(x \quad 5)$ multiplies to give <u>1x and 10x</u>
which <u>add/subtract</u> to give (9x) or 11x

$(2x \quad 1)(x \quad 5)$ ✓

4) Put in the signs: $(2x + 1)(x - 5)$

5) Check:
$(2x + 1)(x - 5) = 2x^2 - 10x + x - 5$
$\qquad\qquad\qquad\quad = 2x^2 - 9x - 5$ ✓

6) Solve:
$(2x + 1) = 0 \Rightarrow x = -\frac{1}{2}$
$\quad (x - 5) = 0 \Rightarrow x = 5$

It's not scary — just think of it as brackets giving algebra a hug...

Learn the step-by-step method for solving quadratics, then have a go at these Exam Practice Questions:

Q1   Factorise $2x^2 - 5x - 12$ [2 marks] (GRADE 7)

Q2   Solve $3x^2 + 10x - 8 = 0$ [3 marks] (GRADE 7)

Q3   Factorise $3x^2 + 32x + 20$ [2 marks] (GRADE 7)

Q4   Solve $5x^2 - 13x = 6$ [3 marks] (GRADE 7)

The Quadratic Formula

The solutions to ANY quadratic equation $ax^2 + bx + c = 0$ are given by this formula:

$$x = \frac{-b \pm \sqrt{b^2 - 4ac}}{2a}$$

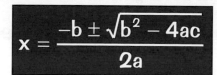

LEARN THIS FORMULA — and <u>how to use it</u>. It's usually given in the exam, but if you don't learn it, you won't know how to use it. Using it isn't that hard, but there are a few pitfalls — so <u>TAKE HEED of these crucial details</u>:

Quadratic Formula — Five Crucial Details ⑦

1) Take it nice and slowly — always write it down in stages as you go.

2) **WHENEVER YOU GET A MINUS SIGN, <u>THE ALARM BELLS SHOULD ALWAYS RING</u>!**

3) Remember it's <u>2a</u> on the bottom line, not just a — and you <u>divide ALL of the top line by 2a</u>.

> If either 'a' or 'c' is negative, the −4ac effectively becomes +4ac, so watch out. Also, be careful if b is negative, as −b will be positive.

4) The ± sign means you end up with <u>two solutions</u> (by replacing it in the final step with '+' and '−').

5) If you get a <u>negative</u> number inside your square root, go back and <u>check your working</u>. Some quadratics do have a negative value in the square root, but they won't come up in the exam.

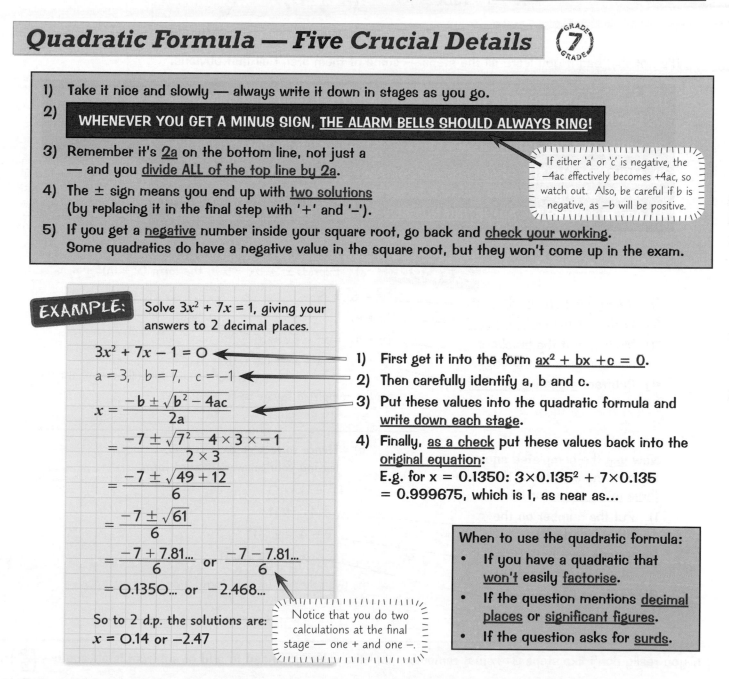

EXAMPLE: Solve $3x^2 + 7x = 1$, giving your answers to 2 decimal places.

$3x^2 + 7x - 1 = 0$

$a = 3, \quad b = 7, \quad c = -1$

$x = \dfrac{-b \pm \sqrt{b^2 - 4ac}}{2a}$

$= \dfrac{-7 \pm \sqrt{7^2 - 4 \times 3 \times -1}}{2 \times 3}$

$= \dfrac{-7 \pm \sqrt{49 + 12}}{6}$

$= \dfrac{-7 \pm \sqrt{61}}{6}$

$= \dfrac{-7 + 7.81...}{6}$ or $\dfrac{-7 - 7.81...}{6}$

$= 0.1350...$ or $-2.468...$

So to 2 d.p. the solutions are:
$x = 0.14$ or -2.47

> Notice that you do two calculations at the final stage — one + and one −.

1) First get it into the form $\underline{ax^2 + bx + c = 0}$.

2) Then carefully identify a, b and c.

3) Put these values into the quadratic formula and <u>write down each stage</u>.

4) Finally, <u>as a check</u> put these values back into the <u>original equation</u>:
E.g. for x = 0.1350: $3 \times 0.135^2 + 7 \times 0.135$ = 0.999675, which is 1, as near as...

> **When to use the quadratic formula:**
> • If you have a quadratic that <u>won't</u> easily <u>factorise</u>.
> • If the question mentions <u>decimal places</u> or <u>significant figures</u>.
> • If the question asks for <u>surds</u>.

Enough number crunches? Now it's time to work on your quads...

Learn the crucial details and how to use the quadratic formula. Done it? Now it's time to practise your mad new skillz with these handy Exam Practice Questions...

Q1 Solve $x^2 + 10x - 4 = 0$, giving your answers to 2 decimal places. [3 marks] ⑦

Q2 Solve $3x^2 - 3x = 2$, giving your answers to 2 decimal places. [3 marks] ⑦

Completing the Square

There's just one more method to learn for solving quadratics — and it's a bit of a nasty one.
It's called 'completing the square', and takes a bit to get your head round it.

Solving Quadratics by 'Completing the Square'

To 'complete the square' you have to:

1) Write down a __SQUARED__ bracket, and then   2) Stick a number on the end to '__COMPLETE__' it.

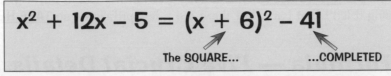

$$x^2 + 12x - 5 = (x + 6)^2 - 41$$

The SQUARE...   ...COMPLETED

It's not that bad if you learn all the steps — some of them aren't all that obvious.

1) As always, __REARRANGE THE QUADRATIC INTO THE STANDARD FORMAT__: $ax^2 + bx + c$ (the rest of this method is for a = 1).

2) __WRITE OUT THE INITIAL BRACKET__: $(x + \frac{b}{2})^2$ — just divide the value of b by 2.

3) __MULTIPLY OUT THE BRACKETS__ and __COMPARE TO THE ORIGINAL__ to find what you need to add or subtract to complete the square.

4) Add or subtract the __ADJUSTING NUMBER__ to make it __MATCH THE ORIGINAL__.

If a isn't 1, you have to divide through by 'a' or take out a factor of 'a' at the start — see next page.

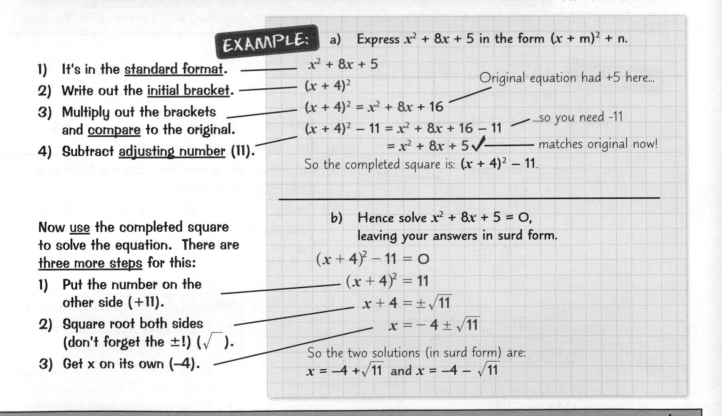

__EXAMPLE:__ a) Express $x^2 + 8x + 5$ in the form $(x + m)^2 + n$.

1) It's in the __standard format__. ——— $x^2 + 8x + 5$

2) Write out the __initial bracket__. ——— $(x + 4)^2$ Original equation had +5 here...

3) Multiply out the brackets and __compare__ to the original. ——— $(x + 4)^2 = x^2 + 8x + 16$ ...so you need –11

4) Subtract __adjusting number__ (11). ——— $(x + 4)^2 - 11 = x^2 + 8x + 16 - 11$
$$= x^2 + 8x + 5 \checkmark \quad\text{— matches original now!}$$

So the completed square is: $(x + 4)^2 - 11$.

Now __use__ the completed square to solve the equation. There are __three more steps__ for this:

b) Hence solve $x^2 + 8x + 5 = 0$, leaving your answers in surd form.

1) Put the number on the other side (+11). ——— $(x + 4)^2 - 11 = 0$
$$(x + 4)^2 = 11$$

2) Square root both sides (don't forget the ±!) ($\sqrt{\ }$). ——— $x + 4 = \pm\sqrt{11}$

3) Get x on its own (–4). ——— $x = -4 \pm \sqrt{11}$

So the two solutions (in surd form) are:
$$x = -4 + \sqrt{11} \text{ and } x = -4 - \sqrt{11}$$

If you really don't like steps 3-4, just remember that the value you need to add or subtract is __always__ $c - \left(\frac{b}{2}\right)^2$.

But if a square's not complete, is it really a square...?

Go over this carefully, 'cos it's pretty gosh darn confusing at first, then try these Exam Practice Questions.

Q1   Write $x^2 - 12x + 23$ in the form $(x + p)^2 + q$.   [3 marks]

Q2   Solve $x^2 + 10x + 7 = 0$, by first writing it in the form $(x + m)^2 + n = 0$.
Give your answers as simplified surds.   [5 marks]

Completing the Square

If you're a fan of <u>completing the square</u>, good news — there's another page on it here.
If you're not a fan of completing the square, bad news — there's another page on it here.

Completing the Square When 'a' Isn't 1 (9)

If 'a' isn't 1, completing the square is a bit trickier. You follow the <u>same method</u> as on the previous page, but you have to take out a <u>factor of 'a'</u> from the x^2 and x-terms before you start (which often means you end up with awkward <u>fractions</u>). This time, the number in the brackets is $\frac{b}{2a}$.

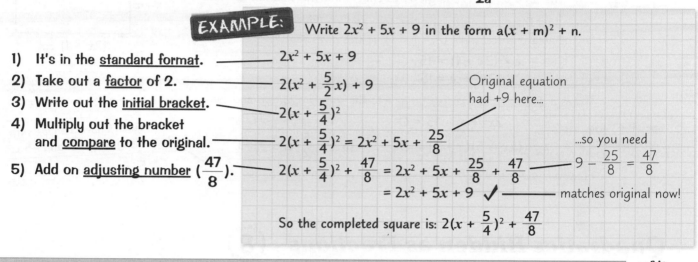

EXAMPLE: Write $2x^2 + 5x + 9$ in the form $a(x + m)^2 + n$.

1) It's in the <u>standard format</u>. —— $2x^2 + 5x + 9$
2) Take out a <u>factor</u> of 2. —— $2(x^2 + \frac{5}{2}x) + 9$
3) Write out the <u>initial bracket</u>. —— $2(x + \frac{5}{4})^2$
4) Multiply out the bracket and <u>compare</u> to the original. —— $2(x + \frac{5}{4})^2 = 2x^2 + 5x + \frac{25}{8}$
5) Add on <u>adjusting number</u> ($\frac{47}{8}$). —— $2(x + \frac{5}{4})^2 + \frac{47}{8} = 2x^2 + 5x + \frac{25}{8} + \frac{47}{8}$
$= 2x^2 + 5x + 9$ ✓ —— matches original now!

Original equation had +9 here... ...so you need $9 - \frac{25}{8} = \frac{47}{8}$

So the completed square is: $2(x + \frac{5}{4})^2 + \frac{47}{8}$

The Completed Square Helps You Sketch the Graph (9)

You can use the <u>completed square</u> to work out key details about the graph — like the <u>turning point</u> (maximum or minimum) and whether it <u>crosses</u> the x-axis.

1) For a <u>positive</u> quadratic (where the x^2 coefficient is positive), the <u>adjusting number</u> tells you the <u>minimum</u> y-value of the graph. If the completed square is $a(x + m)^2 + n$, this minimum y-value will occur when the brackets are equal to 0 (because the bit in brackets is squared, so is never negative) — i.e. when $x = -m$.

2) The <u>solutions</u> to the equation tell you where the graph <u>crosses</u> the <u>x-axis</u>. If the adjusting number is <u>positive</u>, the graph will <u>never</u> cross the x-axis as it will always be greater than 0 (this means that the quadratic has <u>no real roots</u>).

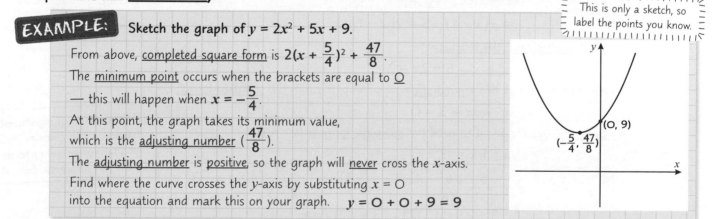

EXAMPLE: Sketch the graph of $y = 2x^2 + 5x + 9$.

From above, <u>completed square form</u> is $2(x + \frac{5}{4})^2 + \frac{47}{8}$.
The <u>minimum point</u> occurs when the brackets are equal to <u>0</u>
— this will happen when $x = -\frac{5}{4}$.
At this point, the graph takes its minimum value, which is the <u>adjusting number</u> ($\frac{47}{8}$).
The <u>adjusting number</u> is <u>positive</u>, so the graph will <u>never</u> cross the x-axis.
Find where the curve crosses the y-axis by substituting $x = 0$ into the equation and mark this on your graph. $y = 0 + 0 + 9 = 9$

This is only a sketch, so label the points you know.

$(0, 9)$
$(-\frac{5}{4}, \frac{47}{8})$

Complete the following square: ☐

I'm not going to lie, this page was rather challenging (I got a bit confused myself). Be careful taking out the factor of a — you only do it for the first two terms. Take care with your fractions too.

Q1 a) Write $2x^2 + 3x - 5$ in the form $a(x + b)^2 + c$. [4 marks]
    b) Hence solve $2x^2 + 3x - 5 = 0$. [2 marks] (9)
    c) Use your answer to part a) to find the coordinates of the minimum point of the graph of $y = 2x^2 + 3x - 5$. [1 mark]

Quadratic Equations — Tricky Ones

Now it's time to have a go at some tricky 'hidden quadratic' questions that sometimes pop up in the exam.

Shape Questions Involving Quadratics (7)

Sometimes examiners like to disguise quadratic equations by pretending the question is about a shape — it might look like an area or volume question where you have to find the length of a side. Don't be fooled though.

EXAMPLE: The rectangle on the right has sides of length x cm and $(2x + 1)$ cm. The area of the rectangle is 15 cm². Find the value of x.

x cm

$(2x + 1)$ cm

You're told the side lengths and the area, and you know the formula for the area of a rectangle ($A = l \times w$), so this gives you:

$$x \times (2x + 1) = 15$$
$$2x^2 + x = 15$$

This is a quadratic, so just rearrange into the standard format and solve:

See p.41-42 if you need some help factorising.

$$2x^2 + x - 15 = 0$$
$$(2x - 5)(x + 3) = 0 \qquad \text{so } x = \frac{5}{2} \text{ or } x = -3.$$

You couldn't have a shape with sides of length −3 cm and −5 cm.

However, you're looking for a length, which means x can't be negative — so $x = \frac{5}{2}$

Quadratics Hidden as Fractions (8)

This is a nasty exam question — you're given an equation to solve that looks like it's an algebraic fractions question (more about these on the next page), but after some rearranging, it turns out you've got a quadratic.

EXAMPLE: Solve $x - \dfrac{5}{x - 1} = 2$, giving your answers to 3 significant figures.

At first glance, this doesn't look like a quadratic, but wait and see...

The first thing to do is to get rid of the fraction (by multiplying every term by $(x - 1)$):

This is using the method for solving equations from p.38.

$$x(x - 1) - \frac{5(x - 1)}{x - 1} = 2(x - 1)$$
$$\Rightarrow x(x - 1) - 5 = 2(x - 1)$$

Next, multiply out the brackets:

$$x^2 - x - 5 = 2x - 2$$

It's starting to look like a quadratic now, so write it out in the standard format:

$$x^2 - 3x - 3 = 0$$

Solve it — you're going to need the quadratic formula (see p.43):

$$a = 1, b = -3, c = -3$$

The mention of significant figures in the question is a hint that you're going to need to use the quadratic formula.

$$x = \frac{-b \pm \sqrt{b^2 - 4ac}}{2a} = \frac{-(-3) \pm \sqrt{(-3)^2 - (4 \times 1 \times -3)}}{2 \times 1}$$
$$= \frac{3 \pm \sqrt{9 - (-12)}}{2} = \frac{3 \pm \sqrt{21}}{2}$$

$$x = \frac{3 + \sqrt{21}}{2} = 3.7912... = 3.79 \text{ (3 s.f.) or } x = \frac{3 - \sqrt{21}}{2} = -0.7912... = -0.791 \text{ (3 s.f.)}$$

I'd like to hide FROM quadratics...

There's no telling what might come up in an exam — be prepared to spot hidden quadratics and solve them.

Q1   Find the exact solutions of $2x + \dfrac{3}{x - 2} = -2$. Give your answers in surd form.   **[4 marks]** (8)

Algebraic Fractions

Unfortunately, fractions aren't limited to numbers — you can get <u>algebraic fractions</u> too.
Fortunately, everything you learnt about fractions on p.9-10 can be applied to algebraic fractions as well.

Simplifying Algebraic Fractions (6)

You can <u>simplify</u> algebraic fractions by <u>cancelling</u> terms on the top and bottom — just deal with each <u>letter</u> individually and cancel as much as you can. You might have to <u>factorise</u> first (see pages 35 and 41-42).

EXAMPLES:

1. Simplify $\dfrac{21x^3y^2}{14xy^3}$

÷7 on the top and bottom

÷x on the top and bottom to leave x^2 on the top

÷y^2 on the top and bottom to leave y on the bottom

$$\dfrac{\overset{3}{\cancel{21}}\,\overset{x^2}{\cancel{x^3}}y^2}{\underset{2}{\cancel{14}}x\underset{y}{\cancel{y^3}}} = \dfrac{3x^2}{2y}$$

2. Simplify $\dfrac{x^2-16}{x^2+2x-8}$

Factorise the top using D.O.T.S.

Factorise the quadratic on the bottom

Then cancel the common factor of $(x+4)$

$$\dfrac{(x+4)(x-4)}{(x-2)(x+4)} = \dfrac{x-4}{x-2}$$

Multiplying/Dividing Algebraic Fractions (8)

1) To <u>multiply</u> two fractions, just multiply tops and bottoms <u>separately</u>.

EXAMPLE: Simplify $\dfrac{x^2}{4} \times \dfrac{2}{x+1}$

Cancel the number terms first...

$$\dfrac{x^2}{\underset{2}{\cancel{4}}} \times \dfrac{\cancel{2}}{x+1} = \dfrac{x^2}{2(x+1)}$$

2) To <u>divide</u>, turn the second fraction <u>upside down</u> then <u>multiply</u>.

EXAMPLE: Simplify $\dfrac{2}{x} \div \dfrac{x^3}{5}$

$$\dfrac{2}{x} \div \dfrac{x^3}{5} = \dfrac{2}{x} \times \dfrac{5}{x^3} = \dfrac{10}{x^4}$$

Adding/Subtracting Algebraic Fractions (8)

For the common denominator, find something both denominators divide into.

Adding or subtracting is a bit more difficult:
1) Work out the <u>common denominator</u> (see p.10).
2) Multiply <u>top and bottom</u> of each fraction by whatever gives you the common denominator.
3) Add or subtract the <u>numerators</u> only.

Fractions		
$\dfrac{1}{x}+\dfrac{1}{3x}$	$\dfrac{1}{x+1}+\dfrac{1}{x-2}$	$\dfrac{1}{x}+\dfrac{1}{x(x+1)}$
$3x$	$(x+1)(x-2)$	$x(x+1)$
Common denominator		

EXAMPLE: Write $\dfrac{3x}{(x+3)} + \dfrac{x-3}{(x-2)}$ as a single fraction.

1st fraction: × top & bottom by $(x-2)$
2nd fraction: × top & bottom by $(x+3)$
Add the numerators

$$\dfrac{3x}{(x+3)} + \dfrac{x-3}{(x-2)} = \dfrac{3x(x-2)}{(x+3)(x-2)} + \dfrac{(x+3)(x-3)}{(x+3)(x-2)}$$

Common denominator will be $(x+3)(x-2)$

$$= \dfrac{3x^2-6x}{(x+3)(x-2)} + \dfrac{x^2-9}{(x+3)(x-2)} = \dfrac{4x^2-6x-9}{(x+3)(x-2)}$$

I'd like to cancel the Summer Term...

One more thing... never do this: $\dfrac{\cancel{x}}{\cancel{x}+y} = \dfrac{1}{y}$ ✗ It's wrong wrong WRONG! Got that? Good, now try these:

Q1 Simplify $\dfrac{18ab^3}{6a^2b}$ [2 marks] (6)

Q2 Simplify $\dfrac{x+3}{2} \div \dfrac{2}{x}$ [2 marks] (8)

Q3 Write $\dfrac{3}{x+4} - \dfrac{2}{x-1}$ as a single fraction in its simplest form. [3 marks] (8)

Inequalities

Inequalities aren't <u>half as difficult as they look</u>. Once you've learned the tricks involved, most of the algebra for them is <u>identical to ordinary equations</u> (have a look back at p.37-38 if you need a reminder).

The Inequality Symbols (3)

> means '<u>Greater than</u>'   ≥ means '<u>Greater than or equal to</u>'
< means '<u>Less than</u>'   ≤ means '<u>Less than or equal to</u>'

I > All of you.

<u>REMEMBER</u> — the one at the <u>BIG</u> end is <u>BIGGEST</u> so x > 4 and 4 < x both say: '<u>x is greater than 4</u>'.

Algebra with Inequalities (5)

The key thing about inequalities is to solve them <u>just like regular equations</u> but <u>WITH ONE BIG EXCEPTION</u>:

Whenever you <u>MULTIPLY OR DIVIDE</u> by a <u>NEGATIVE NUMBER</u>, you must <u>FLIP THE INEQUALITY SIGN</u>.

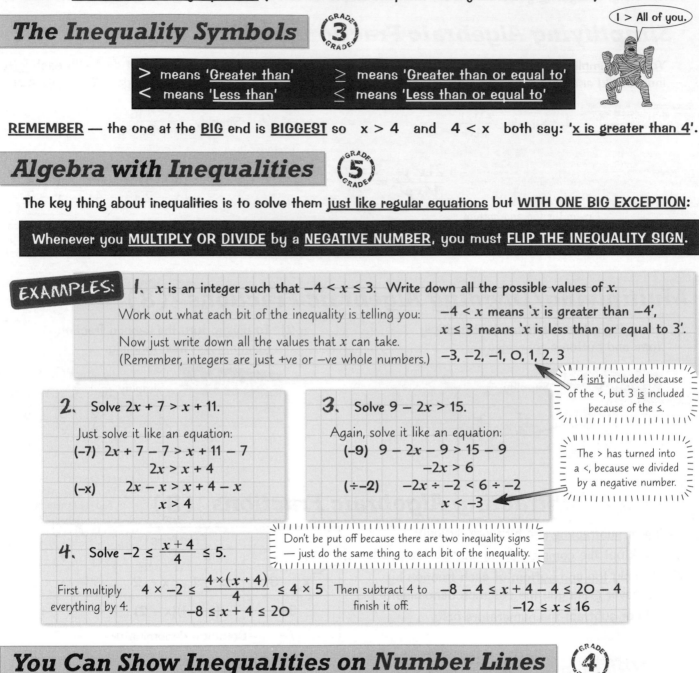

You Can Show Inequalities on Number Lines (4)

Drawing inequalities on a <u>number line</u> is dead easy — all you have to remember is that you use an <u>open circle</u> (O) for > or < and a <u>coloured-in circle</u> (●) for ≥ or ≤.

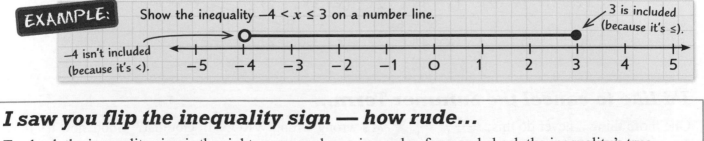

I saw you flip the inequality sign — how rude...

To check the inequality sign is the right way round, pop in a value for x and check the inequality's true.

Q1   Solve: a) $11x + 3 < 47$ [2 marks]   b) $4x \geq 18 - 2x$ [2 marks] (4)

Q2   Solve the inequality $-8 \leq 5x + 2 \leq 22$ and represent the solution on a number line.   [3 marks] (5)

Inequalities

Quadratic inequalities can get pretty tough. Because they involve an x^2 term, they'll have <u>two</u> bounds for x...

Take Care with Quadratic Inequalities (6)

If $x^2 = 4$, then $x = \underline{+2 \text{ or } -2}$. Remember this when solving quadratic inequalities.

EXAMPLES:

1. Solve the inequality $x^2 \leq 25$.

If $x^2 = 25$, then $x = \pm 5$.
As $x^2 \leq 25$, then $\mathbf{-5 \leq x \leq 5}$

This means x is between -5 and 5, possibly equal to either. It looks like this on a number line:

2. Solve the inequality $x^2 > 9$.

If $x^2 = 9$, then $x = \pm 3$.
As $x^2 > 9$, then $\mathbf{x < -3 \text{ or } x > 3}$

This means x is less than -3 or greater than 3. It looks like this on a number line:

Harder Quadratic Inequalities (7)

If the examiners are feeling particularly mean, you might get a harder quadratic inequality that <u>takes more steps</u> to solve. Worst case scenario, you might even need to sketch a graph...

EXAMPLES:

1. Solve the inequality $3x^2 \geq 48$.

Just solve it like an equation:

$(\div 3) \quad \dfrac{3x^2}{3} \geq \dfrac{48}{3}$

$x^2 \geq 16$

$x \leq -4 \text{ or } x \geq 4$

2. Solve the inequality $-2x^2 + 8 > 0$.

$(-8) \quad -2x^2 + 8 - 8 > 0 - 8$

$-2x^2 > -8$

$(\div -2) \quad -2x^2 \div -2 < -8 \div -2$

$x^2 < 4$

$-2 < x < 2$

You're dividing by a <u>negative number</u>, so flip the sign.

3. Solve the inequality $-x^2 + 2x + 3 > 0$. (9)

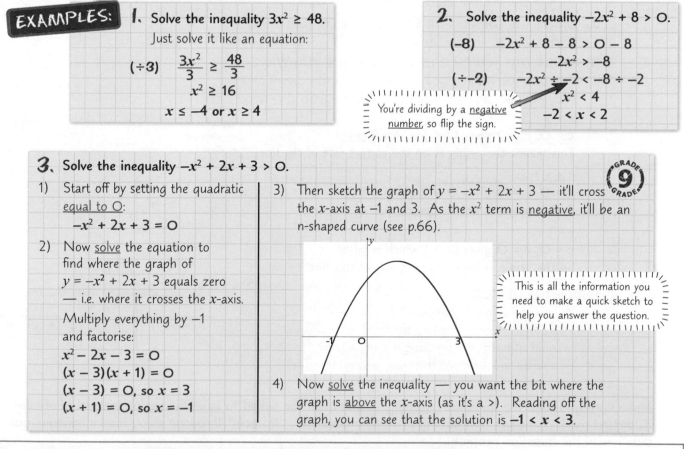

1) Start off by setting the quadratic <u>equal to 0</u>:

$-x^2 + 2x + 3 = 0$

2) Now <u>solve</u> the equation to find where the graph of $y = -x^2 + 2x + 3$ equals zero — i.e. where it crosses the x-axis.

Multiply everything by -1 and factorise:

$x^2 - 2x - 3 = 0$

$(x - 3)(x + 1) = 0$

$(x - 3) = 0$, so $x = 3$

$(x + 1) = 0$, so $x = -1$

3) Then sketch the graph of $y = -x^2 + 2x + 3$ — it'll cross the x-axis at -1 and 3. As the x^2 term is <u>negative</u>, it'll be an n-shaped curve (see p.66).

This is all the information you need to make a quick sketch to help you answer the question.

4) Now <u>solve</u> the inequality — you want the bit where the graph is <u>above</u> the x-axis (as it's a $>$). Reading off the graph, you can see that the solution is $\mathbf{-1 < x < 3}$.

Pie charts — apple pie ≥ steak pie > chicken pie...

It's those tricky quadratics that might catch you out. But like I said on the previous page, if you test a few values in the inequality you can check you've got the signs the right way round.

Q1   Solve these inequalities: a) $p^2 < 49$ [2 marks] (6)   b) $-\frac{1}{2}p^2 \leq -32$ [3 marks] (7)

Q2   Write down all the integer values that satisfy the inequality $x^2 - 4x \leq 0$.   [3 marks] (9)

Graphical Inequalities

These questions always involve <u>shading a region on a graph</u>. The method sounds very complicated, but once you've seen it in action with an example, you see that it's OK...

Showing Inequalities on a Graph (5)

Here's the method to follow:

> 1) <u>CONVERT each INEQUALITY to an EQUATION</u>
>   by simply putting an '=' in place of the inequality sign.
>
> 2) <u>DRAW THE GRAPH FOR EACH EQUATION</u> — if the inequality sign is < or >
>   draw a <u>dotted line</u>, but if it's ≥ or ≤ draw a <u>solid line</u>.
>
> 3) <u>Work out WHICH SIDE of each line you want</u> — put a point (usually the
>   origin, (0, 0)) into the inequality to see if it's on the correct side of the line.
>
> 4) <u>SHADE THE REGION</u> this gives you.

> If using the origin doesn't work (e.g. if the origin lies on a line), just pick another point with easy coordinates and use that instead.

EXAMPLE: Shade the region that satisfies all three of the following inequalities:
$x + y < 5$ $y \le x + 2$ $y > 1$.

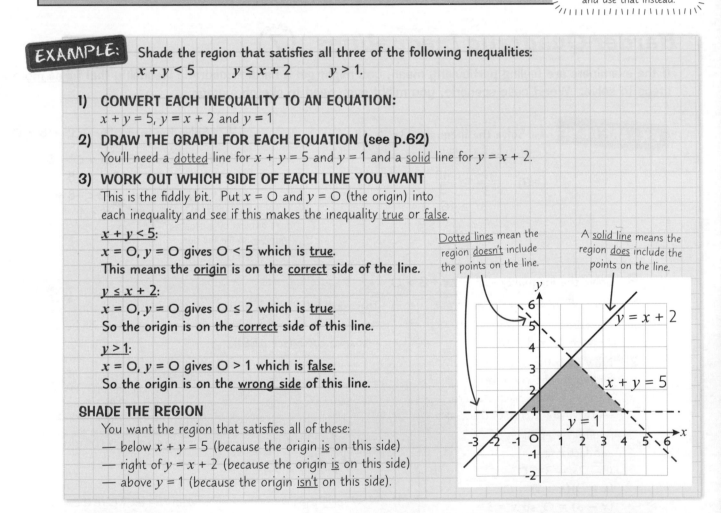

1) **CONVERT EACH INEQUALITY TO AN EQUATION:**
    $x + y = 5$, $y = x + 2$ and $y = 1$

2) **DRAW THE GRAPH FOR EACH EQUATION (see p.62)**
    You'll need a <u>dotted</u> line for $x + y = 5$ and $y = 1$ and a <u>solid</u> line for $y = x + 2$.

3) **WORK OUT WHICH SIDE OF EACH LINE YOU WANT**
    This is the fiddly bit. Put $x = 0$ and $y = 0$ (the origin) into
    each inequality and see if this makes the inequality <u>true</u> or <u>false</u>.

    <u>$x + y < 5$:</u>
    $x = 0$, $y = 0$ gives $0 < 5$ which is <u>true</u>.
    This means the <u>origin</u> is on the <u>correct</u> side of the line.

    <u>$y \le x + 2$:</u>
    $x = 0$, $y = 0$ gives $0 \le 2$ which is <u>true</u>.
    So the origin is on the <u>correct</u> side of this line.

    <u>$y > 1$:</u>
    $x = 0$, $y = 0$ gives $0 > 1$ which is <u>false</u>.
    So the origin is on the <u>wrong side</u> of this line.

    <u>Dotted lines</u> mean the region <u>doesn't</u> include the points on the line.

    A <u>solid line</u> means the region <u>does</u> include the points on the line.

    SHADE THE REGION
    You want the region that satisfies all of these:
    — below $x + y = 5$ (because the origin <u>is</u> on this side)
    — right of $y = x + 2$ (because the origin <u>is</u> on this side)
    — above $y = 1$ (because the origin <u>isn't</u> on this side).

Make sure you read the question <u>carefully</u> — you might be asked to <u>label</u> the region instead of shade it, or just <u>mark on points</u> that satisfy all three inequalities. No point throwing away marks because you didn't read the question properly.

Graphical inequalities — it's a shady business...

Once you've found the region, it's a good idea to pick a point inside it and check that it satisfies ALL the inequalities. Try it out on this Exam Practice Question:

Q1   On a grid, shade the region that satisfies $x \le 5$, $y > -1$ and $y < x + 1$.   [3 marks] (5)

Simultaneous Equations and Graphs

You can use <u>graphs</u> to solve <u>simultaneous equations</u> — just plot the graph of each equation, and the solutions are the points where the graphs <u>cross</u> (you can usually just read off the coordinates from the graph).

Plot Both Graphs and See Where They Cross

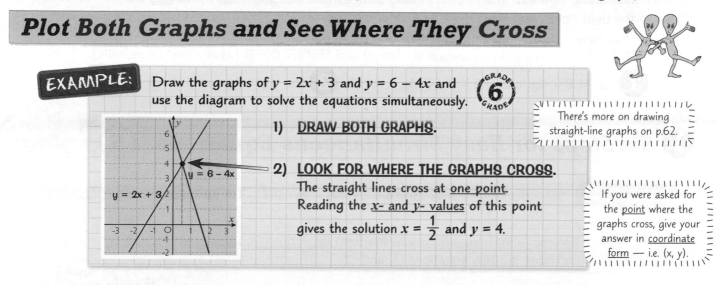

EXAMPLE: Draw the graphs of $y = 2x + 3$ and $y = 6 - 4x$ and use the diagram to solve the equations simultaneously. **(GRADE 6)**

1) **DRAW BOTH GRAPHS.**

2) **LOOK FOR WHERE THE GRAPHS CROSS.**
The straight lines cross at <u>one point</u>.
Reading the <u>x-</u> and <u>y-</u> values of this point gives the solution $x = \frac{1}{2}$ and $y = 4$.

There's more on drawing straight-line graphs on p.62.

If you were asked for the <u>point</u> where the graphs cross, give your answer in <u>coordinate form</u> — i.e. (x, y).

The point at which the two graphs cross is actually the <u>solution</u> you'd find if you set the two equations <u>equal to each other</u> (so in the first example, you're actually solving $2x + 3 = 6 - 4x$).
This fact comes in handy for the next (trickier) example.

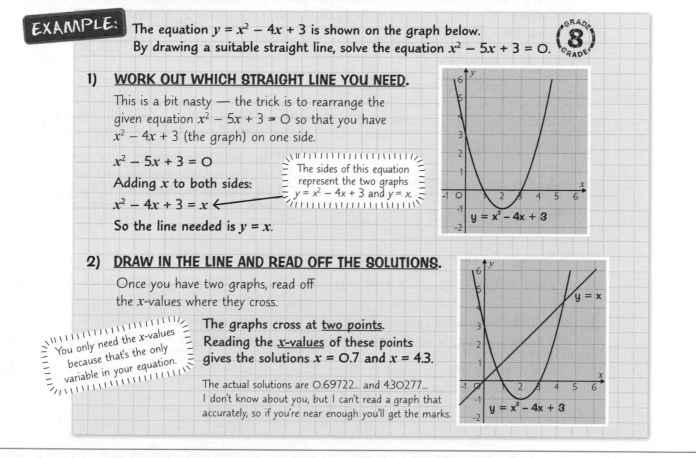

EXAMPLE: The equation $y = x^2 - 4x + 3$ is shown on the graph below. By drawing a suitable straight line, solve the equation $x^2 - 5x + 3 = 0$. **(GRADE 8)**

1) **WORK OUT WHICH STRAIGHT LINE YOU NEED.**

This is a bit nasty — the trick is to rearrange the given equation $x^2 - 5x + 3 = 0$ so that you have $x^2 - 4x + 3$ (the graph) on one side.

$x^2 - 5x + 3 = 0$

Adding x to both sides:

$x^2 - 4x + 3 = x$

So the line needed is $y = x$.

The sides of this equation represent the two graphs $y = x^2 - 4x + 3$ and $y = x$.

2) **DRAW IN THE LINE AND READ OFF THE SOLUTIONS.**

Once you have two graphs, read off the x-values where they cross.

You only need the x-values because that's the only variable in your equation.

The graphs cross at <u>two points</u>.
Reading the <u>x-values</u> of these points gives the solutions $x = 0.7$ and $x = 4.3$.

The actual solutions are 0.69722... and 4.30277...
I don't know about you, but I can't read a graph that accurately, so if you're near enough you'll get the marks.

What do you call a giraffe with no eyes? A graph...

Have a go at these Exam Practice Questions to make sure you're a graph expert:

Q1 By sketching the graphs, find the solutions of the simultaneous equations $y = 4x - 4$ and $y = 6 - x$. [3 marks] **(GRADE 6)**

Q2 Clare wants to use the graph of $x^3 + 4x^2 - 3x + 2$ to solve the equation $x^3 + 4x^2 - 3x - 1 = 0$. Find the equation of the straight line she should draw on the graph. [2 marks] **(GRADE 8)**

Simultaneous Equations

You've seen one way to solve simultaneous equations using graphs. Now it's time to learn how to solve them using algebra. The rules are really quite simple, but you must follow <u>ALL</u> the steps, in the <u>right order</u>, and treat them as a strict method.

There are two types of simultaneous equations you could get
— **EASY ONES** (where both equations are linear) and **TRICKY ONES** (where one's quadratic).

1 $2x = 6 - 4y$ and $-3 - 3y = 4x$ **2** $7x + y = 1$ and $2x^2 - y = 3$

1 *Six Steps for Easy Simultaneous Equations*

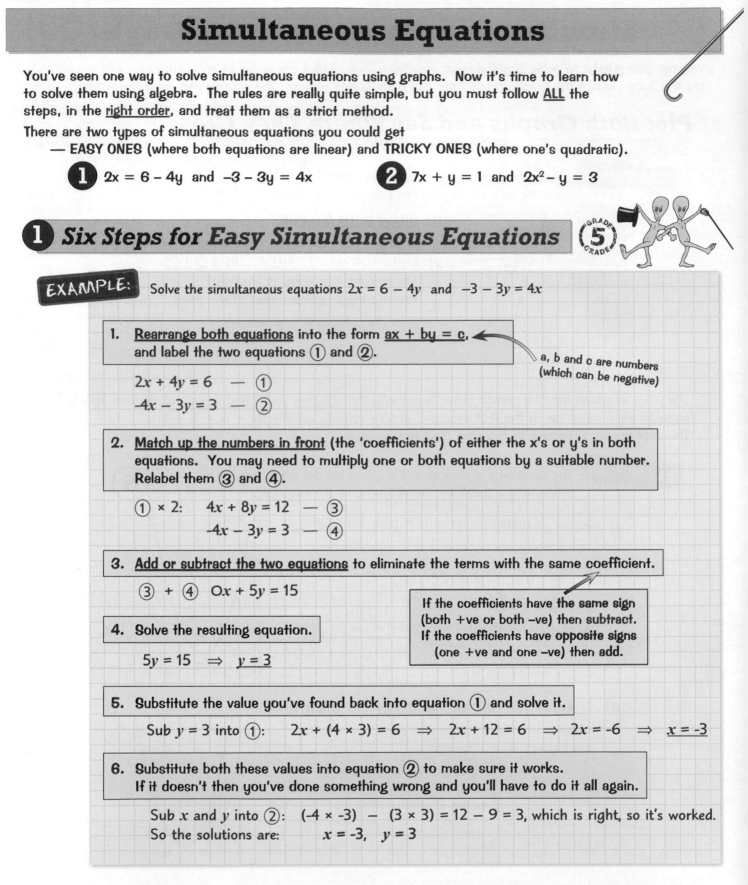

EXAMPLE: Solve the simultaneous equations $2x = 6 - 4y$ and $-3 - 3y = 4x$

1. <u>Rearrange both equations</u> into the form <u>ax + by = c</u>, and label the two equations ① and ②.

   a, b and c are numbers (which can be negative)

   $2x + 4y = 6$ — ①
   $-4x - 3y = 3$ — ②

2. <u>Match up the numbers in front</u> (the 'coefficients') of either the x's or y's in both equations. You may need to multiply one or both equations by a suitable number. Relabel them ③ and ④.

   ① × 2: $4x + 8y = 12$ — ③
   $-4x - 3y = 3$ — ④

3. <u>Add or subtract the two equations</u> to eliminate the terms with the same coefficient.

   ③ + ④ $0x + 5y = 15$

   If the coefficients have the same sign (both +ve or both –ve) then subtract. If the coefficients have opposite signs (one +ve and one –ve) then add.

4. Solve the resulting equation.

   $5y = 15 \Rightarrow \underline{y = 3}$

5. Substitute the value you've found back into equation ① and solve it.

   Sub $y = 3$ into ①: $2x + (4 \times 3) = 6 \Rightarrow 2x + 12 = 6 \Rightarrow 2x = -6 \Rightarrow \underline{x = -3}$

6. Substitute both these values into equation ② to make sure it works. If it doesn't then you've done something wrong and you'll have to do it all again.

   Sub x and y into ②: $(-4 \times -3) - (3 \times 3) = 12 - 9 = 3$, which is right, so it's worked.
   So the solutions are: $x = -3$, $y = 3$

Sunday morning, lemon squeezy and simultaneous linear equations...

You need to learn the 6 steps on this page. When you think you've got them, try them out on these Exam Practice Questions:

Q1   Solve the simultaneous equations $3x - 2y = 9$ and $2x + 3y = 19$.   [4 marks] **5**

Q2   Find x and y given that $2x - 10 = 4y$ and $3y = 4x - 15$.   [4 marks] **5**

Simultaneous Equations

② Seven Steps for TRICKY Simultaneous Equations ⑧

EXAMPLE: Solve these two equations simultaneously:

$$7x + y = 1 \quad \text{and} \quad 2x^2 - y = 3$$

1. **Rearrange the quadratic equation** so that you have the non-quadratic unknown on its own. Label the two equations ① and ②.

   $7x + y = 1 \quad — ①$

   $y = 2x^2 - 3 \quad — ②$

2. **Substitute** the **quadratic expression** into the other equation. You'll get another equation — label it ③.

   $7x + y = 1 \quad — ①$

   $y = \boxed{2x^2 - 3} \quad — ②$

   $\Rightarrow 7x + (2x^2 - 3) = 1 \quad — ③$

   In this example you just shove the expression for y into equation ① in place of y.

3. **Rearrange** to get a **quadratic equation**. And guess what... You've got to **solve** it.

   $2x^2 + 7x - 4 = 0$

   $(2x - 1)(x + 4) = 0$

   So $2x - 1 = 0$ OR $x + 4 = 0$

   $x = 0.5$ OR $x = -4$

   Remember — if it won't factorise, you can use the formula. Have a look at p.43 for more details.

4. **Stick the first value** back in one of the **original equations** (pick the easy one).

   ① $7x + y = 1$

   Substitute in $x = 0.5$: $\quad 3.5 + y = 1$, so $y = 1 - 3.5 = -2.5$

5. **Stick the second value** back in the **same original equation** (the easy one again).

   ① $7x + y = 1$

   Substitute in $x = -4$: $\quad -28 + y = 1$, so $y = 1 + 28 = 29$

6. **Substitute both pairs** of answers back into the **other original equation** to check they work.

   ② $y = 2x^2 - 3$

   Substitute in $x = 0.5$: $\quad y = (2 \times 0.25) - 3 = -2.5$ — jolly good.

   Substitute in $x = -4$: $\quad y = (2 \times 16) - 3 = 29$ — smashing.

7. **Write the pairs of answers** out again, clearly, at the bottom of your working.

   The two pairs of solutions are: $\quad x = 0.5, y = -2.5$ and $x = -4, y = 29$

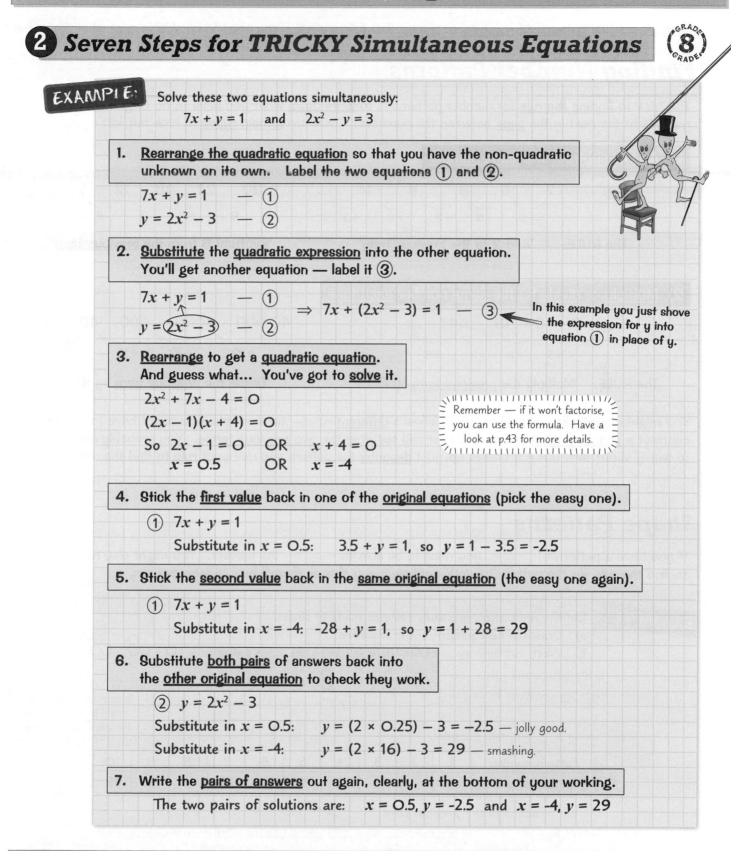

Simultaneous pain and pleasure — it must be algebra...

Don't make the mistake of thinking that there are 4 **separate** solutions — you end up with 2 pairs of solutions to the simultaneous equations. Now try these:

Q1 Solve the simultaneous equations $\quad y = x^2 + 4$ and $y - 6x - 4 = 0$ [6 marks] ⑧

Q2 Solve the simultaneous equations $\quad y = 2 - 3x$ and $y = x^2 - 2$ [6 marks] ⑧

Number Patterns and Sequences

Sequences are just patterns of numbers or shapes that follow a rule. You need to be able to spot what the rule is.

Finding Number Patterns (3)

The trick to finding the rule for number patterns is to write down what you have to do to get from one number to the next in the gaps between the numbers. There are 2 main types to look out for:

1) Add or subtract the same number

E.g.

2 5 8 11 14 ...   30 24 18 12 ...
 +3 +3 +3 +3 +3   −6 −6 −6 −6

The RULE: 'Add 3 to the previous term'   'Subtract 6 from the previous term'

2) Multiply or divide by the same number each time

E.g.

2 6 18 54 ...   40 000 4000 400 40 ...
 ×3 ×3 ×3   ÷10   ÷10 ÷10 ÷10

The RULE: 'Multiply the previous term by 3'   'Divide the previous term by 10'

You might sometimes get patterns that follow a different rule — for example, you might have to add or subtract a changing number each time, or add together the two previous terms. You probably don't need to worry about this, but if it comes up, just describe the pattern and use your rule to find the next term.

Shape Patterns (3)

If you have a pattern of shapes, you need to be able to continue the pattern. You might also have to find the rule for the pattern to work out how many shapes there'll be in a later pattern.

EXAMPLE:

On the right, there are some patterns made of circles.
a) Draw the next pattern in the sequence.
b) Work out how many circles there will be in the 10th pattern.

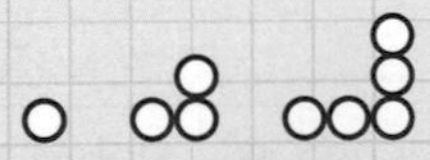

a) Just continue the pattern —
each 'leg' increases by one circle.

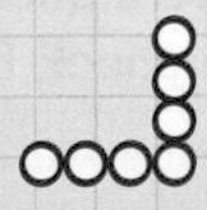

In an exam question, you might be given a table and asked to complete it.

b) Set up a table to find the rule:

Pattern number	1	2	3	4	5	6	7	8	9	10
Number of circles	1	3	5	7	9	11	13	15	17	19

The rule is 'add 2 to the previous term'.

So just keep on adding 2 to extend the table until you get to the 10th term — which is **19**.

Knitting patterns follow the rule knit one, purl one...

Remember, you always need to work out what to do to get from one term to the next — that's the rule.

Q1   A sequence starts 27, 22, 17, 12. Write down the next term in the sequence and explain how you worked it out.

[2 marks] (3)

Number Patterns and Sequences

You'll often be asked to "find an <u>expression</u> for the <u>nth term</u> of a sequence" — this is just a formula with n in, like 5n – 3. It gives you <u>every term in a sequence</u> when you put in different values for n.

Finding the nth Term of a Sequence

The two methods below work for <u>linear</u> sequences — ones with a <u>common difference</u> (where the sequence <u>increases</u> or <u>decreases</u> by the <u>same number</u> each time).

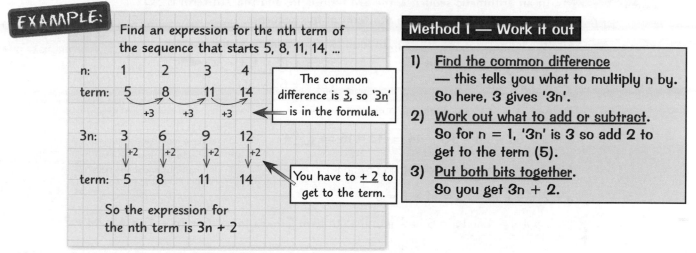

EXAMPLE:

Find an expression for the nth term of the sequence that starts 5, 8, 11, 14, ...

n:	1	2	3	4
term:	5	8	11	14

+3   +3   +3

The common difference is <u>3</u>, so '<u>3n</u>' is in the formula.

3n:	3	6	9	12

+2   +2   +2   +2

term:	5	8	11	14

You have to <u>+ 2</u> to get to the term.

So the expression for the nth term is 3n + 2

Method 1 — Work it out

1) <u>Find the common difference</u> — this tells you what to multiply n by. So here, 3 gives '3n'.
2) <u>Work out what to add or subtract</u>. So for n = 1, '3n' is 3 so add 2 to get to the term (5).
3) <u>Put both bits together</u>. So you get 3n + 2.

Always <u>check</u> your formula by putting the first few values of n back in, e.g. putting n = 1 into 3n + 2 gives 5, n = 2 gives 8, etc. which is the <u>original sequence</u> you were given — hooray!

Method 2 — Learn the formula The other approach is to simply <u>learn this formula</u> and stick in the values of <u>a</u> and <u>d</u> (you don't need to replace the n though):

$$\text{nth term} = a + (n - 1)d$$

<u>d</u> is the <u>common difference</u> and <u>a</u> is the <u>first term</u>.

So for the example above, d = 3 and a = 5. Putting these in the formula gives:
nth term = $5 + (n - 1) \times 3 = 5 + 3n - 3 = \underline{3n + 2}$. Again, <u>check</u> it by putting in values for n.

Deciding if a Term is in a Sequence

You might be given the nth term and asked if a <u>certain value</u> is in the sequence. The trick here is to <u>set the expression equal to that value</u> and solve to find n. If n is a <u>whole number</u>, the value is <u>in</u> the sequence.

EXAMPLE: The nth term of a sequence is given by 3n + 8.

a) **Find the 6th term in the sequence.**

This is dead easy — just put n = 6 into the expression:

$3 \times 6 + 8 = 18 + 8$
$= 26$

b) **Is 45 a term in this sequence?**

Set it equal to 45... $3n + 8 = 45$

$3n = 37$ ...and solve for n.

$n = \frac{37}{3} = 12.33333...$

n is not a whole number, so 45 is <u>not</u> in the sequence 3n + 8.

Have a look at p.37 for more on solving equations.

If I've told you n times, I've told you n + 1 times — learn this page...

Right, I've given you two methods for working out the rule, so pick your favourite out of Method 1 and Method 2 and make sure you learn it. Then have a go at this Exam Practice Question:

Q1   A sequence starts 2, 9, 16, 23, ...

    a) Find an expression for the *n*th term of the sequence.   [2 marks]

    b) Use your expression to find the 8th term in the sequence.   [1 mark]

    c) Is 63 a term in the sequence? Explain your answer.   [2 marks]

Number Patterns and Sequences

Sometimes you might have to do a bit more <u>working out</u> before you can get an <u>expression</u> for the <u>nth term</u>.

Finding the nth Term from any Two Terms (7)

Any two terms can be used to find the nth term. As long as you know <u>where</u> they are in the sequence, you can set up <u>simultaneous equations</u> to find a and d.

An arithmetic sequence is just a fancier way of saying linear sequence.

EXAMPLE:

In an arithmetic sequence, the 3rd term is 14, and the 7th term is 30. Find an expression for the nth term of this sequence.

Use the formula for the nth term to form two equations in a and d:

$a + (3 - 1)d = 14$ $\qquad$ $a + (7 - 1)d = 30$

① $a + 2d = 14$ $\qquad$ ② $a + 6d = 30$

From the question, you know that when n = 3 the term is 14, and when n = 7 the term is 30.

Doing ② − ① cancels the a's out:

$a - a + 6d - 2d = 30 - 14 \Rightarrow 4d = 16 \Rightarrow \underline{d = 4}$

Have a look back at pages 52-53 to brush up on your simultaneous equations skills.

Now, substitute d = 4 back into ① to find a:

$a + 2 \times 4 = 14 \Rightarrow \underline{a} = 14 - 8 = \underline{6}$

Now put d = 4 and a = 6 back into the nth term formula to get $6 + (n - 1) \times 4 = 4n + 2$

A Series is when you Add the Terms to Find the Total (8)

You could be asked to find the <u>sum</u> of the first n terms of an arithmetic series, written S_n.
There are <u>two different formulas</u>, depending on whether or not you know the <u>last term</u> in the sum...

1) If you <u>know</u> the last term...

...the formula you use is dead easy: $S_n = \dfrac{n}{2}(a + \text{the last term})$

EXAMPLE: An arithmetic series has 1st term 3 and 22nd term 87. Find the sum of the first 22 terms.

a = 3, n = 22 and the last term is 87.
Put these values into the formula to get:
$S_{22} = \dfrac{22}{2}(3 + 87) = 11 \times 90 = 990$

2) If you <u>don't know</u> the last term...

...the formula is a bit trickier: $S_n = \dfrac{n}{2}[2a + (n - 1)d]$

You might get a question in the exam where you have to calculate a and d first, before substituting them into the formula (see the practice question below).

EXAMPLE: For the arithmetic series starting −5 + −2 + 1 + 4 + 7 +... find the sum of the first 20 terms.

a = −5, d = 3 and n = 20.
$S_{20} = \dfrac{20}{2}[2 \times -5 + (20 - 1) \times 3] = 10[-10 + 19 \times 3]$

$S_{20} = 470$

Ugh, this page is so formulaic...

Lots of tricky stuff here. The only way to be sure it's sunk in is by doing this practice question...

Q1   The 9th term of an arithmetic series is 48. The 12th term of the same
series is 63. Find the sum of the first 20 terms of the series.   **[5 marks]** (9)

Proof

I'm not going to lie — <u>proof questions</u> can look a bit terrifying. The trick is to understand which <u>bit of maths</u> the question actually <u>wants</u> you to do. Once you've got that, it's a walk in the <u>park</u> (sort of)...

Show Things Are Odd, Even or Multiples by Rearranging

Before you get started, there are a few things you need to know — they'll come in very handy when you're trying to prove things.

- Any <u>even number</u> can be written as <u>2n</u> — i.e. 2 × something.
- Any <u>odd number</u> can be written as <u>2n + 1</u> — i.e. 2 × something + 1.
- <u>Consecutive numbers</u> can be written as <u>n, n + 1, n + 2</u> etc. — you can apply this to e.g. consecutive even numbers too (they'd be written as 2n, 2n + 2, 2n + 4). (In all of these statements, n is just any <u>integer</u>.)
- The <u>sum</u>, <u>difference</u> and <u>product</u> of integers is <u>always</u> an integer.

This can be extended to multiples of other numbers too — e.g. to prove that something is a <u>multiple of 3</u>, show that it can be written as <u>3 × something</u>.

EXAMPLE: Prove that the sum of any three odd numbers is odd.

So what you're trying to do here is show that the sum of three odd numbers can be written as (2 × integer) + 1.

Take three odd numbers:
$2a + 1$, $2b + 1$ and $2c + 1$
(they don't have to be consecutive)

Add them together:
$2a + 1 + 2b + 1 + 2c + 1 = 2a + 2b + 2c + 2 + 1$

You'll see why I've written 3 as 2 + 1 in a second.

$= 2(a + b + c + 1) + 1$
$= 2n + 1$ where n is an integer $(a + b + c + 1)$

So the sum of any three odd numbers is odd.

EXAMPLE: Prove that for any integer n, $(n + 3)^2 - (n - 2)^2$ is a multiple of 5.

Play about with the expression until you get it into the form '5 × something':
$(n + 3)^2 - (n - 2)^2 = n^2 + 6n + 9 - (n^2 - 4n + 4)$
$= n^2 + 6n + 9 - n^2 + 4n - 4$
$= 10n + 5$
$= 5(2n + 1)$

Because you can take a 5 outside the brackets, this must be a multiple of 5 for any integer n.

As n is an integer, $2n + 1$ is also an integer, so $5(2n + 1)$ is a multiple of 5 for any integer n.

Disprove Things by Finding a Counter Example

If you're asked to prove a statement <u>isn't</u> true, all you have to do is find <u>one example</u> that the statement doesn't work for — this is known as <u>disproof by counter example</u>.

EXAMPLE: Ellie says, "If $x > y$, then $x^2 > y^2$". Is she correct? Explain your answer.

Try some different values for x and y:
$x = 2$, $y = 1$: $x > y$ and $x^2 = 4 > 1 = y^2$
$x = 5$, $y = 2$: $x > y$ and $x^2 = 25 > 4 = y^2$

Make sure you try positive and negative numbers when you're trying to find a counter example. Sometimes it's worth trying zero too.

At first glance, Ellie seems to be correct. BUT... $x = -1$, $y = -2$: $x > y$ but $x^2 = 1 < 4 = y^2$, so Ellie is wrong as the statement does not hold for all values of x and y.

Prove that maths isn't fun...

The only way to get on top of proof questions is practice — so start with these:

Q1 Prove that the sum of two consecutive even numbers is even. [3 marks]

Q2 $4x + 2 = 3(3a + x)$. For odd integer values of a, prove that x is never a multiple of 8. [3 marks]

Direct and Inverse Proportion

Proportion questions involve two variables (often x and y) which are linked in some way. You'll have to figure out the relationship between them, and use this to find values of x or y, given one value.

Simple Proportions (7)

∝ means 'is proportional to'.

The easiest types of proportions you might get are direct proportion ($y \propto x$) and inverse proportion ($y \propto \frac{1}{x}$).

Direct Proportion   BOTH INCREASE TOGETHER

The graph is a straight line through the origin: $y = kx$

> If it doesn't go through the origin, it's not a direct proportion.

Inverse Proportion   One INCREASES, one DECREASES

The graph is $y = \frac{k}{x}$:

> See p.67 for more on these graphs.

Trickier Proportions (7)

More complex proportions involve y varying proportionally or inversely to some function of x, e.g. x^2, x^3, $\sqrt{x}$ etc. You can always turn a proportion statement into an equation by replacing '∝' with '= k' like this:

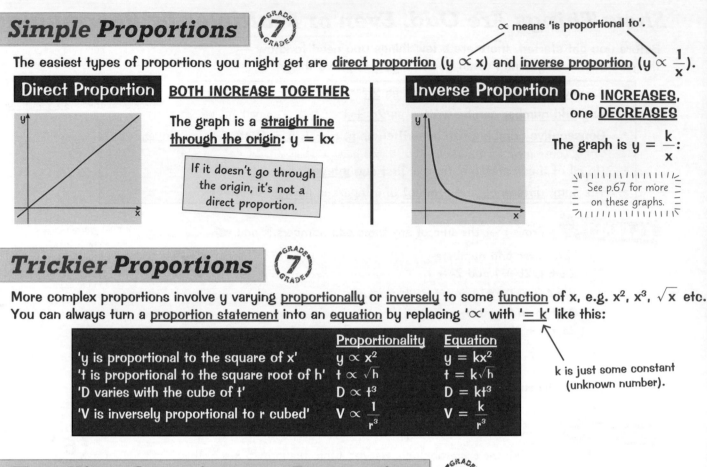

	Proportionality	Equation
'y is proportional to the square of x'	$y \propto x^2$	$y = kx^2$
't is proportional to the square root of h'	$t \propto \sqrt{h}$	$t = k\sqrt{h}$
'D varies with the cube of t'	$D \propto t^3$	$D = kt^3$
'V is inversely proportional to r cubed'	$V \propto \frac{1}{r^3}$	$V = \frac{k}{r^3}$

k is just some constant (unknown number).

Handling Questions on Proportion (7)

1) Convert the sentence into a proportionality.

2) Replace '∝' with '= k' to make an equation (as above).

> Once you've got it in the form of an equation with k, the rest is easy.

3) Find a pair of values of x and y somewhere in the question, and substitute them into the equation with the sole purpose of finding k.

4) Put the value of k into the equation and it's now ready to use, e.g. $y = 3x^2$.

5) Inevitably, they'll ask you to find y, having given you a value for x (or vice versa).

EXAMPLE:

G is inversely proportional to the square root of H. When G = 2, H = 16.
Find an equation for G in terms of H, and use it to work out the value of G when H = 36.

1) Convert to a proportionality. $G \propto \frac{1}{\sqrt{H}}$

2) Replace ∝ with '= k' to form an equation. $G = \frac{k}{\sqrt{H}}$

3) Use the values of G and H (2 and 16) to find k. $2 = \frac{k}{\sqrt{16}} = \frac{k}{4} \Rightarrow k = 8$

4) Put the value of k back into the equation. $G = \frac{8}{\sqrt{H}}$ ← This is the equation for G in terms of H.

5) Use your equation to find the value of G.

$$G = \frac{8}{\sqrt{H}} = \frac{8}{\sqrt{36}}$$
$$= \frac{8}{6}$$
$$= \frac{4}{3}$$

Joy ∝ 1/algebra...

Learn the 5-step method for dealing with proportionality questions, then have a go at this one:

Q1   t is proportional to the square of s, and when $t = 27$, $s = 3$.
Find the value of s when $t = 48$ (given that s is positive).   [4 marks] (7)

Revision Questions for Section Two

There's no denying, Section Two is grisly grimsdike algebra — so check now how much you've learned.
- Try these questions and <u>tick off each one</u> when you <u>get it right</u>.
- When you've done <u>all the questions</u> for a topic and are <u>completely happy</u> with it, tick off the topic.

Algebra (p31-40) ☑

1) Simplify the following: a) $x^3 \times x^6$ b) $y^7 \div y^5$ c) $(z^3)^4$
2) Simplify by collecting like terms: $3x + 2y - 5 - 6y + 2x$
3) Imran buys d DVDs and c CDs. DVDs cost £7 each and CDs cost £5 each. He spends £P in total. Write a formula for P in terms of d and c.
4) Multiply out these brackets: a) $3(2x + 1)$ b) $(x + 2)(x - 3)$ c) $(x - 1)(x + 3)(x + 5)$
5) Factorise: a) $7x^2y + 21xz^2$ b) $49 - 81p^2q^2$ c) $12x^2 - 48y^2$
6) Simplify the following: a) $\sqrt{27}$ b) $\sqrt{125} \div \sqrt{5}$
7) Solve these equations: a) $5(x + 2) = 8 + 4(5 - x)$ b) $x^2 - 21 = 3(5 - x^2)$
8) Make p the subject of these: a) $\frac{1}{p} = \frac{1}{q} + \frac{1}{r}$ b) $\frac{p}{p + y} = 4$

Quadratics (p41-46) ☑

9) Solve the following by factorising them first: a) $x^2 + 9x + 18 = 0$ b) $5x^2 - 17x - 12 = 0$
10) Find the solutions of these equations (to 2 d.p.) using the quadratic formula:
   a) $x^2 + x - 4 = 0$ b) $5x^2 + 6x = 2$ c) $(2x + 3)^2 = 15$
11) Find the exact solutions of these equations by completing the square:
   a) $x^2 + 12x + 15 = 0$ b) $2x^2 - 5x = 3$

Algebraic Fractions (p47) ☑

12) Write $\frac{2}{x + 3} + \frac{1}{x - 1}$ as a single fraction.

Inequalities (p48-50) ☑

13) Solve these inequalities: a) $4x + 3 \leq 6x + 7$ b) $-9 \leq 3 - 2x < 5$
14) Solve: $4x^2 > 100$
15) Show on a graph the region described by these conditions: $x + y \leq 6$, $y > 0.5$, $y \leq 2x - 2$

Simultaneous Equations (p51-53) ☑

16) Solve the following pair of simultaneous equations: $4x + 5y = 23$ and $3y - x = 7$
17) Solve these simultaneous equations: $y = 3x + 4$ and $x^2 + 2y = 0$

Number Patterns and Sequences (p54-56) ☑

18) For each of the following sequences, find the next term and write down the rule you used.
   a) 3, 10, 17, 24, ...   b) 1, 4, 16, 64, ...   c) 2, 5, 7, 12, ...
19) Find the expression for the nth term in the following sequences: a) 5, 9, 13, 17   b) 11, 8, 5, 2.
20) Find the sum of the first 30 terms of these series:
   a) 7 + 9 + 11 + 13...   b) 12 + 23 + 34 + 45...

Proof (p57) ☑

21) Prove that the product of an odd number and an even number is even.

Direct and Inverse Proportion (p58) ☑

22) Write the following statement as an equation: "y is proportional to the square of x".
23) p is proportional to the cube of q. When p = 9, q = 3. Find the value of p when q = 6.

Coordinates

What could be more fun than points in one quadrant? Points in <u>four quadrants</u>, that's what...

The Four Quadrants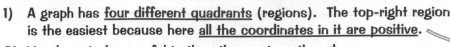

1) A graph has <u>four different quadrants</u> (regions). The top-right region is the easiest because here <u>all the coordinates in it are positive</u>.

2) You have to be careful in the <u>other regions</u> though, because the x- and y- coordinates could be <u>negative</u>, and that makes life much more difficult.

3) Coordinates are always written in brackets like this: **(x, y)**
   — remember x is <u>across</u>, and y is <u>up</u>.

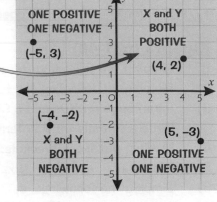

Finding the Midpoint of a Line Segment

Finding the coordinates of a midpoint is pretty easy...

> 1) Find the <u>average</u> of the <u>two x-coordinates</u>, then do the same for the <u>y-coordinates</u>.
>
> 2) These will be the coordinates of the <u>midpoint</u>.

A line segment is <u>part of a line</u>. Lines continue forever in both directions, but line segments have <u>two end points</u>. Things that are actually line segments are often referred to as <u>lines</u> though.

EXAMPLE: Point P has coordinates (8, 3) and point Q has coordinates (−4, 8). Find the <u>midpoint</u> of the line PQ.

See p.106 for finding the length of a line segment.

① Average of x-coordinates $= \dfrac{8 + (-4)}{2} = \underline{2}$

Average of y-coordinates $= \dfrac{3 + 8}{2} = \underline{5.5}$

② So, coordinates of midpoint = (2, 5.5)

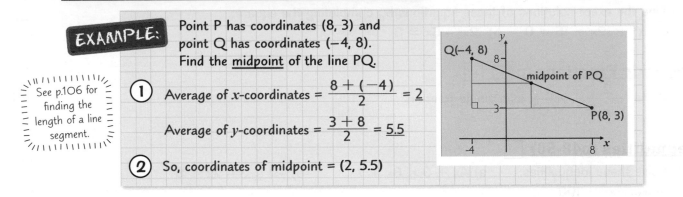

Finding Coordinates Using Geometrical Information

EXAMPLE: A parallelogram has vertices (3, 1), (5, 4) and (9, 1). The x and y coordinates of its fourth vertex are both positive. What are their values?

Do a quick <u>sketch</u> and it's dead easy — just mark in the 4th vertex by eye.

Check: to get from (3, 1) to (5, 4) you go <u>along 2 and up 3</u> — the missing point needs to be the same distance from (9, 1).

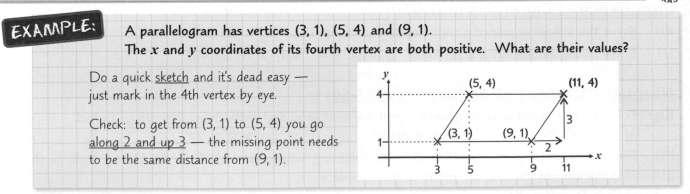

I prefer an orange segment, but there's no accounting for taste...

Learn how to find the midpoint of a line segment and the fourth vertex of a parallelogram.

Q1 Point A has coordinates (−5, −2) and point B has coordinates (6, 0). Find the midpoint of the line AB. **[2 marks]**

Q2 A parallelogram has vertices (1, 1), (4, 1) and (0, 5). Find the coordinates of its fourth vertex, given that both x and y are positive. **[2 marks]**

Straight-Line Graphs

If you thought I-spy was a fun game, wait 'til you play 'recognise the straight-line graph from the equation'.

Horizontal and Vertical lines: 'x = a' and 'y = a' (3)

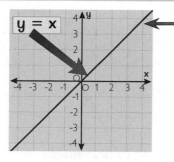

x = a is a <u>vertical line</u> <u>through 'a'</u> on the x-axis

y = a is a <u>horizontal line</u> <u>through 'a'</u> on the y-axis

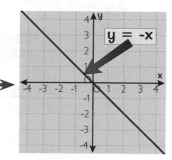

A common error is to mix up x = 3 and y = 3, etc. Remember — all the points on x = 3 have an <u>x-coordinate of 3</u>, and all the points on y = 3 have a <u>y-coordinate of 3</u>.

The Main Diagonals: 'y = x' and 'y = −x' (3)

'y = x' is the <u>main diagonal</u> that goes <u>UPHILL</u> from left to right.
The x- and y-coordinates of each point are <u>the same</u>.

'y = -x' is the <u>main diagonal</u> that goes <u>DOWNHILL</u> from left to right.
The x- and y-coordinates of each point are <u>negatives of each other</u>, e.g. (−4, 4).

Other Sloping Lines Through the Origin: 'y = ax' and 'y = −ax'

<u>y = ax</u> and <u>y = -ax</u> are the equations for <u>A SLOPING LINE THROUGH THE ORIGIN</u>.

The value of '<u>a</u>' (known as the <u>gradient</u>) tells you the steepness of the line. The bigger 'a' is, the steeper the slope. A <u>MINUS SIGN</u> tells you it slopes <u>DOWNHILL</u>.

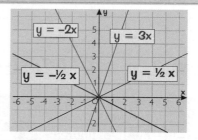

See p.63 for how to find a gradient.

Learn to Spot Straight Lines from Their Equations (3)

All straight-line equations just contain '<u>something x, something y and a number</u>'.

EXAMPLE: Decide whether each of the following are equations of straight lines.
$$2y - 4x = 7 \quad y = x^2 + 3 \quad xy + 3 = 0 \quad 6y - 8 = x \quad \frac{2}{y} - \frac{1}{x} = 7$$

Straight lines: $2y - 4x = 7$
$6y - 8 = x$

These equations only have <u>something x</u>, <u>something y</u> and <u>a number</u>. These 'terms' can be added or subtracted in any order.

Not straight lines: $y = x^2 + 3$
$xy + 3 = 0$
$\frac{2}{y} - \frac{1}{x} = 7$

'x²', 'xy', '2/y' and '1/x' mean that these <u>aren't</u> straight-line equations.

It's no Shakespeare, but my favourite line's y = 3x...

It's definitely worth learning all the graphs on this page. Now try this question:

Q1 Write down the equation of the straight line which passes through the points (−1, −2) and (3, −2). [1 mark] (3)

Plotting Straight-Line Graphs

You could be asked to <u>draw</u> a <u>straight-line graph</u> in the exam. We'll cover <u>two</u> methods on this page:

The 'Table of 3 Values' Method (3)

You can <u>easily</u> draw the graph of
<u>any equation</u> using this <u>easy</u> method:

Don't forget to use a <u>ruler</u> to draw your line — you can lose exam marks if you don't.

1) Choose <u>3 values of x</u> and <u>draw up a wee table</u>,
2) <u>Work out</u> the corresponding <u>y-values</u>,
3) <u>Plot the coordinates</u>, and <u>draw the line</u>.

If it's a <u>straight-line equation</u>, the 3 points will be in a <u>dead straight line</u> with each other.
If they <u>aren't</u>, you need to go back and <u>CHECK YOUR WORKING</u>.

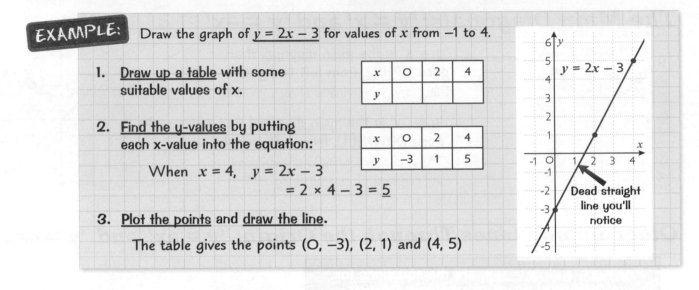

EXAMPLE: Draw the graph of $y = 2x - 3$ for values of x from −1 to 4.

1. <u>Draw up a table</u> with some suitable values of x.

x	0	2	4
y			

2. <u>Find the y-values</u> by putting each x-value into the equation:

x	0	2	4
y	−3	1	5

When $x = 4$, $y = 2x - 3$
$= 2 \times 4 - 3 = \underline{5}$

3. <u>Plot the points</u> and <u>draw the line</u>.

The table gives the points (0, −3), (2, 1) and (4, 5)

The 'x = 0, y = 0' Method (4)

1) <u>Set x=0</u> in the equation, and <u>find y</u> — this is where it <u>crosses the y-axis</u>.
2) <u>Set y=0</u> in the equation and <u>find x</u> — this is where it <u>crosses the x-axis</u>.
3) <u>Plot these two points</u> and <u>join them up with a straight line</u>.

Make sure it's definitely a straight line before using this method — have a look at the previous page to see how you can check.

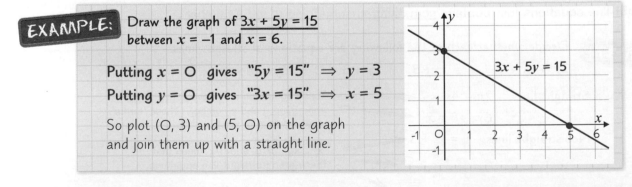

EXAMPLE: Draw the graph of $3x + 5y = 15$ between $x = -1$ and $x = 6$.

Putting $x = 0$ gives "$5y = 15$" $\Rightarrow y = 3$
Putting $y = 0$ gives "$3x = 15$" $\Rightarrow x = 5$

So plot (0, 3) and (5, 0) on the graph and join them up with a straight line.

"No!" cried y "You won't cross me again" — extract from a Maths thriller...

Learn the details of these two easy methods. Then you'll be ready for some Exam Practice Questions.

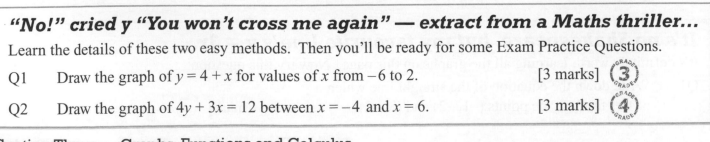

Q1   Draw the graph of $y = 4 + x$ for values of x from −6 to 2.   [3 marks] (3)

Q2   Draw the graph of $4y + 3x = 12$ between $x = -4$ and $x = 6$.   [3 marks] (4)

Finding the Gradient

Time to hit the slopes. Well, find them anyway...

The Gradient is the Steepness of the Line — GRADE 3

The <u>gradient</u> of the line is how <u>steep</u> it is — the <u>larger</u> the gradient, the <u>steeper</u> the slope.
A <u>negative gradient</u> tells you it slopes <u>downhill</u>. You find it by dividing the <u>change in y</u> by the <u>change in x</u>.

EXAMPLE: Find the gradient of the straight line to the right.

1 Choose <u>two accurate points</u> on the line.

A: (6, 50)
B: (1, 10)

2 Find the <u>change in y</u> and <u>change in x</u>.

Change in y = 50 − 10 = 40
Change in x = 6 − 1 = 5

Make sure you subtract the y and x-coordinates in the
same order. E.g. $y_A - y_B$ and $x_A - x_B$

3 Use this <u>formula</u>:

$$\text{GRADIENT} = \frac{\text{CHANGE IN Y}}{\text{CHANGE IN X}}$$

Gradient = $\frac{40}{5}$ = 8

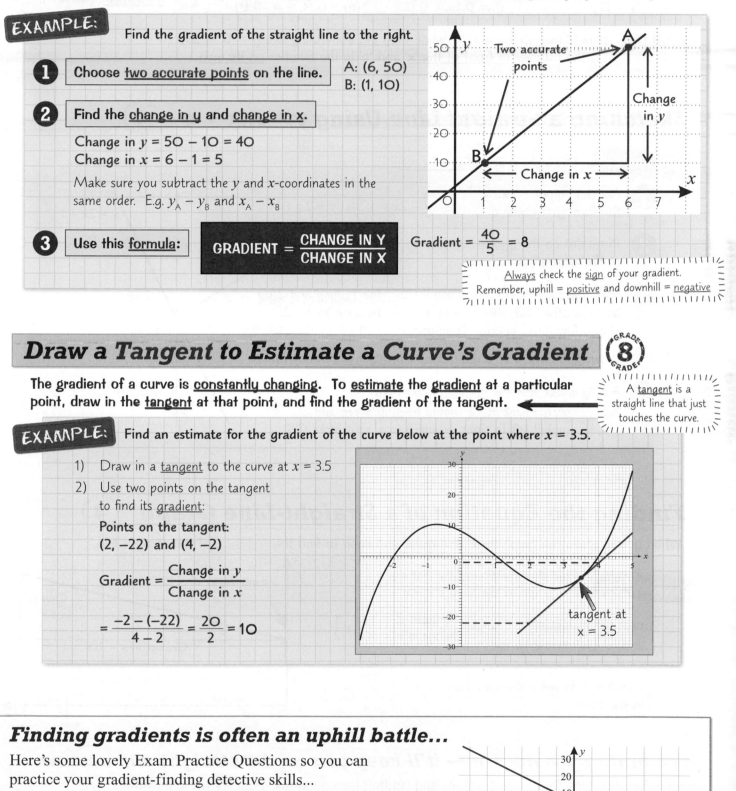

*Always check the <u>sign</u> of your gradient.
Remember, uphill = <u>positive</u> and downhill = <u>negative</u>*

Draw a Tangent to Estimate a Curve's Gradient — GRADE 8

The gradient of a curve is <u>constantly changing</u>. To <u>estimate</u> the <u>gradient</u> at a particular
point, draw in the <u>tangent</u> at that point, and find the gradient of the tangent.

*A <u>tangent</u> is a
straight line that just
touches the curve.*

EXAMPLE: Find an estimate for the gradient of the curve below at the point where $x = 3.5$.

1) Draw in a <u>tangent</u> to the curve at $x = 3.5$

2) Use two points on the tangent
to find its <u>gradient</u>:

Points on the tangent:
(2, −22) and (4, −2)

$$\text{Gradient} = \frac{\text{Change in } y}{\text{Change in } x}$$

$$= \frac{-2 - (-22)}{4 - 2} = \frac{20}{2} = 10$$

tangent at
x = 3.5

Finding gradients is often an uphill battle...

Here's some lovely Exam Practice Questions so you can
practice your gradient-finding detective skills...

Q1 Find the gradient of the line on the right. [2 marks] — GRADE 3

Q2 Find an estimate for the gradient of the
curve above at the point where $x = -2$. [3 marks] — GRADE 8

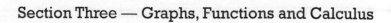

"y = mx + c"

Using 'y = mx + c' is perhaps the 'proper' way of dealing with straight-line equations, and it's a nice trick if you can do it. The first thing you have to do though is <u>rearrange</u> the equation into the standard format like this:

Straight line:		Rearranged into 'y = mx +c'	
y = 2 + 3x	→	y = 3x + 2	(m = 3, c = 2)
x – y = 0	→	y = x + 0	(m = 1, c = 0)
4x – 3 = 5y	→	y = 0.8x – 0.6	(m = 0.8, c = –0.6)

<u>REMEMBER</u>:

'<u>m</u>' = <u>gradient</u> of the line.

'<u>c</u>' = '<u>y-intercept</u>' (where it hits the y-axis)

<u>WATCH OUT</u>: people mix up 'm' and 'c' when they get something like y = 5 + 2x.
Remember, 'm' is the number <u>in front of the 'x'</u> and 'c' is the number <u>on its own</u>.

Sketching a Straight Line Using y = mx + c — GRADE 4

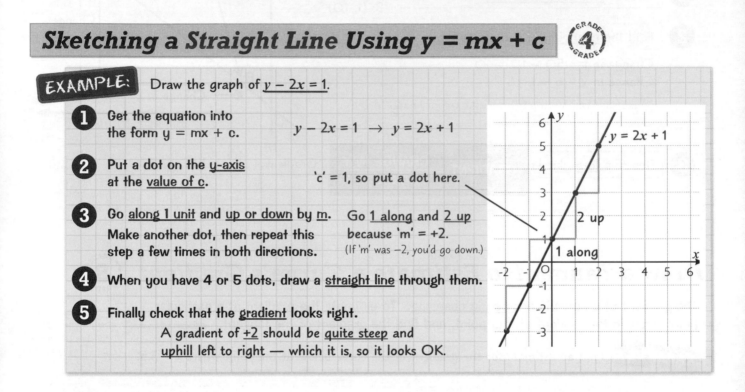

EXAMPLE: Draw the graph of <u>y – 2x = 1</u>.

1 Get the equation into the form y = mx + c.

$$y - 2x = 1 \rightarrow y = 2x + 1$$

2 Put a dot on the <u>y-axis</u> at the <u>value of c</u>.

'c' = 1, so put a dot here.

3 Go <u>along 1 unit</u> and <u>up or down</u> by <u>m</u>. Make another dot, then repeat this step a few times in both directions.

Go <u>1 along</u> and <u>2 up</u> because 'm' = +2. (If 'm' was –2, you'd go down.)

4 When you have 4 or 5 dots, draw a <u>straight line</u> through them.

5 Finally check that the <u>gradient</u> looks right.

A gradient of <u>+2</u> should be <u>quite steep</u> and <u>uphill</u> left to right — which it is, so it looks OK.

y = 2x + 1

2 up

1 along

Finding the Equation of a Straight-Line Graph — GRADE 4

When you're given the graph itself, it's quick and easy to find the <u>equation</u> of the straight line.

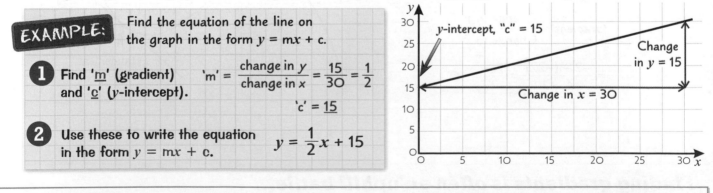

EXAMPLE: Find the equation of the line on the graph in the form y = mx + c.

1 Find '<u>m</u>' (gradient) and '<u>c</u>' (y-intercept).

$$'m' = \frac{\text{change in } y}{\text{change in } x} = \frac{15}{30} = \frac{1}{2}$$

'c' = <u>15</u>

2 Use these to write the equation in the form y = mx + c.

$$y = \frac{1}{2}x + 15$$

y-intercept, "c" = 15

Change in y = 15

Change in x = 30

Remember y = mx + c — it'll keep you on the straight and narrow...

Remember the steps for drawing graphs and finding the equations. And try these questions:

Q1   Draw the graph of $x = 2y + 4$ for values of x between -4 and 4.   [3 marks] (4)

Q2   Line Q goes through (0, 5) and (4, 7).
Find the equation of Line Q in the form $y = mx + c$.   [3 marks] (5)

Section Three — Graphs, Functions and Calculus

Parallel and Perpendicular Lines

On the previous page, you saw how to write the <u>equation of a straight line</u>. Well, you also have to be able to write the equation of a line that's <u>parallel</u> or <u>perpendicular</u> to the straight line you're given.

Parallel Lines Have the Same Gradient (6)

Parallel lines all have the <u>same gradient</u>, which means their $y = mx + c$ equations all have the same value of <u>m</u>.

So the lines: $y = 2x + 3$, $y = 2x$ and $y = 2x - 4$ are all parallel.

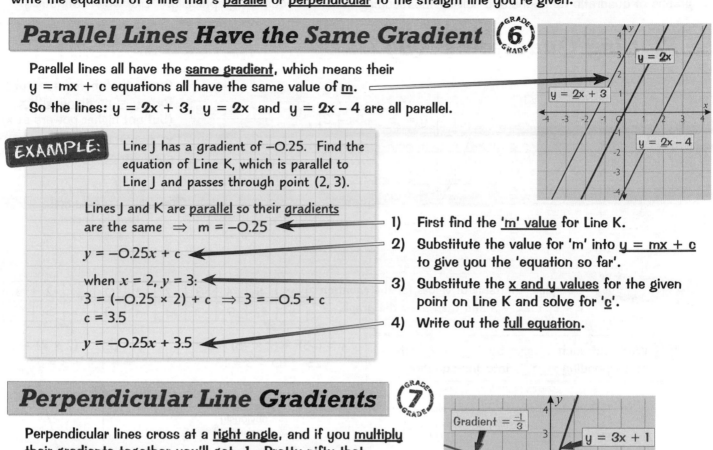

EXAMPLE: Line J has a gradient of −0.25. Find the equation of Line K, which is parallel to Line J and passes through point (2, 3).

Lines J and K are <u>parallel</u> so their <u>gradients</u> are the same $\Rightarrow m = -0.25$

$y = -0.25x + c$

when $x = 2$, $y = 3$:
$3 = (-0.25 \times 2) + c \Rightarrow 3 = -0.5 + c$
$c = 3.5$

$y = -0.25x + 3.5$

1) First find the <u>'m' value</u> for Line K.

2) Substitute the value for 'm' into <u>$y = mx + c$</u> to give you the 'equation so far'.

3) Substitute the <u>x and y values</u> for the given point on Line K and solve for '<u>c</u>'.

4) Write out the <u>full equation</u>.

Perpendicular Line Gradients (7)

Perpendicular lines cross at a <u>right angle</u>, and if you <u>multiply</u> their <u>gradients</u> together you'll get <u>−1</u>. Pretty nifty that.

> If the gradient of the first line is m, the gradient of the other line will be $-\dfrac{1}{m}$, because $m \times -\dfrac{1}{m} = -1$.

Gradient $= \dfrac{-1}{3}$

$y = 3x + 1$

Product of gradients $= -\dfrac{1}{3} \times 3 = \underline{-1}$

EXAMPLE: Lines A and B are perpendicular and intersect at (3, 3). If Line A has the equation $3y - x = 6$, what is the equation of Line B?

Find '<u>m</u>' (the gradient) for Line A.	$3y - x = 6 \Rightarrow 3y = x + 6$ $\Rightarrow y = \frac{1}{3}x + 2$, so $m_A = \frac{1}{3}$
Find the 'm' value for the <u>perpendicular</u> line (Line B).	$m_B = -\dfrac{1}{m_A} = -1 \div \dfrac{1}{3} = -3$
Put this into $y = mx + c$ to give the 'equation so far'.	$y = -3x + c$
Put in the <u>x and y values</u> of the point and solve for '<u>c</u>'.	$x = 3$, $y = 3$ gives: $3 = (-3 \times 3) + c$ $\Rightarrow 3 = -9 + c \Rightarrow c = 12$
Write out the full equation.	$y = -3x + 12$

This stuff is a way to get one over on the examiners (well −1 actually)...

So basically, use one gradient to find the other, then use the known x and y values to work out c.

Q1 Find the equation of the line parallel to $2x + 2y = 3$ which passes through the point (1, 4). Give your answer in the form $y = mx + c$. [3 marks] (6)

Q2 Show that the lines $y + 5x = 2$ and $5y = x + 3$ are perpendicular. [3 marks] (7)

Quadratic Graphs

Quadratic functions can sound pretty darn impressive — "What did you do in Maths today, dear?", "Drawing the graphs of quadratic functions and solving the resulting quadratic equation graphically." Like wow. Seriously.

Plotting Quadratics (GRADE 5)

$y = x^2$

$y = 3x^2 - 6x - 3$

Line of symmetry

$y = -2x^2 - 4x + 3$

Line of symmetry

Quadratic functions are of the form $\underline{y = \text{anything with } x^2}$ (but not higher powers of x).

x^2 graphs all have the same <u>symmetrical</u> bucket shape.

If the x^2 bit has a '–' in front of it then the bucket is <u>upside down</u>.

EXAMPLE: Complete the table of values for the equation $y = x^2 + 2x - 3$ and then draw the graph.

x	-5	-4	-3	-2	-1	0	1	2	3
y	12	5	0	-3	-4	-3	0	5	12

1 Work out each <u>y-value</u> by <u>substituting</u> the corresponding <u>x-value</u> into the equation.

$y = (-5)^2 + (2 \times -5) - 3$
$= 25 - 10 - 3 = 12$

$y = (2)^2 + (2 \times 2) - 3$
$= 4 + 4 - 3 = 5$

To check you're doing it right, make sure you can <u>reproduce the y-values</u> they've already given you.

This point is <u>obviously wrong</u>

2 Plot the points and join them with a <u>completely smooth curve</u>. Definitely <u>DON'T</u> use a ruler.

<u>NEVER EVER</u> let one point drag your line off in some ridiculous direction. When a graph is generated from an equation, you never get spikes or lumps — only <u>MISTAKES</u>.

Solving Quadratic Equations (GRADE 5)

Now celebrate the only way graphs know how: line dancing.

EXAMPLE: Use the graph of $y = x^2 + 2x - 3$ to solve the equation $x^2 + 2x - 3 = 0$.

The equation $x^2 + 2x - 3 = 0$ is what you get when you put $\underline{y = 0}$ into the graph's equation, $y = x^2 + 2x - 3$.

So to <u>solve</u> the equation, all you do is <u>read the x-values</u> where $y = 0$, i.e. where it crosses the x-axis.

So the solutions are $\underline{x = -3}$ and $\underline{x = 1}$.

Quadratic equations usually have <u>2 solutions</u>.

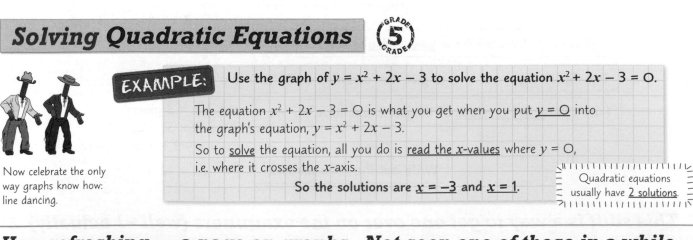

How refreshing — a page on graphs. Not seen one of those in a while...

You know the deal by now — learn what's on this page, then treat yourself to answering the question below.

Q1   a) Draw the graph of $y = x^2 - 4x - 1$ for values of x between –2 and 6.   **[4 marks]** (GRADE 5)

      b) Use your graph to estimate the solutions to $5 = x^2 - 4x - 1$.   **[1 mark]** (GRADE 5)

Harder Graphs

Graphs come in all sorts of shapes, sizes and wiggles — here are three more types you need to know:

x^3 Graphs: $y = ax^3 + bx^2 + cx + d$ (b, c and/or d can be zero) **GRADE 6**

All x^3 graphs have a <u>wiggle</u> in the middle — sometimes it's a flat wiggle, sometimes it's more pronounced.
$-x^3$ graphs always go down from <u>top left</u>, $+x^3$ ones go up from <u>bottom left</u>.

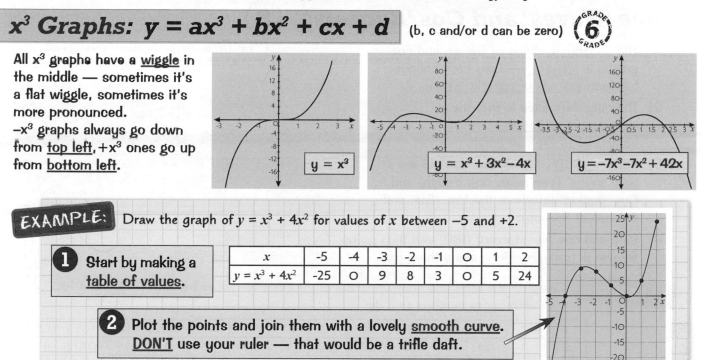

$y = x^3$

$y = x^3 + 3x^2 - 4x$

$y = -7x^3 - 7x^2 + 42x$

EXAMPLE: Draw the graph of $y = x^3 + 4x^2$ for values of x between -5 and $+2$.

1 Start by making a <u>table of values</u>.

x	-5	-4	-3	-2	-1	0	1	2
$y = x^3 + 4x^2$	-25	0	9	8	3	0	5	24

2 Plot the points and join them with a lovely <u>smooth curve</u>. <u>DON'T</u> use your ruler — that would be a trifle daft.

1/x (Reciprocal) Graphs: $y = A/x$ or $xy = A$ **GRADE 6**

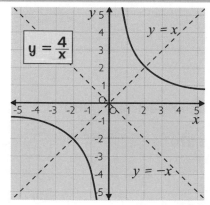

$y = \dfrac{4}{x}$

These are <u>all the same basic shape</u>, except the negative ones are in <u>opposite quadrants</u> to the positive ones (as shown). The two halves of the graph don't touch. The graphs <u>don't exist</u> for <u>x = 0</u>.

They're all <u>symmetrical</u> about the lines <u>y = x</u> and <u>y = -x</u>.

(You get this type of graph with inverse proportion — see p.58.)

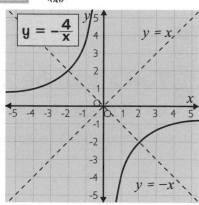

$y = -\dfrac{4}{x}$

1/x² Graphs: $y = A/x^2$ or $x^2y = A$ **GRADE 7**

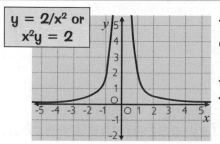

$y = 2/x^2$ or $x^2y = 2$

These are a bit like the $y = A/x$ graphs — except the two bits are <u>next to each other</u>.

The <u>positive</u> ones are <u>above</u> the x-axis and the <u>negative</u> ones are <u>below</u> the x-axis.

They're all <u>symmetrical</u> about the y-axis.

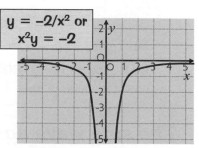

$y = -2/x^2$ or $x^2y = -2$

Phew — that page could seriously drive you round the x^2y...

Learn what type of graph you get from each sort of equation. Then try this Exam Practice Question:

Q1 a) Complete this table for $y = x^3 - 2x + 1$. [2 marks] **GRADE 6**

b) Draw the graph of $y = x^3 - 2x + 1$ for $-2 \le x \le 2$. [2 marks]

x	−2	−1	0	1	2
y				0	

Harder Graphs

The graphs of cos, sine and tan all have a <u>different pattern</u>. Make sure you learn all <u>three</u>.

Sine 'Waves' and Cos 'Buckets'

1) The underlying shape of the sin and cos graphs is <u>identical</u> — they both bounce between <u>y-limits of exactly +1 and –1</u>.

2) The only difference is that the <u>sin graph</u> is <u>shifted right by 90°</u> compared to the cos graph.

3) <u>For 0° – 360°</u>, the shapes you get are a <u>Sine 'Wave'</u> (one peak, one trough) and a <u>Cos 'Bucket'</u> (starts at the top, dips, and finishes at the top).

4) Sine and cos repeat every 360° and they go on forever in <u>both directions</u> along the <u>x-axis</u>.

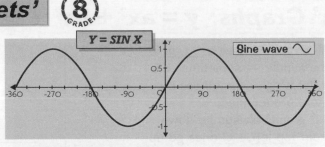

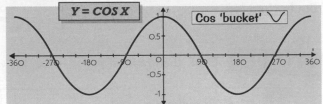

EXAMPLE: Complete the table and draw the graph of $y = \cos x$ for values between –180° and 180°. Give all rounded numbers to 2 d.p.

x	–180°	–150°	–120°	–90°	–60°	–30°	0°	30°	60°	90°	120°	150°	180°
cos x	–1	–0.87	–0.5	0	0.5	0.87	1	0.87	0.5	0	–0.5	–0.87	–1

Plot the points and join them up with a smooth curve.

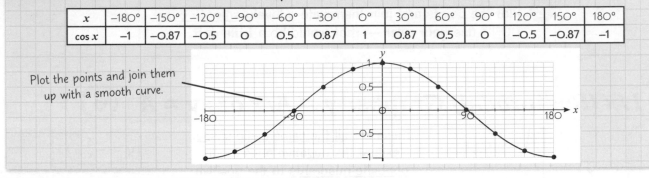

Tan x can be Any Value at all

tan x is <u>different</u> from sin x or cos x — it goes between -∞ and +∞. It also repeats every 180°.

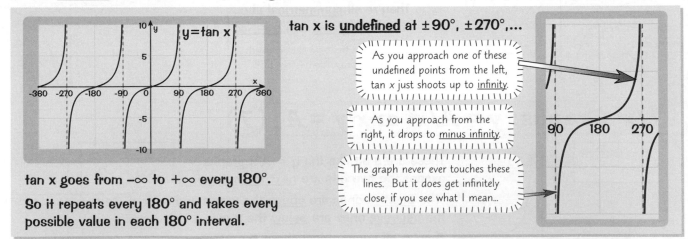

tan x is <u>undefined</u> at ±90°, ±270°,...

As you approach one of these undefined points from the left, tan x just shoots up to <u>infinity</u>.

As you approach from the right, it drops to <u>minus infinity</u>.

The graph never ever touches these lines. But it does get infinitely close, if you see what I mean...

tan x goes from -∞ to +∞ every 180°.

So it repeats every 180° and takes every possible value in each 180° interval.

The sine wave and the cos bucket — a great day out at the beach...

Learn the shape of each graph and how they repeat. Once you've got it, try out these practice questions.

Q1   a) Complete this table of values for $y = \cos x$.
Round your answers to 2 d.p.   [2 marks]

x	210°	240°	270°	300°	330°	360°
cos x						

     b) Using this table and the one in the example above, draw the graph of $y = \cos x$ for values of x between 0° and 360°.   [2 marks]

Functions

Functions can look a bit yuck, but they're basically just equations in fancy dress.

Functions Map Numbers from One Set to Another (6)

1) The definition of a function is a <u>rule</u> that <u>maps</u> each number from a set called the <u>domain</u> to <u>exactly one number</u> of a second set called the <u>range</u>.

But different domain values <u>can</u> map to the <u>same value</u> in the range — see the example on the right.

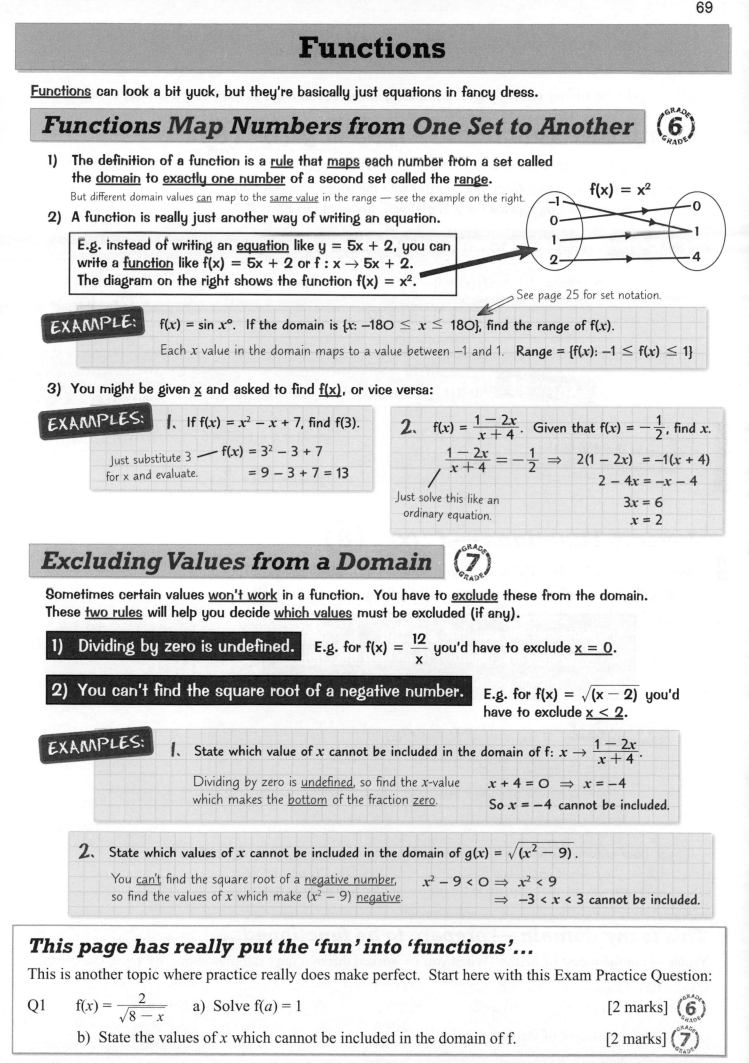

$f(x) = x^2$

2) A function is really just another way of writing an equation.

> E.g. instead of writing an <u>equation</u> like $y = 5x + 2$, you can write a <u>function</u> like $f(x) = 5x + 2$ or $f : x \rightarrow 5x + 2$. The diagram on the right shows the function $f(x) = x^2$.

See page 25 for set notation.

EXAMPLE: $f(x) = \sin x°$. If the domain is $\{x: -180 \leq x \leq 180\}$, find the range of $f(x)$.

Each x value in the domain maps to a value between -1 and 1. Range $= \{f(x): -1 \leq f(x) \leq 1\}$

3) You might be given <u>x</u> and asked to find <u>f(x)</u>, or vice versa:

EXAMPLES:

1. If $f(x) = x^2 - x + 7$, find $f(3)$.

Just substitute 3 for x and evaluate.

$f(x) = 3^2 - 3 + 7$
$= 9 - 3 + 7 = 13$

2. $f(x) = \dfrac{1 - 2x}{x + 4}$. Given that $f(x) = -\dfrac{1}{2}$, find x.

$\dfrac{1 - 2x}{x + 4} = -\dfrac{1}{2} \Rightarrow 2(1 - 2x) = -1(x + 4)$

$2 - 4x = -x - 4$

$3x = 6$

$x = 2$

Just solve this like an ordinary equation.

Excluding Values from a Domain (7)

Sometimes certain values <u>won't work</u> in a function. You have to <u>exclude</u> these from the domain. These <u>two rules</u> will help you decide <u>which values</u> must be excluded (if any).

1) Dividing by zero is undefined. E.g. for $f(x) = \dfrac{12}{x}$ you'd have to exclude <u>x = 0</u>.

2) You can't find the square root of a negative number. E.g. for $f(x) = \sqrt{(x - 2)}$ you'd have to exclude <u>x < 2</u>.

EXAMPLES:

1. State which value of x cannot be included in the domain of $f: x \rightarrow \dfrac{1 - 2x}{x + 4}$.

Dividing by zero is <u>undefined</u>, so find the x-value which makes the <u>bottom</u> of the fraction <u>zero</u>.

$x + 4 = 0 \Rightarrow x = -4$

So $x = -4$ cannot be included.

2. State which values of x cannot be included in the domain of $g(x) = \sqrt{(x^2 - 9)}$.

You <u>can't</u> find the square root of a <u>negative number</u>, so find the values of x which make $(x^2 - 9)$ <u>negative</u>.

$x^2 - 9 < 0 \Rightarrow x^2 < 9$

$\Rightarrow -3 < x < 3$ cannot be included.

This page has really put the 'fun' into 'functions'...

This is another topic where practice really does make perfect. Start here with this Exam Practice Question:

Q1 $f(x) = \dfrac{2}{\sqrt{8 - x}}$ a) Solve $f(a) = 1$ [2 marks] (6)

       b) State the values of x which cannot be included in the domain of f.   [2 marks] (7)

Functions

Functions get a bit trickier on this page. But once you can see through all the f's, g's and (x)'s they're OK.

Composite Functions — fg(x) or gf(x) (8)

You might get a question with two functions, e.g. f(x) and g(x).

- fg(x) means that you <u>replace</u> the <u>x</u> in f(x) with the <u>whole function</u> g(x).
- gf(x) means that you replace the <u>x</u> in g(x) with the <u>whole function</u> f(x).

EXAMPLE: If $f(x) = 2x - 10$ and $g(x) = -\dfrac{x}{2}$, find: a) fg(x)   b) gf(x).

a) Substitute g(x) in place of x in f(x).

$$fg(x) = f\left(-\frac{x}{2}\right)$$
$$= 2\left(-\frac{x}{2}\right) - 10$$
$$= -x - 10$$

b) Substitute f(x) in place of x in g(x).

$$gf(x) = g(2x - 10)$$
$$= -\frac{(2x - 10)}{2}$$
$$= -(x - 5) = 5 - x$$

EXAMPLE: If $f(x) = \dfrac{6}{x}$ and $g(x) = 4 - x$, find fg(−2).

> *Another way to think of this is that you have to do the function closest to x first. So for fg(x), you do g first, then f.*

You could also find fg(x), then substitute –2 for x.

1) First find g(−2): $g(-2) = 4 - (-2) = 6$

2) Now substitute g(−2) = 6 into f(x) to find fg(−2): $fg(-2) = f(6) = \dfrac{6}{6} = 1$

Inverse Functions — f⁻¹(x) (8)

The <u>inverse</u> of a function f(x) is another function, f⁻¹(x), which <u>reverses</u> f(x).

Finding the inverse of a function is only slightly fiddly. Here's the <u>method</u>:

1) Write out the equation <u>x = f(y)</u>
2) <u>Rearrange</u> the equation to <u>make y the subject.</u>
3) You've now got the equation y = f⁻¹(x).

> *f(y) is just the expression f(x), but with y's instead of x's*

See pages 39-40 for more on rearranging.

EXAMPLE: If $f(x) = \dfrac{12 + x}{3}$, find f⁻¹(x).

1) Write out x = f(y): $x = \dfrac{12 + y}{3}$

2) Rearrange to make y the subject: $3x = 12 + y \Rightarrow y = 3x - 12$

3) Now you've got f⁻¹(x): $f^{-1}(x) = 3x - 12$

<u>Check</u> your answer by testing if the inverse function <u>does reverse</u> the original function:

E.g. for the example above, find $f(9) = \dfrac{12+9}{3} = 7$. Now find $f^{-1}(7) = 21 - 12 = 9$.
We're back to the start number, so the inverse function is likely to be right.

This is my domain — prepare to be functioned...

Yeuch — not the nicest of maths. When you've worked through the examples above, try these questions:

Q1 $f(x) = 5x - 1$ $g(x) = 8 - 2x$ $h(x) = x^2 + 3$

Find: a) gf(x)   b) hf(2)   c) f⁻¹(x)   d) g⁻¹(f(x))   [9 marks] (8)

Q2   Find the inverse of the function f: $x \rightarrow \dfrac{2x + 3}{4 - x}$.   [3 marks] (8)

Graph Transformations

The next two pages cover all the types of graph transformation you'll need to know for your exam — translations, reflections and stretches. Learn them all and transform yourself into a maths guru.

Translations on the y-axis: y = f(x) + a (7)

This is where the whole graph is slid up or down the y-axis, and is achieved by simply adding a number onto the end of the equation: $y = f(x) + a$. This can be described as a translation by the vector $\begin{pmatrix} 0 \\ a \end{pmatrix}$.

EXAMPLE:

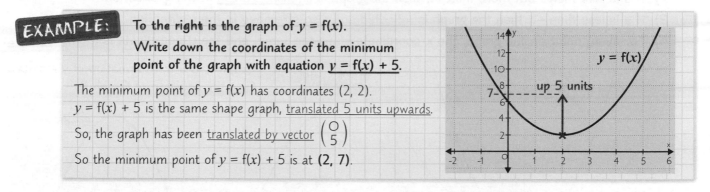

To the right is the graph of $y = f(x)$.
Write down the coordinates of the minimum point of the graph with equation $y = f(x) + 5$.

The minimum point of $y = f(x)$ has coordinates (2, 2).
$y = f(x) + 5$ is the same shape graph, translated 5 units upwards.

So, the graph has been translated by vector $\begin{pmatrix} 0 \\ 5 \end{pmatrix}$

So the minimum point of $y = f(x) + 5$ is at **(2, 7)**.

Translations on the x-axis: y = f(x – a) (8)

1) This is where the whole graph slides left or right and it only happens when you replace 'x' everywhere in the equation with 'x – a'. These are tricky because they go 'the wrong way'. If you want to go from $y = f(x)$ to $y = f(x – a)$ you must move the whole graph a distance 'a' in the positive x-direction →.

2) The translation $f(x – a)$ can be described as a translation by the vector $\begin{pmatrix} a \\ 0 \end{pmatrix}$.

3) Be careful though — with the translation $f(x + a)$, 'a' is negative. E.g. $f(x + 2) = f(x – (–2))$, which means it's a translation by the vector $\begin{pmatrix} -2 \\ 0 \end{pmatrix}$.

EXAMPLE:

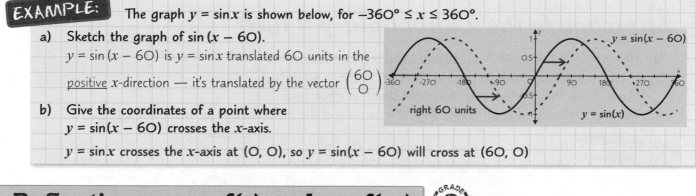

The graph $y = \sin x$ is shown below, for $-360° \leq x \leq 360°$.

a) Sketch the graph of $\sin(x – 60)$.
$y = \sin(x – 60)$ is $y = \sin x$ translated 60 units in the positive x-direction — it's translated by the vector $\begin{pmatrix} 60 \\ 0 \end{pmatrix}$

b) Give the coordinates of a point where $y = \sin(x – 60)$ crosses the x-axis.
$y = \sin x$ crosses the x-axis at (0, 0), so $y = \sin(x – 60)$ will cross at (60, 0)

Reflections: y = –f(x) and y = f(–x) (8)

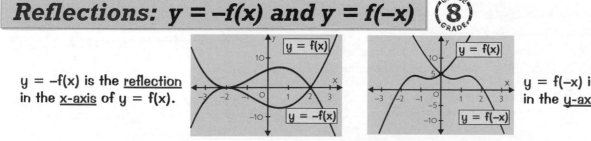

$y = –f(x)$ is the reflection in the x-axis of $y = f(x)$.

$y = f(–x)$ is the reflection in the y-axis of $y = f(x)$.

More sliding and flipping than a martial arts film...

Make sure you don't get translations on the x- and y-axis mixed up. Now, practice question time...

Q1 The coordinates of the maximum point of the graph $y = f(x)$ are (4, 3).
Give the coordinates of the maximum point of the graph with equation:
a) $y = f(–x)$ b) $y = f(x) – 4$ c) $y = f(x – 2) + 1$ [3 marks] (8)

Section Three — Graphs, Functions and Calculus

Graph Transformations

On the last page, you saw graphs sliding and flipping around. On this page you'll see graphs being <u>stretched</u> and <u>squashed</u>. Hold onto your <u>hats</u>, this could get pretty wild... (sort of).

Stretches in the y-direction: $y = af(x)$ (GRADE 9)

1) This is where the original graph is <u>stretched parallel to the y-axis</u> by multiplying the whole function by a number (a <u>scale factor</u>), i.e. $y = f(x)$ becomes $y = af(x)$ (where $a = 2$ or 5 etc.).

2) If a is less than 1 but more than –1, then the graph is <u>squashed down</u> in the y-direction.

3) If a is less than –1, then the graph is <u>reflected and also stretched</u> in the y-direction.

4) For every point on the graph, the x-coordinate <u>stays the same</u>, and the y-coordinate is <u>multiplied by a</u>.

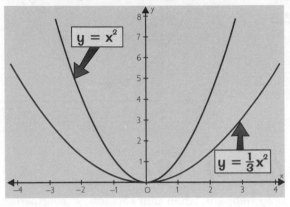

This graph shows $y = f(x)$ and $y = \frac{1}{3}f(x)$

$(y = x^2$ and $y = \frac{1}{3}x^2)$

EXAMPLE: Graph R is a transformation of $y = \sin(x)$. Give the equation of Graph R.

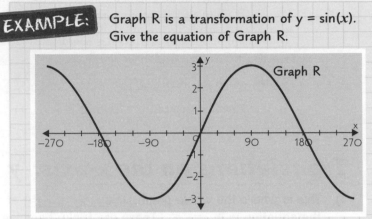

Graph R is $y = \sin x$ <u>stretched in the vertical direction</u>. You saw on p.68 that $y = \sin x$ 'bounces' between 1 and –1 on the y-axis. Graph R 'bounces' between 3 and –3, so the stretch has a <u>scale factor of 3</u>.
So the equation of Graph R is $y = 3\sin x$.

Stretches in the x direction: $y = f(ax)$ (GRADE 9)

1) This is where the graph is <u>stretched parallel to the x-axis</u> by a scale factor of $\frac{1}{a}$.

2) If a is more than 1 or less than –1 then the graph is <u>squashed</u>.
If a is more than –1 but less than 1 the graph is <u>stretched</u>.

3) The y-coordinate of each point stays the same and the x-coordinate is multiplied by $\frac{1}{a}$.

EXAMPLE: The graph of $y = \sin x$ is shown to the right. Sketch the graph $\underline{y = \sin 4x}$ for $0° \le x \le 360°$.

$y = \sin 4x$ has a <u>scale factor</u> of $\frac{1}{4}$, so its graph will be <u>4 times as squashed up</u> as $y = \sin x$.

There is <u>one</u> cycle of up and down on the $y = \sin x$ graph, so you can fit <u>four</u> cycles of the $y = \sin 4x$ graph in the same space.

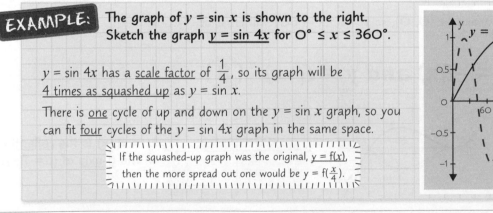

If the squashed-up graph was the original, $\underline{y = f(x)}$, then the more spread out one would be $y = f(\frac{x}{4})$.

And stretch... ... and breathe... ...and relax...

Make sure you learn the different transformations — then try them out on this Exam Practice Question.

Q1 The coordinates of the minimum point of the graph $y = f(x)$ are (2, 2).
Give the coordinates of the minimum point of the graph with equation:

a) $y = f(\frac{x}{2})$ b) $y = f(2x) - 4$ c) $y = 0.5\,f(x)$ [3 marks] (GRADE 9)

Differentiation

This page just shows you <u>how to do</u> differentiation. <u>Why you do it</u> is covered on the next page.

Use the Formula to Differentiate Powers of x (6)

This means 'the result of differentiating the thing in the brackets'.

$$\frac{d}{dx}(x^n) = nx^{n-1}$$

If $y = x^n$, then you write: $\frac{dy}{dx}$

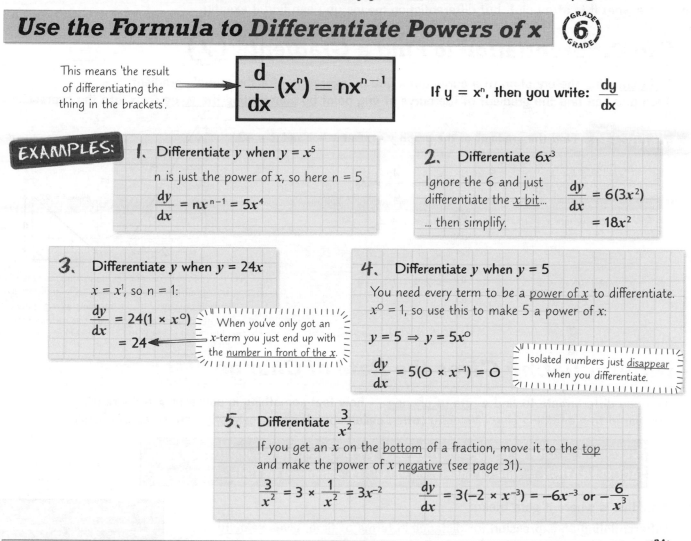

EXAMPLES:

1. Differentiate y when $y = x^5$

n is just the power of x, so here n = 5

$$\frac{dy}{dx} = nx^{n-1} = 5x^4$$

2. Differentiate $6x^3$

Ignore the 6 and just differentiate the x bit...

... then simplify.

$$\frac{dy}{dx} = 6(3x^2)$$
$$= 18x^2$$

3. Differentiate y when $y = 24x$

$x = x^1$, so n = 1:

$$\frac{dy}{dx} = 24(1 \times x^0)$$
$$= 24$$

When you've only got an x-term you just end up with the <u>number in front of the x</u>.

4. Differentiate y when $y = 5$

You need every term to be a <u>power of x</u> to differentiate. $x^0 = 1$, so use this to make 5 a power of x:

$$y = 5 \Rightarrow y = 5x^0$$

$$\frac{dy}{dx} = 5(0 \times x^{-1}) = 0$$

Isolated numbers just <u>disappear</u> when you differentiate.

5. Differentiate $\frac{3}{x^2}$

If you get an x on the <u>bottom</u> of a fraction, move it to the <u>top</u> and make the power of x <u>negative</u> (see page 31).

$$\frac{3}{x^2} = 3 \times \frac{1}{x^2} = 3x^{-2} \qquad \frac{dy}{dx} = 3(-2 \times x^{-3}) = -6x^{-3} \text{ or } -\frac{6}{x^3}$$

Differentiate Each Term in an Equation Separately (6)

Even if there are loads of terms in the equation, it doesn't matter.
Differentiate each bit <u>separately</u> and you'll be fine.

EXAMPLES:

1. Find $\frac{dy}{dx}$ for $y = 6x^4 + 4x^3 - 2x + 1$.

Think of this as four separate differentiations, i.e.

$$\frac{dy}{dx} = \frac{d}{dx}(6x^4) + \frac{d}{dx}(4x^3) - \frac{d}{dx}(2x) + \frac{d}{dx}(1)$$

$$\frac{dy}{dx} = 6(4x^3) + 4(3x^2) - 2(1x^0) + 0$$
$$= 24x^3 + 12x^2 - 2$$

2. Differentiate $\frac{3 + x^2}{5}$

Dividing by 5 is the same as multiplying by $\frac{1}{5}$:

$$\frac{3 + x^2}{5} = \frac{1}{5}(3 + x^2)$$

Now differentiate each term in the brackets:

$$\frac{dy}{dx} = \frac{1}{5}(0 + 2x^1) = \frac{2x}{5}$$

Differentiate yourself from the crowd — wear your clothes backwards...

Luckily, once you can do the simple stuff, you should be all right. Longer equations are just made up of simple little terms, so they're not really that much harder. And another thing — don't panic if the examiners use letters other than x and y — just differentiate in the same way. Now try these Exam Practice Questions:

Q1   Differentiate $4x - x^3 + 3$.   [2 marks] (6)   Q2 $F = \frac{13}{x^2} + x^3$. Find $\frac{dF}{dx}$.   [2 marks] (6)

Differentiation

As you saw on p.63, the gradient of a curve is <u>constantly changing</u>. You can draw a tangent to estimate what it is at a point, but differentiation means you can find it <u>exactly</u>.

Use Differentiation to Find a Gradient (7)

<u>Differentiating</u> the equation of a curve gives you an <u>expression</u> for the curve's gradient.
Then you can find the gradient of the curve at any point by <u>substituting the value for x</u> into the expression.

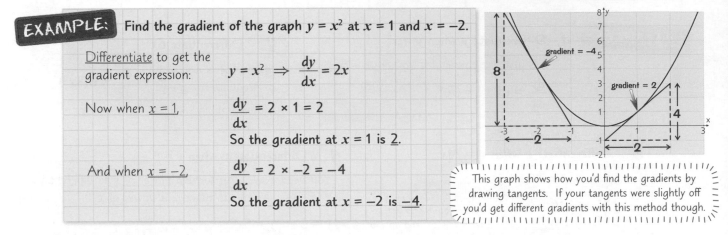

EXAMPLE: Find the gradient of the graph $y = x^2$ at $x = 1$ and $x = -2$.

<u>Differentiate</u> to get the gradient expression:

$$y = x^2 \Rightarrow \frac{dy}{dx} = 2x$$

Now when $\underline{x = 1}$,

$$\frac{dy}{dx} = 2 \times 1 = 2$$

So the gradient at $x = 1$ is <u>2</u>.

And when $\underline{x = -2}$,

$$\frac{dy}{dx} = 2 \times -2 = -4$$

So the gradient at $x = -2$ is <u>−4</u>.

This graph shows how you'd find the gradients by drawing tangents. If your tangents were slightly off you'd get different gradients with this method though.

Differentiating Gives the Rate of Change (9)

You can differentiate to find a <u>rate of change</u> — how fast something is decreasing or increasing <u>compared to something else</u>. <u>Velocity</u> (often called speed) and <u>acceleration</u> are rates of change:

> **VELOCITY** = rate of change of **DISTANCE** (or displacement) compared to **TIME**
> **ACCELERATION** = rate of change of **VELOCITY** compared to **TIME**

's' is commonly used for distance. Yep — weird, isn't it?

Now this is where it gets tricky:

Differentiating an expression for <u>distance in terms of time</u>, gives <u>velocity</u>.
Differentiating an expression for <u>velocity in terms of time</u>, gives <u>acceleration</u>.
An example will make this clearer:

> If s = distance, t = time,
> v = velocity, a = acceleration:
> $$v = \frac{ds}{dt} \quad \text{and} \quad a = \frac{dv}{dt}$$

EXAMPLE: An object's displacement, s metres, from a fixed point after t seconds is $s = 5t^3 + t^2$, $0 \le t \le 10$.
a) Find expressions for the object's velocity and acceleration at time t seconds.
b) Find the velocity after 3 seconds.

a) Differentiate the <u>displacement</u> expression (s) to get the <u>velocity</u> expression.

velocity $= \frac{ds}{dt} = 5(3t^2) + 2t \Rightarrow$ velocity $= \underline{15t^2 + 2t}$

Differentiate the <u>velocity</u> expression (v) to get the <u>acceleration</u> expression.

acceleration $= \frac{dv}{dt} = 15(2t) + 2 \Rightarrow$ acceleration $= \underline{30t + 2}$

Remember to put the correct units.

b) Substitute <u>3 for t</u> in the <u>velocity</u> expression to find the velocity after this many seconds.

$v = 15t^2 + 2t$.
When t = 3, $v = 15(3^2) + 2(3) = 135 + 6 = \underline{141 \text{ m/s}}$

Help me differentiation — you're my only hope...

Understanding that differentiating gives the gradient of the graph is more important than washing regularly — and that's important. Now try these:

Q1 Find the gradient of the graph of $y = 6x^4 + 2x^3$ when $x = 2$. [3 marks] (7)

Q2 If distance, $s = 3t(t^2 + t)$, where t = time, find expressions for velocity and acceleration. [3 marks] (9)

Differentiation

Some graphs have <u>stationary points</u> — places where the graph 'levels off'. You find them by <u>differentiating</u>.

Stationary Points are When the Gradient is Zero (8)

1) A <u>stationary point</u> is a point on a curve where the <u>gradient equals zero</u>.

2) So to find the stationary points of a graph, you need to find the points where:

$$\frac{dy}{dx} = 0$$

3) A <u>turning point</u> is a type of stationary point which can be a <u>maximum</u> or a <u>minimum</u>.

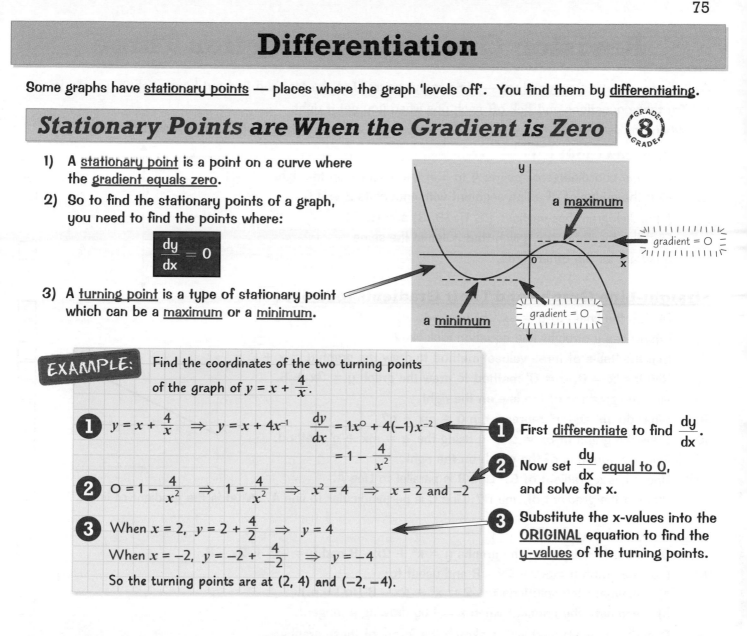

EXAMPLE: Find the coordinates of the two turning points of the graph of $y = x + \frac{4}{x}$.

1 $y = x + \frac{4}{x} \Rightarrow y = x + 4x^{-1}$ $\frac{dy}{dx} = 1x^0 + 4(-1)x^{-2}$

$= 1 - \frac{4}{x^2}$

1 First <u>differentiate</u> to find $\frac{dy}{dx}$.

2 $0 = 1 - \frac{4}{x^2} \Rightarrow 1 = \frac{4}{x^2} \Rightarrow x^2 = 4 \Rightarrow x = 2$ and -2

2 Now set $\frac{dy}{dx}$ equal to 0, and solve for x.

3 When $x = 2$, $y = 2 + \frac{4}{2} \Rightarrow y = 4$

When $x = -2$, $y = -2 + \frac{4}{-2} \Rightarrow y = -4$

So the turning points are at (2, 4) and (−2, −4).

3 Substitute the x-values into the <u>ORIGINAL</u> equation to find the <u>y-values</u> of the turning points.

Maximum or Minimum? (9)

You <u>can't tell</u> if a turning point is a <u>maximum</u> or <u>minimum</u> from the coordinates. The easiest way of telling is to think about the <u>shape</u> of the graph (see p.66-68).

EXAMPLE: Determine whether each turning point of the graph of $y = x + \frac{4}{x}$ identified above is a maximum or a minimum.

This is a y = A/x graph with a bit added on (see page 67). It's a nasty one, so you might be best sketching it using a table of values (see page 62). If you did, you'd get a graph like this:

The turning point at (2, 4) is a minimum.
The turning point at (−2, −4) is a maximum.

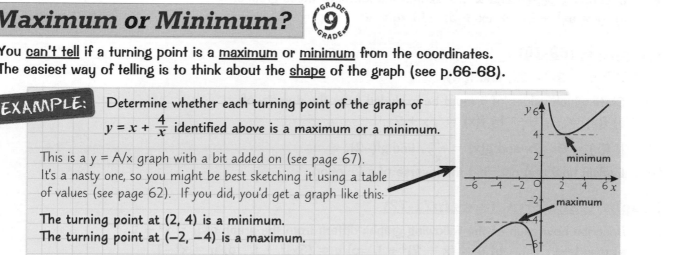

An anagram of differentiation is "Perfect Insomnia Cure"...

There are so many uses for differentiation. Amazing. Check you get it with this lovely question:

Q1 A curve has equation $y = 7x^2 + 42x$.

a) Find $\frac{dy}{dx}$ and use your answer to find the coordinates of the curve's turning point. [4 marks] (9)

b) State, with a reason, whether this is a minimum or maximum. [1 mark]

Revision Questions for Section Three

Well, that wraps up <u>Section Three</u> — time to put yourself to the test and find out <u>how much you really know</u>.

- Try these questions and <u>tick off each one</u> when you <u>get it right</u>.
- When you've done <u>all the questions</u> for a topic and are <u>completely happy</u> with it, tick off the topic.

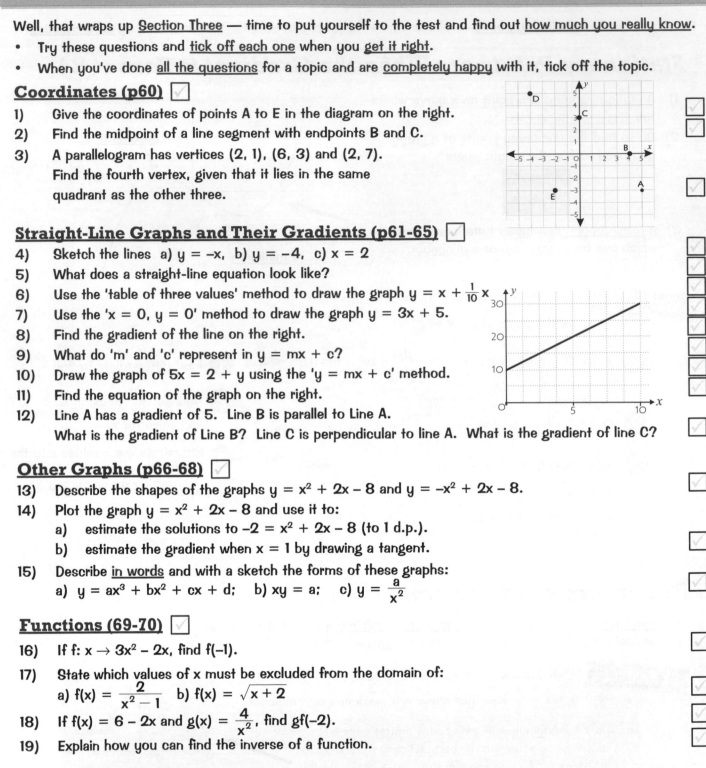

Coordinates (p60) ☑

1) Give the coordinates of points A to E in the diagram on the right.
2) Find the midpoint of a line segment with endpoints B and C.
3) A parallelogram has vertices (2, 1), (6, 3) and (2, 7).
   Find the fourth vertex, given that it lies in the same
   quadrant as the other three.

Straight-Line Graphs and Their Gradients (p61-65) ☑

4) Sketch the lines a) $y = -x$, b) $y = -4$, c) $x = 2$
5) What does a straight-line equation look like?
6) Use the 'table of three values' method to draw the graph $y = x + \frac{1}{10}x$
7) Use the '$x = 0$, $y = 0$' method to draw the graph $y = 3x + 5$.
8) Find the gradient of the line on the right.
9) What do 'm' and 'c' represent in $y = mx + c$?
10) Draw the graph of $5x = 2 + y$ using the '$y = mx + c$' method.
11) Find the equation of the graph on the right.
12) Line A has a gradient of 5. Line B is parallel to Line A.
    What is the gradient of Line B? Line C is perpendicular to line A. What is the gradient of line C?

Other Graphs (p66-68) ☑

13) Describe the shapes of the graphs $y = x^2 + 2x - 8$ and $y = -x^2 + 2x - 8$.
14) Plot the graph $y = x^2 + 2x - 8$ and use it to:
    a) estimate the solutions to $-2 = x^2 + 2x - 8$ (to 1 d.p.).
    b) estimate the gradient when $x = 1$ by drawing a tangent.
15) Describe <u>in words</u> and with a sketch the forms of these graphs:
    a) $y = ax^3 + bx^2 + cx + d$;   b) $xy = a$;   c) $y = \frac{a}{x^2}$

Functions (69-70) ☑

16) If $f: x \rightarrow 3x^2 - 2x$, find $f(-1)$.
17) State which values of x must be excluded from the domain of:
    a) $f(x) = \frac{2}{x^2 - 1}$ b) $f(x) = \sqrt{x + 2}$
18) If $f(x) = 6 - 2x$ and $g(x) = \frac{4}{x^2}$, find $gf(-2)$.
19) Explain how you can find the inverse of a function.

Graphs Transformations (p71-72) ☑

20) Describe how each of the following graphs differs from the graph of $y = x^3 + 1$
    a) $y = (-x)^3 + 1$,   b) $y = (x + 2)^3 + 1$,   c) $y = (3x)^3 + 1$,   d) $y = x^3 - 1$

Differentiation (p73-75) ☑

21) Differentiate $3x^5 + 2x$, and then find the gradient of the graph of $y = 3x^5 + 2x$ at $x = 3$.
22) An object's displacement, s metres, after t seconds is given by $s = t^2 - 2t$.
    Find the object's velocity and acceleration after 4 seconds.
23) Find the coordinates of the turning point of each of these graphs.
    Say if each is a minimum or a maximum.
    a) $y = x^2 - 2x$ b) $y = -x^2 - 2x$.

Maps and Scale Drawings

The added bonus with this page is that it'll come in handy next time the sat nav lands you in a field...

Map Scales (2)

<u>Scales</u> tell you what a <u>distance</u> on a <u>map</u> or <u>drawing</u> represents in <u>real life</u>.

They can be written in various ways, but they all boil down to something like "<u>1 cm represents 5 km</u>":

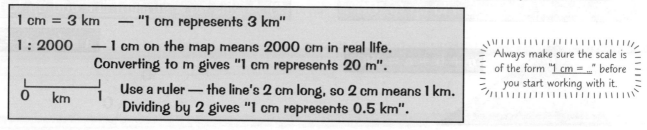

1 cm = 3 km — "1 cm represents 3 km"
1 : 2000 — 1 cm on the map means 2000 cm in real life. Converting to m gives "1 cm represents 20 m".
0   km   1   Use a ruler — the line's 2 cm long, so 2 cm means 1 km. Dividing by 2 gives "1 cm represents 0.5 km".

Always make sure the scale is of the form "<u>1 cm = ...</u>" before you start working with it.

Converting from Map Distance to Real Life — Multiply (2)

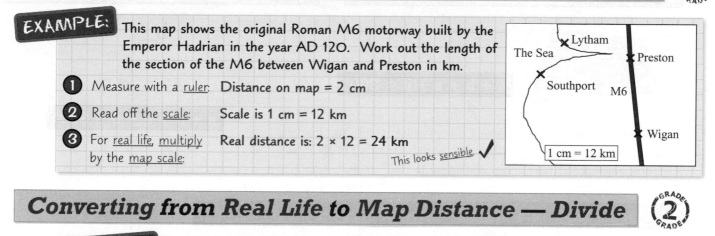

EXAMPLE: This map shows the original Roman M6 motorway built by the Emperor Hadrian in the year AD 120. Work out the length of the section of the M6 between Wigan and Preston in km.

1. Measure with a <u>ruler</u>: Distance on map = 2 cm
2. Read off the <u>scale</u>: Scale is 1 cm = 12 km
3. For <u>real life</u>, <u>multiply</u> by the <u>map scale</u>: Real distance is: 2 × 12 = 24 km

This looks <u>sensible</u>. ✓

Map labels: The Sea, Lytham, Preston, Southport, M6, Wigan, 1 cm = 12 km

Converting from Real Life to Map Distance — Divide (2)

EXAMPLE: Helmsley and Pickering are 18 km apart.
How far apart would they be on a map with a scale of 1 cm = 6 km?

<u>Divide</u> by the <u>scale</u> to find the <u>map distance</u>.
— Real-life distance = 18 km, Scale is 1 cm = 6 km
— Distance on map = 18 ÷ 6 = 3 cm

This looks <u>sensible</u>. ✓

Scale Drawings (2)

To convert between real life and <u>scale drawings</u>, just replace the word 'map' with 'drawing' in the <u>rules</u> above.

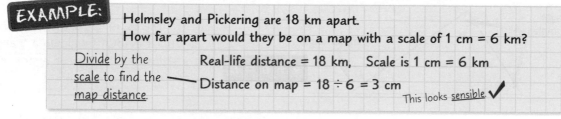

EXAMPLE: 1 cm represents 1.5 m on this scale drawing of a room in Clare's house. Her dining table is 0.9 m wide and 1.8 m long. Draw the table on the scale drawing.

1. <u>Divide</u> to get scale drawing dimensions.
   Width on drawing = 0.9 ÷ 1.5 = 0.6 cm
   Length on drawing = 1.8 ÷ 1.5 = 1.2 cm

2. Draw with a <u>ruler</u> in any sensible position and label.

(Table)

Follow this map of the road to exam glory... What?... Cheesy?... Me?

Give these practice questions a go once you're happy with the two formulas and know when to use them.

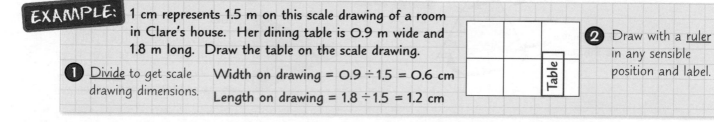

Q1 The diagram is a scale drawing of a flag, where 1 cm represents 20 cm. Calculate the actual length of the vertical side of the flag. [2 marks] (2)

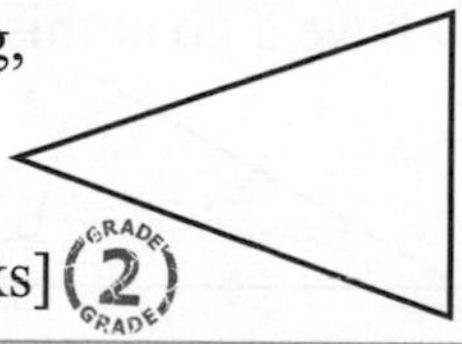

Q2 Sarah's house is 2.25 km away from Luke's house. How far apart in cm would they be on a map where 1 cm represents 500 m? [2 marks] (2)

Geometry

If you know <u>all</u> these rules <u>thoroughly</u>, you'll at least have a fighting chance of working out problems with lines and angles. If you don't — you've no chance. Sorry to break it to you like that.

6 Simple Rules — that's all (3)

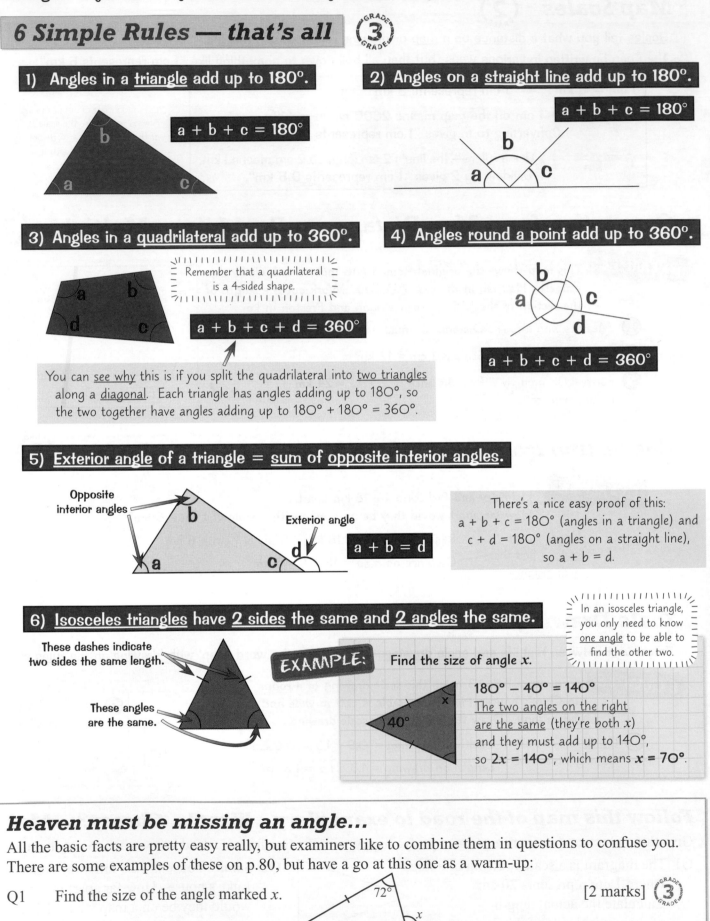

1) Angles in a <u>triangle</u> add up to 180°.

a + b + c = 180°

2) Angles on a <u>straight line</u> add up to 180°.

a + b + c = 180°

3) Angles in a <u>quadrilateral</u> add up to 360°.

Remember that a quadrilateral is a 4-sided shape.

a + b + c + d = 360°

You can <u>see why</u> this is if you split the quadrilateral into <u>two triangles</u> along a <u>diagonal</u>. Each triangle has angles adding up to 180°, so the two together have angles adding up to 180° + 180° = 360°.

4) Angles <u>round a point</u> add up to 360°.

a + b + c + d = 360°

5) <u>Exterior angle</u> of a triangle = <u>sum</u> of <u>opposite interior angles</u>.

Opposite interior angles

Exterior angle

a + b = d

There's a nice easy proof of this:
a + b + c = 180° (angles in a triangle) and
c + d = 180° (angles on a straight line),
so a + b = d.

6) <u>Isosceles triangles</u> have <u>2 sides</u> the same and <u>2 angles</u> the same.

These dashes indicate two sides the same length.

These angles are the same.

In an isosceles triangle, you only need to know <u>one angle</u> to be able to find the other two.

EXAMPLE: Find the size of angle *x*.

40°

180° − 40° = 140°
<u>The two angles on the right
are the same</u> (they're both *x*)
and they must add up to 140°,
so 2*x* = 140°, which means *x* = 70°.

Heaven must be missing an angle...

All the basic facts are pretty easy really, but examiners like to combine them in questions to confuse you. There are some examples of these on p.80, but have a go at this one as a warm-up:

Q1   Find the size of the angle marked *x*.

72°

x

[2 marks] (3)

Parallel Lines

Parallel lines are quite straightforward really. (They're also quite straight. And parallel.)
There are a few rules you need to learn — make sure you don't get them mixed up.

Angles Around Parallel Lines

When a line crosses two parallel lines, it forms special sets of angles.

1)   The two bunches of angles formed at the points of intersection
    are the same.

2)   There are only actually two different angles involved (labelled a and b
    here), and they add up to 180° (from rule 2 on the previous page).

3)   Vertically opposite angles (ones opposite each other) are equal
    (in the diagram, a and a are vertically opposite, as are b and b).

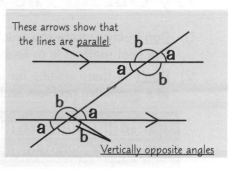
These arrows show that
the lines are parallel.
Vertically opposite angles

Alternate, Allied and Corresponding Angles

The diagram above has some characteristic shapes to look out for — and each shape contains a
specific pair of angles. The angle pairs are known as alternate, allied and corresponding angles.

> You need to spot the characteristic Z, C, U and F shapes:

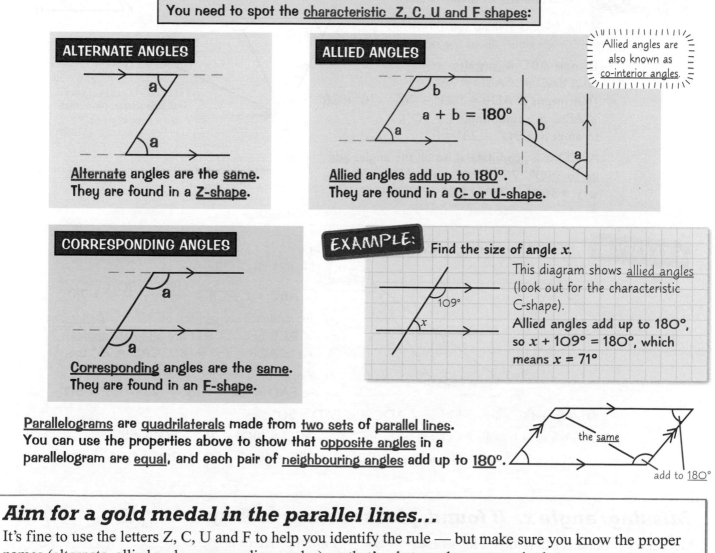

ALTERNATE ANGLES

Alternate angles are the same.
They are found in a Z-shape.

ALLIED ANGLES

$a + b = 180°$

Allied angles are
also known as
co-interior angles.

Allied angles add up to 180°.
They are found in a C- or U-shape.

CORRESPONDING ANGLES

Corresponding angles are the same.
They are found in an F-shape.

EXAMPLE: Find the size of angle x.

109°

This diagram shows allied angles
(look out for the characteristic
C-shape).
Allied angles add up to 180°,
so $x + 109° = 180°$, which
means $x = 71°$

Parallelograms are quadrilaterals made from two sets of parallel lines.
You can use the properties above to show that opposite angles in a
parallelogram are equal, and each pair of neighbouring angles add up to 180°.

the same

add to 180°

Aim for a gold medal in the parallel lines...

It's fine to use the letters Z, C, U and F to help you identify the rule — but make sure you know the proper
names (alternate, allied and corresponding angles), as that's what you have to use in the exam.

Q1   Find the size of the angle marked x.   116°   [2 marks]

x

Geometry Problems

My biggest geometry problem is that I have to do geometry problems in the first place. *Sigh*
Ah well, best get practising — these problems aren't going to solve themselves.

Try Out All The Rules One by One (3)

1) <u>Don't</u> concentrate too much on the angle you have been asked to find.
The best method is to find <u>ALL</u> the angles in <u>whatever order</u> they become obvious.

2) <u>Don't</u> sit there waiting for inspiration to hit you. It's all too easy to find yourself staring
at a geometry problem and <u>getting nowhere</u>. The method is this:

> <u>GO THROUGH ALL THE RULES OF GEOMETRY</u> (including <u>PARALLEL LINES</u>), <u>ONE BY ONE</u>,
> and apply each of them in turn <u>in as many ways as possible</u> — one of them is bound to work.

3) Before we get going, there's one bit of <u>notation</u> you need to be familiar with —
<u>three-letter angle notation</u>. It's not hard — if you get an angle written as $\angle$**ABC**
(or just **ABC**), it's the angle formed at letter <u>**B**</u> (it's always the middle letter).

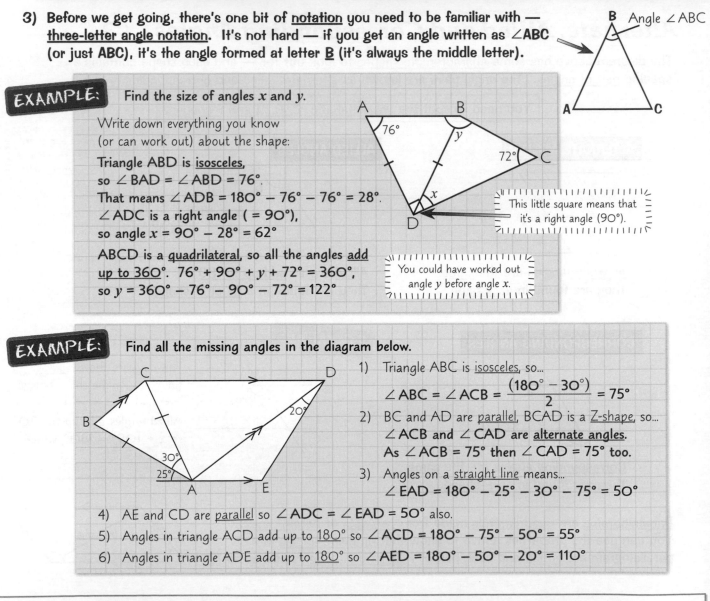

EXAMPLE: Find the size of angles x and y.

Write down everything you know
(or can work out) about the shape:

Triangle ABD is <u>isosceles</u>,
so $\angle$ BAD = $\angle$ ABD = 76°.
That means $\angle$ ADB = 180° − 76° − 76° = 28°.
$\angle$ ADC is a right angle (= 90°),
so angle x = 90° − 28° = 62°

This little square means that
it's a right angle (90°).

ABCD is a <u>quadrilateral</u>, so all the angles <u>add
up to 360°</u>. 76° + 90° + y + 72° = 360°,
so y = 360° − 76° − 90° − 72° = 122°

You could have worked out
angle y before angle x.

EXAMPLE: Find all the missing angles in the diagram below.

1) Triangle ABC is <u>isosceles</u>, so...
$$\angle ABC = \angle ACB = \frac{(180° - 30°)}{2} = 75°$$

2) BC and AD are <u>parallel</u>, BCAD is a <u>Z-shape</u>, so...
$\angle$ ACB and $\angle$ CAD are <u>alternate angles</u>.
As $\angle$ ACB = 75° then $\angle$ CAD = 75° too.

3) Angles on a <u>straight line</u> means...
$\angle$ EAD = 180° − 25° − 30° − 75° = 50°

4) AE and CD are <u>parallel</u> so $\angle$ ADC = $\angle$ EAD = 50° also.

5) Angles in triangle ACD add up to <u>180°</u> so $\angle$ ACD = 180° − 75° − 50° = 55°

6) Angles in triangle ADE add up to <u>180°</u> so $\angle$ AED = 180° − 50° − 20° = 110°

Missing: angle x. If found, please return to Amy...

Geometry problems often look a lot worse
than they are — don't panic, just write down
everything you can work out. Watch out for
hidden parallel lines and isosceles triangles
— they can help you work out angles.

Q1   Find the size of angle x.

[3 marks] (3)

Polygons

A <u>polygon</u> is a <u>many-sided shape</u>, and can be <u>regular</u> or <u>irregular</u>. A <u>regular</u> polygon is one where all the <u>sides</u> and <u>angles</u> are the <u>same</u> (in an <u>irregular</u> polygon, the sides and angles are <u>different</u>).

Regular Polygons

You need to be familiar with the first few <u>regular polygons</u> — ones with up to <u>10 sides</u>. You need to know their <u>names</u> and how many <u>sides</u> they have (remember that all the <u>sides</u> and <u>angles</u> in a regular polygon are the <u>same</u>).

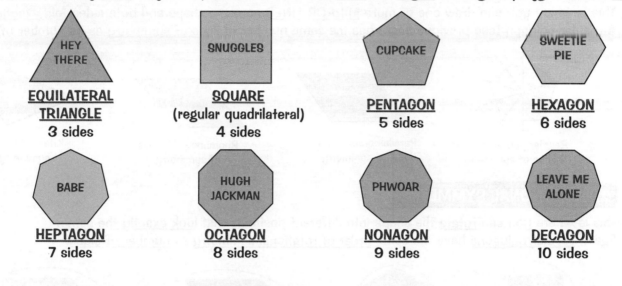

Interior and Exterior Angles

Questions on <u>interior</u> and <u>exterior angles</u> often come up in exams — so you need to know <u>what</u> they are and <u>how to find them</u>. There are a couple of <u>formulas</u> you need to learn as well.

For <u>ANY POLYGON</u> (regular or irregular):

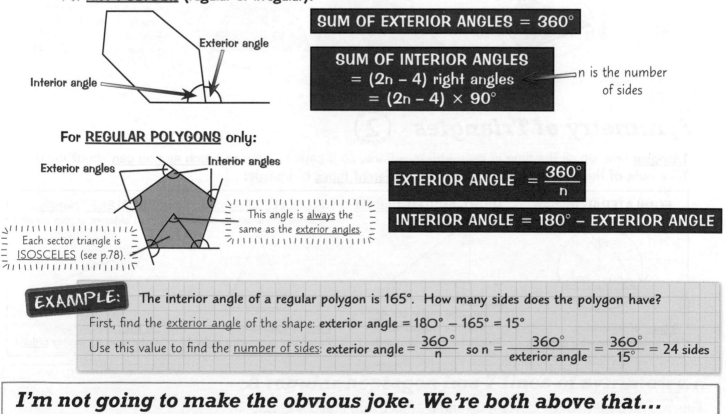

SUM OF EXTERIOR ANGLES = 360°

SUM OF INTERIOR ANGLES = (2n − 4) right angles = (2n − 4) × 90°

n is the number of sides

For <u>REGULAR POLYGONS</u> only:

This angle is <u>always</u> the same as the <u>exterior angles</u>.

Each sector triangle is <u>ISOSCELES</u> (see p.78).

$$\text{EXTERIOR ANGLE} = \frac{360°}{n}$$

INTERIOR ANGLE = 180° − EXTERIOR ANGLE

EXAMPLE: The interior angle of a regular polygon is 165°. How many sides does the polygon have?

First, find the <u>exterior angle</u> of the shape: exterior angle = 180° − 165° = 15°

Use this value to find the <u>number of sides</u>: exterior angle = $\frac{360°}{n}$ so n = $\frac{360°}{\text{exterior angle}}$ = $\frac{360°}{15°}$ = 24 sides

I'm not going to make the obvious joke. We're both above that...

Make sure you learn all the formulas on this page, and which ones go with regular and irregular polygons.

Q1 Find the size of the interior angle of a regular decagon. [2 marks]

Aww man, this was gonna be my big break an' everythin'.

Symmetry

After you've finished this page, remind me that I need to pop out and buy a pint of milk. There'll be none left for my breakfast otherwise. Anyway, sorry, symmetry... Right, yes, there are __TWO types__ of symmetry:

Symmetry (2)

1) LINE SYMMETRY

This is where you can draw one or more __MIRROR LINES__ across a shape and both sides __fold exactly__ together.
A __regular polygon__ (see previous page) has the same number of __lines of symmetry__ as its number of __sides__.

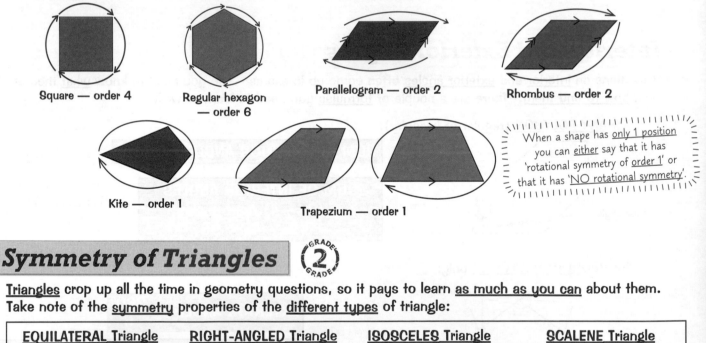

Regular pentagon
— 5 lines of symmetry

Parallelogram — no
lines of symmetry

Rhombus — 2 lines
of symmetry

Kite — 1 line of
symmetry

2) ROTATIONAL SYMMETRY

This is where you can __rotate__ the shape into different positions that __look exactly the same__.
Again, __regular polygons__ have the same __order of rotational symmetry__ as __number of sides__.

Square — order 4

Regular hexagon
— order 6

Parallelogram — order 2

Rhombus — order 2

Kite — order 1

Trapezium — order 1

When a shape has __only 1 position__ you can __either__ say that it has 'rotational symmetry of __order 1__' or that it has '__NO rotational symmetry__'.

Symmetry of Triangles (2)

__Triangles__ crop up all the time in geometry questions, so it pays to learn __as much as you can__ about them.
Take note of the __symmetry__ properties of the __different types__ of triangle:

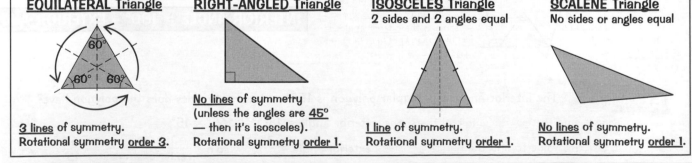

__EQUILATERAL Triangle__	__RIGHT-ANGLED Triangle__	__ISOSCELES Triangle__ 2 sides and 2 angles equal	__SCALENE Triangle__ No sides or angles equal
60° 60° 60°			
__3 lines__ of symmetry. Rotational symmetry __order 3__.	__No lines__ of symmetry (unless the angles are __45°__ — then it's isosceles). Rotational symmetry __order 1__.	__1 line__ of symmetry. Rotational symmetry __order 1__.	__No lines__ of symmetry. Rotational symmetry __order 1__.

A regular heptagon has 7 lines of symmetry...

This is a nice easy page. Cover it up and try this Exam Practice Question:

Q1 Write down the number of lines of symmetry and the order of rotational symmetry of:
   a) an equilateral triangle   b) a parallelogram   c) a regular octagon   [3 marks] (2)

Section Four — Geometry and Measures

Circle Geometry

Brace yourself — there's a 3-page extravaganza on <u>circle theorems</u> coming your way. Sorry.

Parts of a Circle

There are some wacky names for the <u>parts of a circle</u> — make sure you know what they all mean.

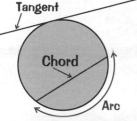

> You should know these two already.

<u>A TANGENT</u> is a straight line that <u>just touches</u> the <u>outside</u> of a circle.
<u>A CHORD</u> is a line drawn <u>across the inside</u> of a circle.
The <u>CIRCUMFERENCE</u> of a circle is the <u>distance all the way around it</u>.
<u>AN ARC</u> is just <u>part of the circumference</u> of a circle.

<u>A SECTOR</u> is a wedge-shaped area (like a slice of cake) cut right from the centre.
<u>SEGMENTS</u> are the areas you get when you cut a circle with a chord.

11 Rules to Learn — 4 Simple Ones to Start With... (5)

1) A <u>TANGENT</u> and a <u>RADIUS</u> meet at <u>90°</u>.

A <u>TANGENT</u> is a line that just touches a single point on the circumference of a circle.
A tangent always makes an angle of <u>exactly 90°</u> with the <u>radius</u> it meets at this point.

2) <u>TANGENTS</u> from the <u>SAME POINT</u> are the <u>SAME LENGTH</u>.

Two tangents drawn from an outside point are <u>always equal in length</u> (up to the point where they touch the circle), so creating an 'isosceles' situation, with <u>two congruent right-angled triangles</u>.

> There's more about congruence on p.89.

3) The <u>PERPENDICULAR BISECTOR</u> of a <u>CHORD</u> passes through the <u>CENTRE</u> of the circle.

A <u>CHORD</u> is any line <u>drawn across a circle</u>. And no matter where you draw a chord, the line that <u>cuts it exactly in half</u> (at 90°), will <u>go through the centre of the circle</u>.

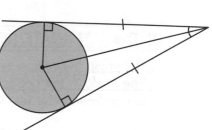

EXAMPLE: A, B and C are points on the circumference of the circle with centre O. Find x.

Line <u>AC is a chord</u>.

Line OB is at <u>right angles</u> to AC and goes through the <u>centre</u> of the circle.

This means that:
OB is the perpendicular bisector of AC, so $x = 5$.

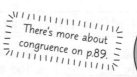

4) <u>TWO RADII</u> form an <u>ISOSCELES TRIANGLE</u>.

> Radii is the plural of radius.

They <u>don't have the little tick marks on the sides</u> to remind you that they are the same — the fact that <u>they are both radii</u> is enough to make it an isosceles triangle.

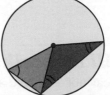

Section Four — Geometry and Measures

Circle Geometry

More circle theorems? But I've had enough. Can't I go home now?

5 Trickier Ones... (GRADE 7)

5) The angle at the <u>CENTRE</u> of a circle is <u>TWICE</u> the angle at the <u>CIRCUMFERENCE</u>.

The angle subtended at the <u>centre</u> of a circle is <u>EXACTLY DOUBLE</u> the angle subtended at the <u>circumference</u> of the circle from the <u>same two points</u> (two ends of the same <u>chord</u>).

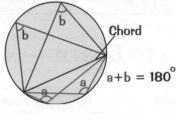

'Angle subtended at' is just a posh way of saying 'angle made at'.

6) The <u>ANGLE</u> in a <u>SEMICIRCLE</u> is <u>90°</u>.

A triangle drawn from the <u>two ends of a diameter</u> will <u>ALWAYS</u> make an <u>angle of 90°</u> where it <u>hits</u> the circumference of the circle, no matter where it hits.

7) Angles in the <u>SAME SEGMENT</u> are <u>EQUAL</u>.

All triangles drawn from a chord will have <u>the same angle where they touch the circumference</u>. Also, the two angles on opposite sides of the chord <u>add up to 180°</u>.

Chord

$a+b = 180°$

8) <u>OPPOSITE ANGLES</u> in a <u>CYCLIC QUADRILATERAL</u> add up to <u>180°</u>.

A <u>cyclic quadrilateral</u> is a 4-sided shape with <u>every corner touching the circle</u>. Both pairs of opposite angles add up to 180°.

$a + c = 180°$
$b + d = 180°$

9) The <u>ALTERNATE SEGMENT THEOREM</u>.

The <u>angle between</u> a <u>tangent</u> and a <u>chord</u> is always <u>equal</u> to 'the angle in the opposite segment' (i.e. the angle made at the circumference by two lines drawn from ends of the chord).

This is probably the hardest rule, so take care.

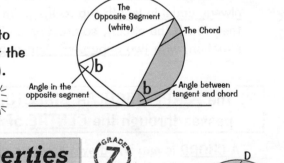

The Opposite Segment (white)

The Chord

b

Angle in the opposite segment

b

Angle between tangent and chord

... and 2 Intersecting Chord Properties (GRADE 7)

10) <u>INTERNAL INTERSECTION</u>.

For any two chords that intersect inside a circle: $AE \times EB = CE \times ED$

11) <u>EXTERNAL INTERSECTION</u>.

If two chords are extended and meet outside the circle:

$AE \times BE = CE \times DE$

Watch out — all these lengths are measured from the point outside the circle.

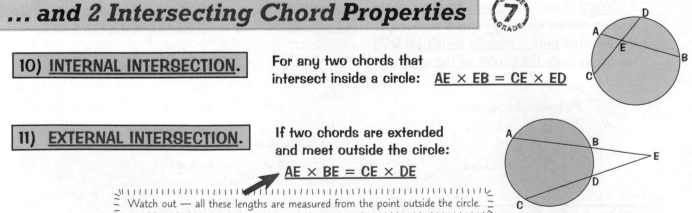

All this talk of segments and tangerines is making me hungry...

Fear not — there are some examples and Exam Practice Questions coming your way on the next page...

Circle Geometry

Using the Circle Theorems ⑦

EXAMPLE: A, B, C and D are points on the circumference of the circle, and O is the centre of the circle. Angle ADC = 109°. Work out the size of angles ABC and AOC.

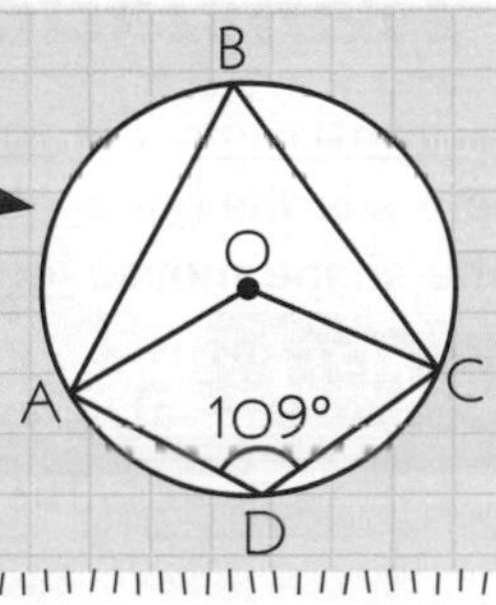

You'll probably have to use more than one rule to solve circle theorem questions — here, ABCD is a <u>cyclic quadrilateral</u>, so use rule 8:

> **8) OPPOSITE ANGLES in a CYCLIC QUADRILATERAL add up to 180°.**

Angles ADC and ABC are <u>opposite</u>, so **angle ABC = 180° − 109° = 71°.**

Now, angles ABC (which you've just found) and AOC both come from chord AC, so you can use rule 5:

> Remember three-letter angle notation from p.80 — angle ADC is the angle formed at D (it's always the middle letter).

> **5) The angle at the CENTRE of a circle is TWICE the angle at the CIRCUMFERENCE.**

So angle AOC is <u>double</u> angle ABC, which means **angle AOC = 71° × 2 = 142°.**

EXAMPLE: Line ABC is a tangent to the circle with centre O, and points B, D and E are points on the circumference. Angle EOB = 88°. Work out the size of angles BEO and ABE.

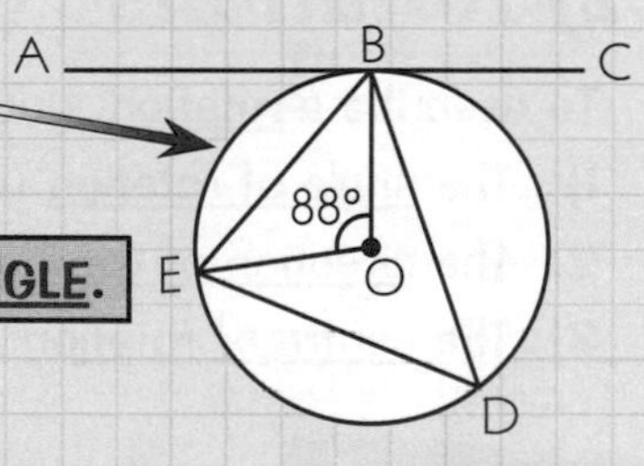

To find <u>angle BEO</u>, use rule 4: | **4) TWO RADII form an ISOSCELES TRIANGLE.**

Triangle <u>EOB</u> is an <u>isosceles triangle</u> with an angle of 88°.
So **angle BEO = (180° − 88°) ÷ 2 = 46°.**

To find <u>angle ABE</u>, use rule 9: | **9) The ALTERNATE SEGMENT THEOREM.**

So angle <u>ABE</u> is the <u>same</u> as angle <u>EDB</u>, which we can find using rule 5:

> **5) The angle at the CENTRE of a circle is TWICE the angle at the CIRCUMFERENCE.**

Angle <u>EDB</u> = 88° ÷ 2 = 44°, so **angle ABE = 44°.**

EXAMPLE: In the diagram, AE = 49 mm, BE = 22 mm and CE = 47 mm. Find the length of chord CD.

1) Use the <u>external intersection</u> formula: **AE × BE = CE × DE**
2) Put in the numbers to find <u>DE</u>: 49 × 22 = 47 × DE
   DE = 22.9 mm
3) <u>Subtract</u> DE from CE to find <u>CD</u>: CE − DE = CD
   47 − 22.9 = 24.1 mm

I can play an intersecting chord if I really stretch my fingers...

And here's what you've been waiting for — time for a bit of practice...

Q1 A, B, C and D are points on the circumference of the circle with centre O. The line EF is a tangent to the circle, and touches the circle at D. Angle ADE is 63°. Find the size of angles ABD and ACD. **[2 marks]** ⑦

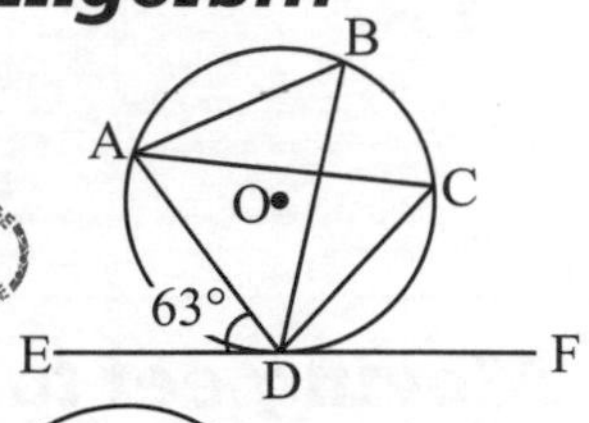

Q2 PQ and RS are chords of the circle on the right. They intersect at T. PT = 3 cm, RT = 2 cm and QT = 5 cm. Find the length of ST. ⑦ **[2 marks]**

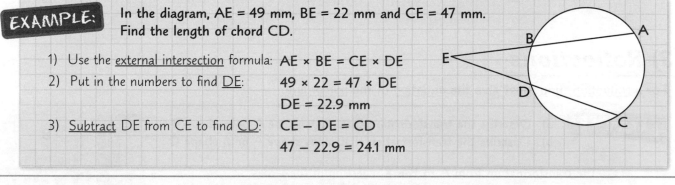

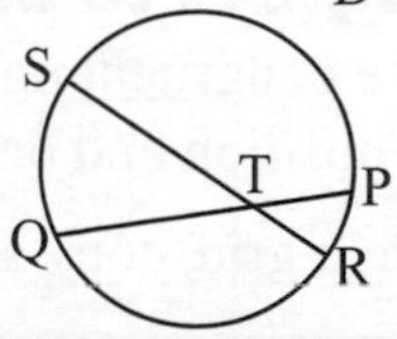

The Four Transformations

There are four <u>transformations</u> you need to know — <u>translation</u>, <u>rotation</u>, <u>reflection</u> and <u>enlargement</u>.

1) Translations (4)

In a <u>translation</u>, the <u>amount</u> the shape moves by is given as a <u>vector</u> (see p.114-115) written $\begin{pmatrix} x \\ y \end{pmatrix}$ — where x is the <u>horizontal movement</u> (i.e. to the <u>right</u>) and y is the <u>vertical movement</u> (i.e. <u>up</u>). If the shape moves <u>left and down</u>, x and y will be <u>negative</u>.

EXAMPLE:

a) Describe the transformation that maps triangle ABC onto A'B'C'.

The transformation from ABC to A'B'C' is a translation of 8 units left and 6 units up.

b) Describe the transformation that maps triangle ABC onto A"B"C". Give your answer as a vector.

To get from A to A", you need to move <u>7 units up</u> (and no units horizontally), so...

The transformation from ABC to A"B"C" is a translation by the vector $\begin{pmatrix} 0 \\ 7 \end{pmatrix}$.

2) Rotations (4)

To describe a <u>rotation</u>, you must give <u>3 details</u>:

1) The <u>angle of rotation</u> (usually 90° or 180°).

2) The <u>direction of rotation</u> (clockwise or anticlockwise).

3) The <u>centre of rotation</u> (often, but not always, the origin).

+ and − signs are sometimes used to show whether a rotation is <u>clockwise (−)</u> or <u>anticlockwise (+)</u>.
+90° means 90° anticlockwise and −90° means 90° clockwise.

EXAMPLE:

a) Describe the transformation that maps triangle ABC onto A'B'C'.
b) Describe the transformation that maps triangle ABC onto A"B"C".

a) The transformation from ABC to A'B'C' is a rotation of <u>90°</u> <u>anticlockwise</u> about the <u>origin</u>.

b) The transformation from ABC to A"B"C" is a rotation of <u>180°</u> clockwise (or anticlockwise) about the <u>origin</u>.

If it helps, you can use tracing paper to help you find the centre of rotation.

3) Reflections (3)

For a <u>reflection</u>, you must give the <u>equation</u> of the <u>mirror line</u>.

EXAMPLE:

a) Describe the transformation that maps shape A onto shape B.
b) Describe the transformation that maps shape A onto shape C.

a) The transformation from A to B is a reflection in the y-axis.

b) The transformation from A to C is a reflection in the line $y = x$.

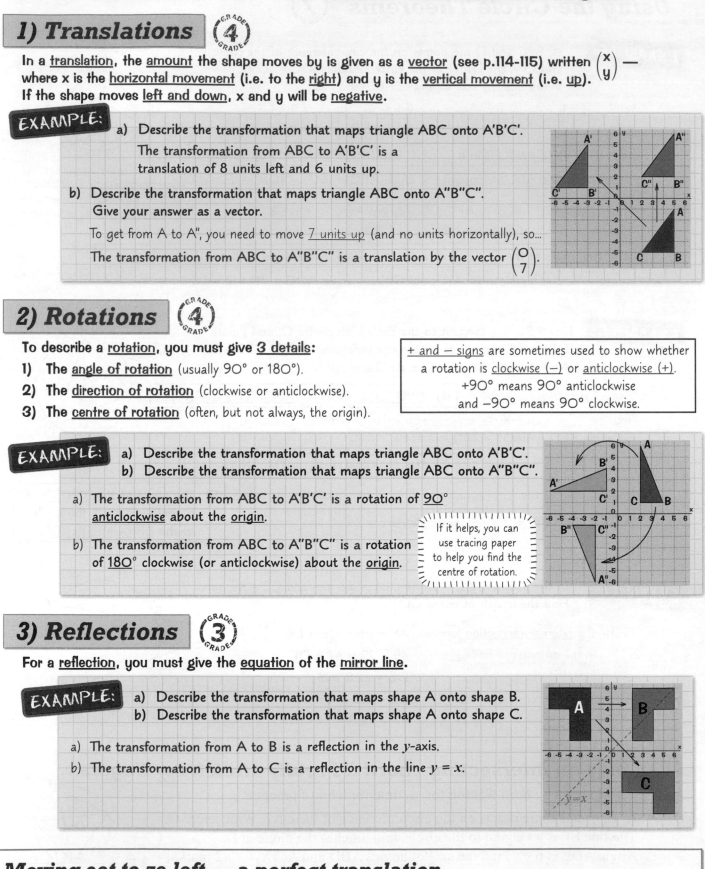

Moving eet to ze left — a perfect translation...

Shapes are <u>congruent</u> under translation, reflection and rotation because their <u>size</u> and <u>shape</u> don't change, just their position and orientation (congruence is on p.89). Now have a go at this question:

Q1 On a grid, copy shape A above and rotate it 90° clockwise about the point (−1, −1). [2 marks] (4)

The Four Transformations

One more transformation coming up — <u>enlargements</u>. They're the trickiest, but also the most fun (honest).

4) Enlargements (5)

For an <u>enlargement</u>, you must specify:

1) The <u>scale factor</u>. ←

2) The <u>centre of enlargement</u>.

$$\text{scale factor} = \frac{\text{new length}}{\text{old length}}$$

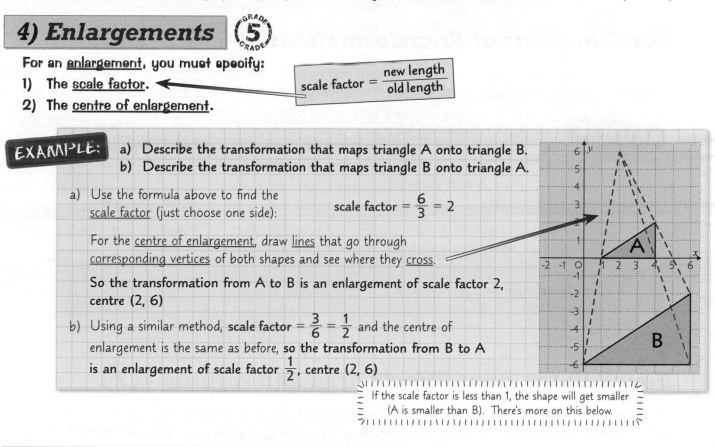

EXAMPLE:
a) Describe the transformation that maps triangle A onto triangle B.
b) Describe the transformation that maps triangle B onto triangle A.

a) Use the formula above to find the <u>scale factor</u> (just choose one side):

$$\text{scale factor} = \frac{6}{3} = 2$$

For the <u>centre of enlargement</u>, draw <u>lines</u> that go through <u>corresponding vertices</u> of both shapes and see where they <u>cross</u>.

So the transformation from A to B is an enlargement of scale factor 2, centre (2, 6)

b) Using a similar method, **scale factor** $= \frac{3}{6} = \frac{1}{2}$ and the centre of enlargement is the same as before, **so the transformation from B to A is an enlargement of scale factor** $\frac{1}{2}$, centre (2, 6)

If the scale factor is less than 1, the shape will get smaller (A is smaller than B). There's more on this below.

Scale Factors — Three Key Facts (5)

1) If the scale factor is <u>bigger than 1</u> the <u>shape gets bigger</u>.

2) If the scale factor is <u>smaller than 1</u> (e.g. ½) it <u>gets smaller</u>.

3) The scale factor also tells you the <u>relative distance</u> of old points and new points from the <u>centre of enlargement</u> — this is very useful for <u>drawing an enlargement</u>, because you can use it to trace out the positions of the new points.

EXAMPLE: Enlarge shape A below by a scale factor of 3, centre (–4, 1). Label the transformed shape B.

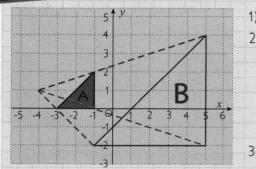

1) First, <u>draw lines</u> from <u>(–4, 1)</u> going through each <u>vertex</u> of shape A.

2) Then, <u>multiply</u> the distance from the centre of enlargement to each vertex by 3, and measure this distance from the centre of enlargement along each of the lines you've drawn.

So on shape A, vertex (–1, 2) is 3 right and 1 up from (–4, 1) — so the corresponding point on shape B will be 3 × 3 = 9 right and 3 × 1 = 3 up from (–4, 1). Do this for every point.

3) <u>Join</u> the points you've drawn to form shape **B**.

Scale factors — they're enough to put the fear of cod into you...

Shapes are <u>similar</u> under enlargement — the <u>position</u> and the <u>size</u> change, but the <u>angles</u> and <u>ratios of the sides</u> don't (see p.89). Make sure you learn the 3 key facts about scale factors.

Q1 On a grid, draw triangle A with vertices (–1, 3), (–5, –1) and (–5, 3), then enlarge it by a scale factor of $\frac{1}{2}$ with centre of enlargement (3, –1). [3 marks] (5)

More Transformation Stuff

Just one more page on transformations, and then you're done. With transformations anyway, not with Maths.

Combinations of Transformations (6 GRADE)

If they're feeling really mean, the examiners might make you do <u>two transformations</u> to the <u>same shape</u>, then ask you to <u>describe</u> the <u>single transformation</u> that would get you to the <u>final shape</u>. It's not as bad as it looks.

EXAMPLE:
a) Reflect shape A in the x-axis. Label this shape B.
b) Reflect shape B in the y-axis. Label this shape C.
c) Describe the single transformation that will map shape A onto shape C.

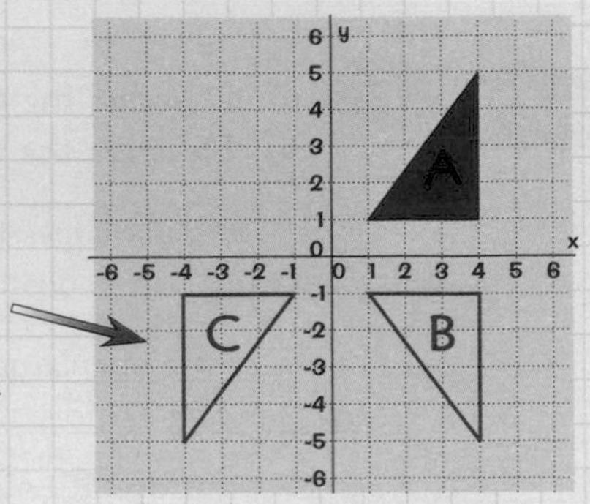

For a) and b), just draw the reflections.

For c), you can ignore shape B and just work out how to get from A to C. You can see it's a <u>rotation</u>, but the tricky bit is working out the <u>centre of rotation</u>. Use <u>tracing paper</u> if you need to.

The transformation from A to C is a <u>rotation of 180°</u> clockwise (or anticlockwise) about the <u>origin</u>.

How Enlargement Affects Area and Volume (7 GRADE)

If a shape is enlarged by a <u>scale factor</u> (see previous page), its <u>area</u>, or <u>surface area</u> and <u>volume</u> (if it's a 3D shape), will change too. However, they <u>don't</u> change by the <u>same value</u> as the scale factor:

For a SCALE FACTOR n:		Or... AS RATIOS:	
The <u>SIDES</u> are $\quad$ n times bigger	$n = \dfrac{\text{new length}}{\text{old length}} \qquad n^2 = \dfrac{\text{new area}}{\text{old area}}$	Lengths	a : b
The <u>AREAS</u> are $\quad n^2$ times bigger		Areas	$a^2 : b^2$
The <u>VOLUMES</u> are $\quad n^3$ times bigger	$n^3 = \dfrac{\text{new volume}}{\text{old volume}}$	Volumes	$a^3 : b^3$

So if the <u>scale factor</u> is <u>2</u>, the lengths are <u>2 times</u> as long, the area is $2^2 = \underline{4\text{ times}}$ as big, and the volume is $2^3 = \underline{8\text{ times}}$ as big. As <u>ratios</u>, these enlargements are <u>1:2</u> (length), $1^2:2^2 = \underline{1:4}$ (area) and $1^3:2^3 = \underline{1:8}$ (volume).

There's more on areas on p.90-92 and volumes on p.93-94.

EXAMPLE: Cylinder A has surface area 6π cm², and cylinder B has surface area 54π cm². The volume of cylinder A is 2π cm³. Find the volume of cylinder B, given that B is an enlargement of A.

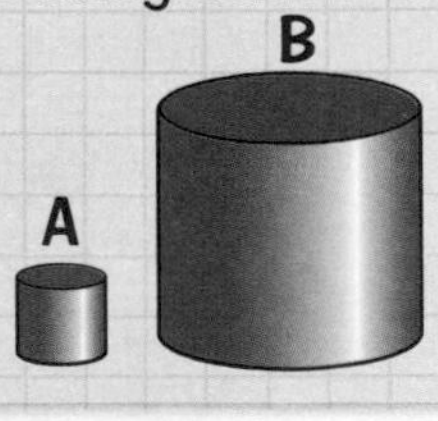

First, work out the <u>scale factor</u>, n: $\quad n^2 = \dfrac{\text{Area B}}{\text{Area A}} = \dfrac{54\pi}{6\pi} = 9$, so $\underline{n = 3}$

Use this in the volume formula: $\quad n^3 = \dfrac{\text{Volume B}}{\text{Volume A}} \Rightarrow 3^3 = \dfrac{\text{Volume B}}{2\pi}$

$\Rightarrow$ Volume of B = $2\pi \times 27 = 54\pi$ cm³

This shows that if the scale factor is <u>3</u>, lengths are <u>3 times as long</u>, the surface area is <u>9 times as big</u> and the volume is <u>27 times as big</u>.

Twice as much learning, 4 times better results, 8 times more fun...

Make sure you don't get the scale factors mixed up — try them out on this Exam Practice Question:

Q1 There are 3 stacking dolls in a set. The dolls are mathematically similar and have heights of 5 cm, 10 cm and 15 cm. The surface area of the middle doll is 80 cm², and the volume of the largest doll is 216 cm³. Find the surface area and volume of the smallest doll. [4 marks] (7 GRADE)

Congruence and Similarity

Shapes can be <u>similar</u> or <u>congruent</u>. And I bet you really want to know what that means —
I can already picture your eager face. Well, lucky you — I've written a page all about it.

Congruent Shapes — Same Shape, Same Size (2)

<u>Congruence</u> is another ridiculous maths word which sounds really complicated
when it's not. If two shapes are congruent, they are simply <u>the same</u> —
the <u>same size</u> and the <u>same shape</u>. That's all it is.

It doesn't matter which way round the shape is, so <u>translations</u>, <u>reflections</u> and <u>rotations</u>
all produce a shape that's congruent to the original shape.

Similar Shapes Have the Same Angles (4)

<u>Similar</u> shapes are <u>exactly the same shape</u>, but can be <u>different sizes</u>
(they can also be <u>rotated</u> or <u>reflected</u>).

For two shapes to be <u>similar</u>, all the <u>angles</u> must match and the <u>sides</u> must be <u>proportional</u>.

If one shape is an <u>enlargement</u> of another shape then they're similar — this applies to 3D shapes too.
Exam questions often <u>tell you</u> that two shapes are similar, then ask you to find the <u>length</u> of a <u>missing side</u>.
You need to find the <u>scale factor</u> to get from one shape to the other.

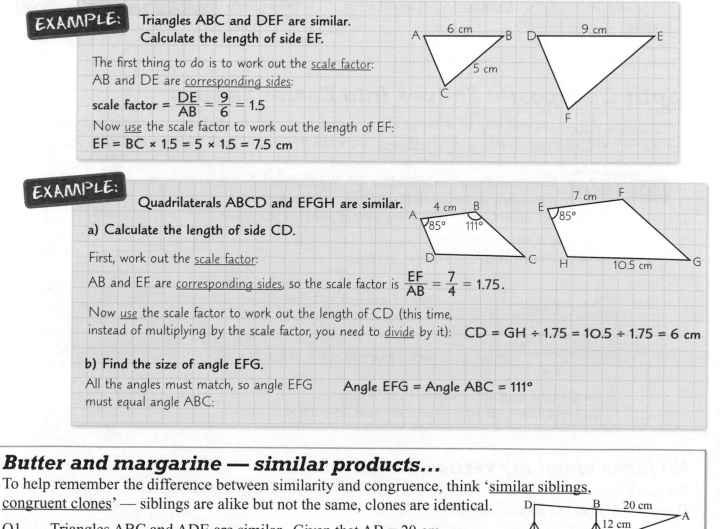

EXAMPLE: Triangles ABC and DEF are similar.
Calculate the length of side EF.

The first thing to do is to work out the <u>scale factor</u>:
AB and DE are <u>corresponding sides</u>:

scale factor $= \dfrac{DE}{AB} = \dfrac{9}{6} = 1.5$

Now <u>use</u> the scale factor to work out the length of EF:
EF = BC × 1.5 = 5 × 1.5 = 7.5 cm

EXAMPLE: Quadrilaterals ABCD and EFGH are similar.

a) Calculate the length of side CD.

First, work out the <u>scale factor</u>:

AB and EF are <u>corresponding sides</u>, so the scale factor is $\dfrac{EF}{AB} = \dfrac{7}{4} = 1.75$.

Now <u>use</u> the scale factor to work out the length of CD (this time,
instead of multiplying by the scale factor, you need to <u>divide</u> by it): CD = GH ÷ 1.75 = 10.5 ÷ 1.75 = 6 cm

b) Find the size of angle EFG.

All the angles must match, so angle EFG
must equal angle ABC: Angle EFG = Angle ABC = 111°

Butter and margarine — similar products...

To help remember the difference between similarity and congruence, think '<u>similar siblings</u>,
<u>congruent clones</u>' — siblings are alike but not the same, clones are identical.

Q1   Triangles ABC and ADE are similar. Given that AB = 20 cm,
find the length of AD.   [2 marks] (4)

Areas

Be warned — there are lots of <u>area formulas</u> coming up on the next two pages for you to <u>learn</u>. By the way, I'm assuming that you know the formulas for the area of a <u>rectangle</u> (A = l × w) and the area of a <u>square</u> (A = l²).

Areas of Triangles and Quadrilaterals

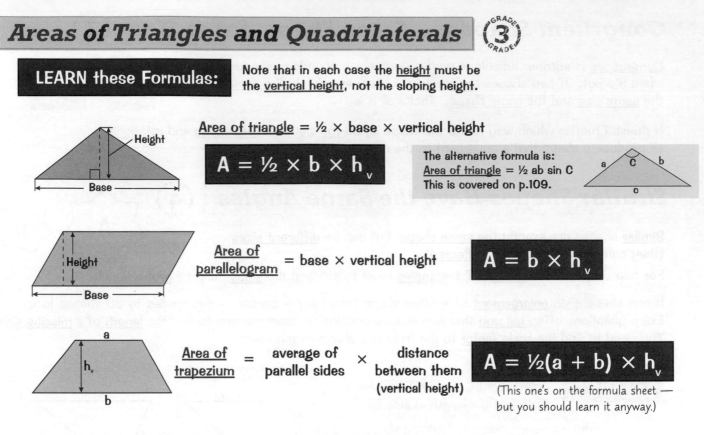

LEARN these Formulas: Note that in each case the <u>height</u> must be the <u>vertical height</u>, not the sloping height.

<u>Area of triangle</u> = ½ × base × vertical height

$$A = ½ × b × h_v$$

The alternative formula is:
<u>Area of triangle</u> = ½ ab sin C
This is covered on p.109.

$$\frac{\text{Area of}}{\text{parallelogram}} = \text{base} × \text{vertical height}$$

$$A = b × h_v$$

$$\frac{\text{Area of}}{\text{trapezium}} = \frac{\text{average of}}{\text{parallel sides}} × \frac{\text{distance between them (vertical height)}}{}$$

$$A = ½(a + b) × h_v$$

(This one's on the formula sheet — but you should learn it anyway.)

Split Composite Shapes into Easier Shapes

<u>Composite shapes</u> are made up of different shapes <u>stuck together</u>. Finding their area is actually dead easy — just <u>split them up</u> into <u>separate shapes</u>, work out the area of each bit, then add them up.

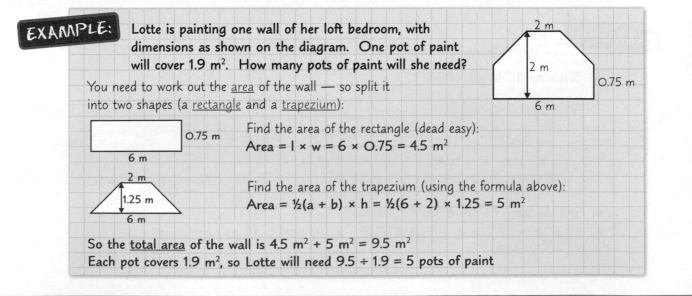

EXAMPLE: Lotte is painting one wall of her loft bedroom, with dimensions as shown on the diagram. One pot of paint will cover 1.9 m². How many pots of paint will she need?

You need to work out the <u>area</u> of the wall — so split it into two shapes (a <u>rectangle</u> and a <u>trapezium</u>):

Find the area of the rectangle (dead easy):
Area = l × w = 6 × 0.75 = 4.5 m²

Find the area of the trapezium (using the formula above):
Area = ½(a + b) × h = ½(6 + 2) × 1.25 = 5 m²

So the <u>total area</u> of the wall is 4.5 m² + 5 m² = 9.5 m²
Each pot covers 1.9 m², so Lotte will need 9.5 ÷ 1.9 = 5 pots of paint

No jokes about my vertical height please...

Not much to say about this page really — LEARN the formulas and practise using them.
Then have a go at this Exam Practice Question:

Q1 The triangle and rectangle shown on the right have the same area. Find the value of x. [4 marks] 5 cm / 16 cm / 4 cm / x cm

Areas

Yes, I thought I could detect some groaning when you realised that this is another page of formulas. You know the drill...

LEARN these Formulas

Area and Circumference of Circles (3)

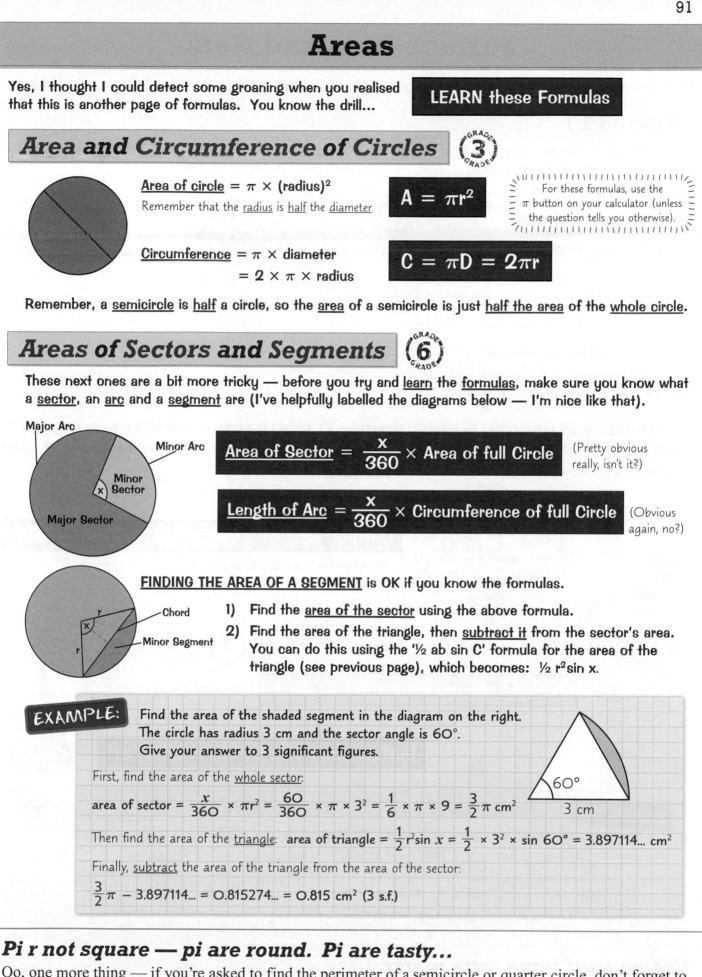

Area of circle = $\pi \times$ (radius)^2
Remember that the radius is half the diameter.

$$A = \pi r^2$$

For these formulas, use the π button on your calculator (unless the question tells you otherwise).

Circumference = $\pi \times$ diameter
= $2 \times \pi \times$ radius

$$C = \pi D = 2\pi r$$

Remember, a semicircle is half a circle, so the area of a semicircle is just half the area of the whole circle.

Areas of Sectors and Segments (6)

These next ones are a bit more tricky — before you try and learn the formulas, make sure you know what a sector, an arc and a segment are (I've helpfully labelled the diagrams below — I'm nice like that).

Major Arc
Minor Arc
Minor Sector
x
Major Sector

Area of Sector = $\dfrac{x}{360} \times$ Area of full Circle *(Pretty obvious really, isn't it?)*

Length of Arc = $\dfrac{x}{360} \times$ Circumference of full Circle *(Obvious again, no?)*

r
Chord
x
Minor Segment
r

FINDING THE AREA OF A SEGMENT is OK if you know the formulas.

1) Find the area of the sector using the above formula.

2) Find the area of the triangle, then subtract it from the sector's area. You can do this using the '½ ab sin C' formula for the area of the triangle (see previous page), which becomes: ½ r^{2}sin x.

EXAMPLE: Find the area of the shaded segment in the diagram on the right. The circle has radius 3 cm and the sector angle is 60°. Give your answer to 3 significant figures.

60°
3 cm

First, find the area of the whole sector:

area of sector = $\dfrac{x}{360} \times \pi r^2 = \dfrac{60}{360} \times \pi \times 3^2 = \dfrac{1}{6} \times \pi \times 9 = \dfrac{3}{2}\pi$ cm^2

Then find the area of the triangle: area of triangle = $\dfrac{1}{2}r^2$sin $x = \dfrac{1}{2} \times 3^2 \times$ sin 60° = 3.897114... cm^2

Finally, subtract the area of the triangle from the area of the sector:

$\dfrac{3}{2}\pi$ − 3.897114... = 0.815274... = 0.815 cm^2 (3 s.f.)

Pi r not square — pi are round. Pi are tasty...

Oo, one more thing — if you're asked to find the perimeter of a semicircle or quarter circle, don't forget to add on the straight edges too. It's an easy mistake to make, and it'll cost you marks.

Q1 For the sector on the right, find to 2 decimal places:
  a) the area [2 marks] b) the arc length [2 marks] (6)

150°
8 cm

Surface Area and Nets

It's time now to move on to the next <u>dimension</u> — yep, that's right, <u>3D shapes</u>. I can hardly contain myself.

Nets

A <u>NET</u> is just a hollow <u>3D shape</u> folded out flat.
Here are the nets of some <u>common shapes</u> — make sure you can recognise them.

> Note that these are just some of the nets for these shapes — there are many other nets that will produce the same shapes (particularly for a cube).

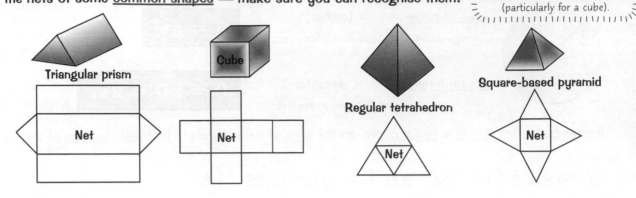

Triangular prism | Cube | Regular tetrahedron | Square-based pyramid

Surface Area (5)

1) <u>SURFACE AREA</u> only applies to solid 3D objects — it's simply the <u>total area</u> of all the <u>faces</u> added together.

2) <u>SURFACE AREA OF SOLID = AREA OF NET</u>. So if it helps, imagine the net and add up the area of <u>each bit</u>.

3) There's a formula for the surface area of a <u>CYLINDER</u>:

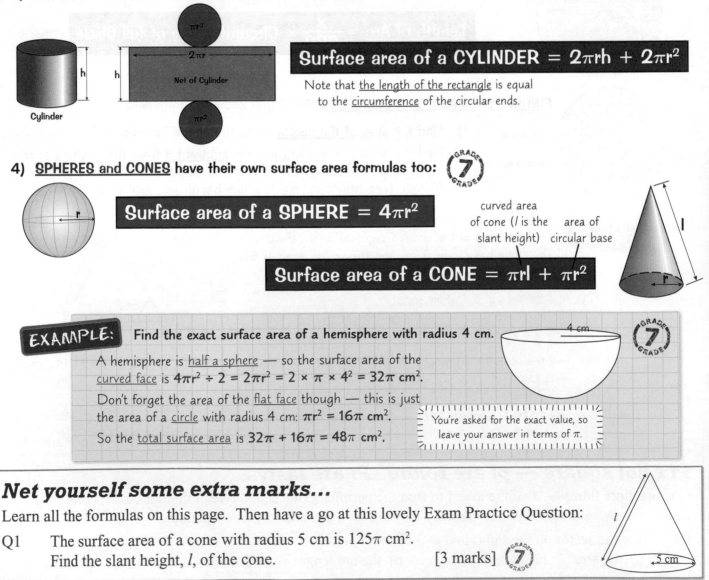

Surface area of a CYLINDER = 2πrh + 2πr²

Note that <u>the length of the rectangle</u> is equal to the <u>circumference</u> of the circular ends.

4) <u>SPHERES</u> and <u>CONES</u> have their own surface area formulas too: (7)

Surface area of a SPHERE = 4πr²

curved area of cone (*l* is the slant height)   area of circular base

Surface area of a CONE = πrl + πr²

EXAMPLE: Find the exact surface area of a hemisphere with radius 4 cm.

A hemisphere is <u>half a sphere</u> — so the surface area of the <u>curved face</u> is $4\pi r^2 \div 2 = 2\pi r^2 = 2 \times \pi \times 4^2 = 32\pi$ cm².

Don't forget the area of the <u>flat face</u> though — this is just the area of a <u>circle</u> with radius 4 cm: $\pi r^2 = 16\pi$ cm².

So the <u>total surface area</u> is $32\pi + 16\pi = 48\pi$ cm².

> You're asked for the exact value, so leave your answer in terms of π.

Net yourself some extra marks...

Learn all the formulas on this page. Then have a go at this lovely Exam Practice Question:

Q1   The surface area of a cone with radius 5 cm is 125π cm².
Find the slant height, *l*, of the cone.   [3 marks] (7)

Volume

You might think you know some of this already, but I bet you don't know it all. There's only one thing for it...

LEARN these volume formulas... (Another word for volume is **CAPACITY**.)

Volumes of Cuboids (2)

A <u>cuboid</u> is a <u>rectangular block</u>. Finding its volume is dead easy:

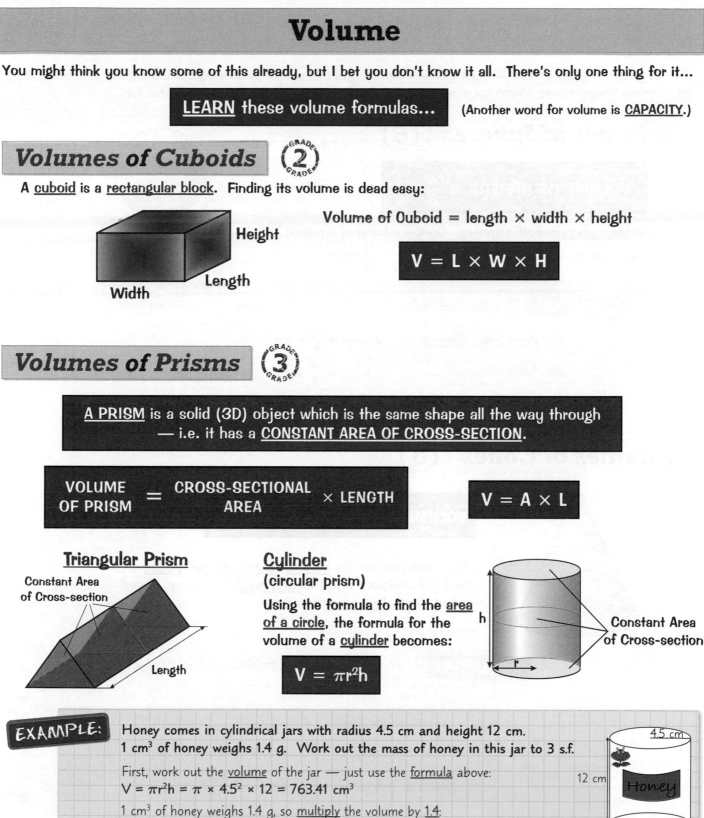

Height
Length
Width

Volume of Ouboid = length × width × height

$$V = L \times W \times H$$

Volumes of Prisms (3)

<u>A PRISM</u> is a solid (3D) object which is the same shape all the way through
— i.e. it has a <u>CONSTANT AREA OF CROSS-SECTION</u>.

| VOLUME OF PRISM | = | CROSS-SECTIONAL AREA | × LENGTH |

$$V = A \times L$$

Triangular Prism

Constant Area of Cross-section

Length

Cylinder
(circular prism)

Using the formula to find the <u>area of a circle</u>, the formula for the volume of a <u>cylinder</u> becomes:

$$V = \pi r^2 h$$

h

r

Constant Area of Cross-section

EXAMPLE: Honey comes in cylindrical jars with radius 4.5 cm and height 12 cm.
1 cm³ of honey weighs 1.4 g. Work out the mass of honey in this jar to 3 s.f.

First, work out the <u>volume</u> of the jar — just use the <u>formula</u> above:
V = πr²h = π × 4.5² × 12 = 763.41 cm³

1 cm³ of honey weighs 1.4 g, so <u>multiply</u> the volume by <u>1.4</u>:
mass of honey = 1.4 × 763.41 = 1068.8 = 1070 g (3 s.f.)

4.5 cm
12 cm
Honey

Don't make it any more angry — it's already a cross-section...

Learn the volume formulas on this page — and make sure you know the area formulas from
p.90-91 as well (you might need them to find the area of the cross-section of a prism).
Now try this Exam Practice Question:

Q1   a) Find the volume of the triangular prism on the right.   (3)   [3 marks]
     b) The prism is made out of glass, which weighs 1.8 g per cm³.
        Work out the mass of the prism.   [1 mark]

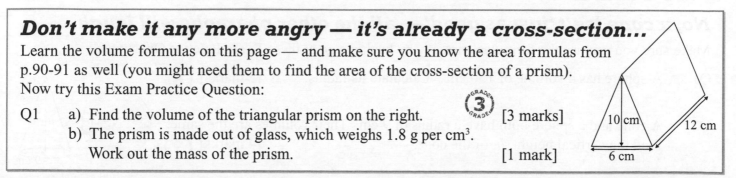

10 cm   12 cm
6 cm

Volume

This page has a great bonus — once you've learnt it you can amaze people by calculating the volume of their ice cream cones. Who says revision isn't fun? I love it. I take exams just for fun.

Volumes of Spheres (6)

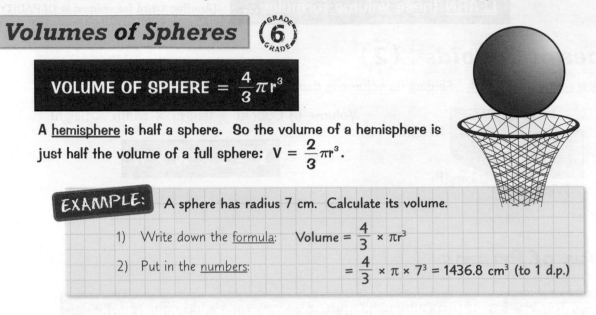

$$\text{VOLUME OF SPHERE} = \frac{4}{3}\pi r^3$$

A <u>hemisphere</u> is half a sphere. So the volume of a hemisphere is just half the volume of a full sphere: $V = \frac{2}{3}\pi r^3$.

EXAMPLE: A sphere has radius 7 cm. Calculate its volume.

1) Write down the <u>formula</u>: $\text{Volume} = \frac{4}{3} \times \pi r^3$

2) Put in the <u>numbers</u>: $= \frac{4}{3} \times \pi \times 7^3 = 1436.8 \text{ cm}^3$ (to 1 d.p.)

Volumes of Cones (6)

$$\text{VOLUME OF CONE} = \frac{1}{3} \times \pi r^2 \times h_v$$

Make sure you use the <u>vertical (perpendicular) height</u> — don't get confused with the <u>slant height</u>, which you used to find the <u>surface area</u> of a cone.

EXAMPLE: A cone has a vertical height of 20 cm. Its volume is 170 cm³. Find the radius of the cone.

1) Write down the <u>formula</u>: $\text{Volume} = \frac{1}{3} \times \pi r^2 \times h_v$

2) Put in the <u>numbers</u>: $170 = \frac{1}{3} \times \pi r^2 \times 20$

3) <u>Rearrange</u> to find r: $r = \sqrt{\dfrac{170 \times 3}{20\pi}}$

$= 2.8 \text{ cm}$ (to 1 d.p.)

No, a cone isn't 'just as good' — all the other pharaohs will laugh...

Make sure you can use the formulas correctly by having a go at these Exam Practice Questions:

Q1 A sphere has a volume of 150 cm³. Calculate its radius. [2 marks] (6)

Q2 A cone and a sphere both have a radius of 9 cm. Their volumes are the same. Find the vertical height, h, of the cone. [4 marks] (7)

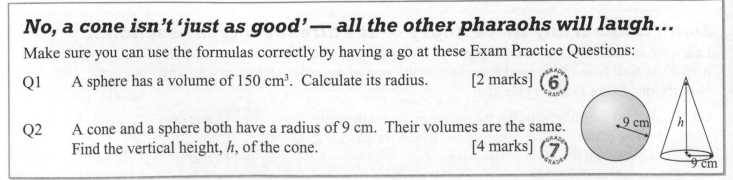

Time

I'm sure you're a dab hand at reading <u>clocks</u>, but here's a quick reminder...

<u>am</u> means <u>morning</u>
<u>pm</u> means <u>afternoon</u> or <u>evening</u>.

<u>12 am</u> (<u>OO:OO</u>) means <u>midnight</u>.
<u>12 pm</u> (<u>12:OO</u>) means <u>noon</u>.

12-hour clock	24-hour clock
12.00 am	OO:OO
1.12 am	O1:12
12.15 pm	12:15
1.47 pm	13:47
11.32 pm	23:32

The hour parts of times on 12- and 24- hour clocks are <u>different after 1 pm</u>:
<u>add 12 hours</u> to go from <u>12-hour to 24-hour</u>, and subtract 12 to go the other way.

3.24 pm $\xrightarrow{+ 12 \text{ h}}$ 15:24 $\xleftarrow{- 12 \text{ h}}$

Break Time Calculations into Simple Stages

EXAMPLE: Angela watched a film that started at 7.2O pm and finished at 1O.O5 pm. How long was the film in minutes?

1) Split the time between 7.2O pm and 1O.O5 pm into <u>simple stages</u>.

7.2O pm → 9.2O pm → 1O.OO pm → 1O.O5 pm
+ 2 hours + 4O minutes + 5 minutes

2) <u>Convert</u> the hours to minutes.   2 hours = 2 × 6O = 12O minutes

3) <u>Add</u> to get the total minutes.   12O + 4O + 5 = 165 minutes

> <u>Avoid calculators</u> — the decimal answers they give are confusing, e.g. <u>2.5 hours = 2 hours 3O mins</u>, <u>NOT 2 hours 5O mins</u>.

Timetable Exam Questions

EXAMPLE:

Use the timetable to answer these questions:

a) How long does it take for the bus to get from <u>Market Street</u> to the hospital?

Bus Timetable				
Bus Station	18 45	19 OO	19 15	19 3O
Market Street	18 52	19 O7	19 22	19 37
Long Lane Shops	19 O1	19 16	19 31	19 46
Train Station	19 11	19 26	19 41	19 56
Hospital	19 23	19 38	19 53	2O O8

Read times from the <u>same column</u> (I've used the 1st) — break the <u>time</u> into <u>stages</u>.

Market Street 18:52 → 19:OO → Hospital 19:23
+ 8 mins   + 23 mins   8 + 23 = 31 minutes

b) Harry wants to get a bus from the <u>bus station</u> to the <u>train station</u> in time for a train that leaves at <u>19:30</u>. What is the latest bus he can catch?

1) Read along the <u>train station</u> row.

19 11   (19 26)   19 41   19 56

This is the latest time he could arrive before 19:3O.

2) Move up this column to the <u>bus station</u> row and read off the entry.

The bus that gets to the train station at 19:26 leaves the bus station at 19:OO.

BREAKING NEWS: Public panic after warning over calculator use...

Have a go at these Exam Practice Questions and use the timetable above to answer Q2.

Q1 A plane takes off at 9.37 am and lands at 11.16 am. How long is the flight in minutes? [1 mark]

Q2 Amy lives 10 minutes' walk from the Market Street bus stop. She wants to be at Long Lane shops by 19:45. Write a schedule for her journey from her house to the shops. [2 marks]

Speed, Density and Pressure

Speed, density and pressure. Just a matter of <u>learning the formulas</u>, bunging the <u>numbers</u> in and watching the <u>units</u>.

Speed = Distance ÷ Time

Speed is the <u>distance travelled per unit time</u>, e.g. the number of <u>km per hour</u> or <u>metres per second</u>.

$$\text{SPEED} = \frac{\text{DISTANCE}}{\text{TIME}} \qquad \text{TIME} = \frac{\text{DISTANCE}}{\text{SPEED}} \qquad \text{DISTANCE} = \text{SPEED} \times \text{TIME}$$

<u>Formula triangles</u> are a handy tool for remembering formulas like these. The speed one is shown below.

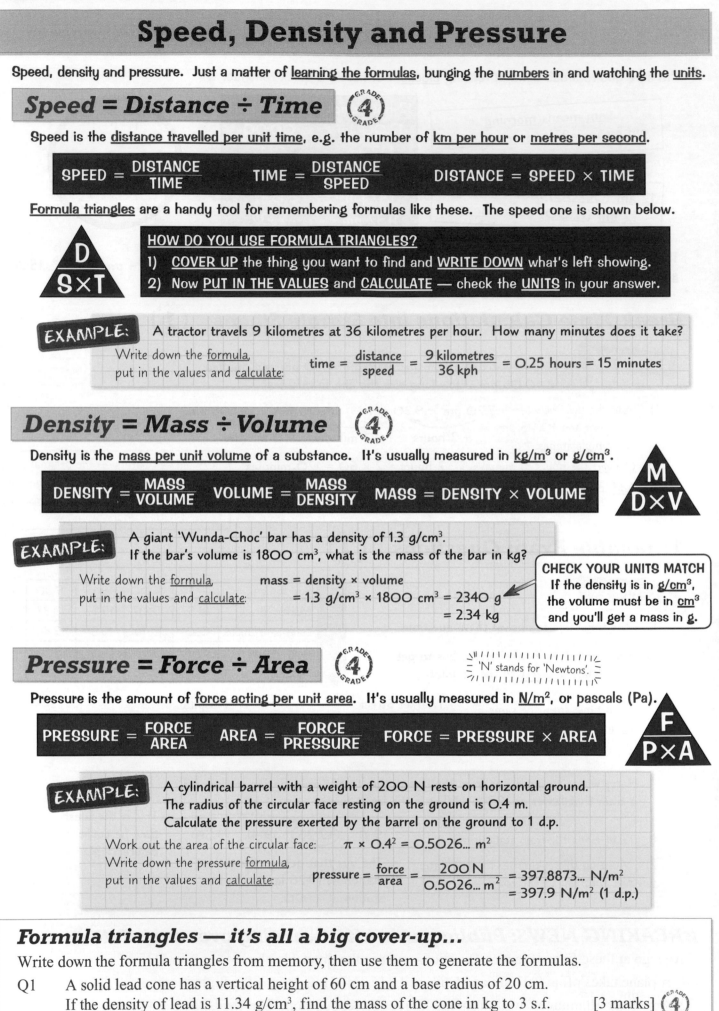

HOW DO YOU USE FORMULA TRIANGLES?
1) <u>COVER UP</u> the thing you want to find and <u>WRITE DOWN</u> what's left showing.
2) Now <u>PUT IN THE VALUES</u> and <u>CALCULATE</u> — check the <u>UNITS</u> in your answer.

EXAMPLE: A tractor travels 9 kilometres at 36 kilometres per hour. How many minutes does it take?

Write down the <u>formula</u>, put in the values and <u>calculate</u>:

$$\text{time} = \frac{\text{distance}}{\text{speed}} = \frac{9 \text{ kilometres}}{36 \text{ kph}} = 0.25 \text{ hours} = 15 \text{ minutes}$$

Density = Mass ÷ Volume

Density is the <u>mass per unit volume</u> of a substance. It's usually measured in <u>kg/m³</u> or <u>g/cm³</u>.

$$\text{DENSITY} = \frac{\text{MASS}}{\text{VOLUME}} \qquad \text{VOLUME} = \frac{\text{MASS}}{\text{DENSITY}} \qquad \text{MASS} = \text{DENSITY} \times \text{VOLUME}$$

EXAMPLE: A giant 'Wunda-Choc' bar has a density of 1.3 g/cm³.
If the bar's volume is 1800 cm³, what is the mass of the bar in kg?

Write down the <u>formula</u>, put in the values and <u>calculate</u>:

$$\text{mass} = \text{density} \times \text{volume}$$
$$= 1.3 \text{ g/cm}^3 \times 1800 \text{ cm}^3 = 2340 \text{ g}$$
$$= 2.34 \text{ kg}$$

CHECK YOUR UNITS MATCH
If the density is in <u>g/cm³</u>, the volume must be in <u>cm³</u> and you'll get a mass in <u>g</u>.

Pressure = Force ÷ Area

'N' stands for 'Newtons'.

Pressure is the amount of <u>force acting per unit area</u>. It's usually measured in <u>N/m²</u>, or pascals (Pa).

$$\text{PRESSURE} = \frac{\text{FORCE}}{\text{AREA}} \qquad \text{AREA} = \frac{\text{FORCE}}{\text{PRESSURE}} \qquad \text{FORCE} = \text{PRESSURE} \times \text{AREA}$$

EXAMPLE: A cylindrical barrel with a weight of 200 N rests on horizontal ground.
The radius of the circular face resting on the ground is 0.4 m.
Calculate the pressure exerted by the barrel on the ground to 1 d.p.

Work out the area of the circular face: $\pi \times 0.4^2 = 0.5026... \text{ m}^2$
Write down the pressure <u>formula</u>, put in the values and <u>calculate</u>:

$$\text{pressure} = \frac{\text{force}}{\text{area}} = \frac{200 \text{ N}}{0.5026... \text{ m}^2} = 397.8873... \text{ N/m}^2$$
$$= 397.9 \text{ N/m}^2 \text{ (1 d.p.)}$$

Formula triangles — it's all a big cover-up...

Write down the formula triangles from memory, then use them to generate the formulas.

Q1   A solid lead cone has a vertical height of 60 cm and a base radius of 20 cm.
If the density of lead is 11.34 g/cm³, find the mass of the cone in kg to 3 s.f.   [3 marks]
(Hint: you'll need to find the volume of the cone — see p.94)

Distance-Time Graphs

Ah, what could be better than some nice D/T graphs? They're quite possibly the <u>best</u> use of straight lines <u>ever</u>.

Distance-Time Graphs (3)

Distance-time graphs are pretty common in exams.
They're not too bad once you get your head around them.

Just remember these 4 important points:

1) At any point, <u>GRADIENT = SPEED</u>, but watch out for the UNITS.
2) The <u>STEEPER</u> the graph, the <u>FASTER</u> it's going.
3) <u>FLAT SECTIONS</u> are where it is <u>STOPPED</u>.
4) If the gradient's negative, it's <u>COMING BACK</u>.

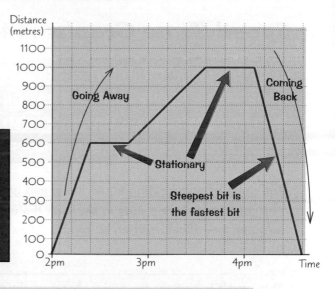

EXAMPLE: Henry went out for a ride on his bike. After a while he got a puncture and stopped to fix it. This graph shows the first part of Henry's journey.

a) **What time did Henry leave home?**

He left home at the point where the line starts. **At 8:15**

b) **How far did Henry cycle before getting a puncture?**

The horizontal part of the graph is where Henry stopped. **12 km**

c) **What was Henry's speed before getting a puncture?**

Using the speed formula is the same as finding the gradient.

$$speed = \frac{distance}{time} = \frac{12\,km}{0.5\,hours}$$
$$= 24\,km/h$$

d) **At 9:30 Henry turns round and cycles home at 24 km/h. Complete the graph to show this.**

You have to work out how long it will take Henry to cycle the 18 km home:

$$time = \frac{distance}{speed} = \frac{18\,km}{24\,km/h} = \underline{0.75\,hours}$$

$$0.75 \times 60\,mins = \underline{45\,mins}$$

Decimal times are yuck, so convert it to <u>minutes</u>.

45 minutes after 9:30 is 10:15, so that's the time Henry gets home. Now you can complete the graph.

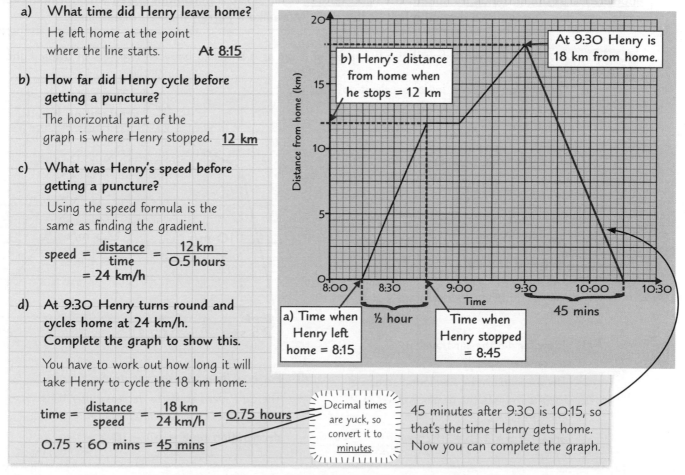

D-T Graphs — filled with highs and lows, an analogy of life...

The only way to get good at distance-time graphs is to practise, practise, practise...

Q1 a) Using the graph above, how long did Henry stop for? [1 mark] (3)

b) How far from home was Henry at 8:30? [1 mark] (3)

Speed-Time Graphs

This page <u>looks</u> pretty much the same as the last page — but there are some huge differences.

Speed-Time Graphs (4)

1) At any point, <u>GRADIENT = ACCELERATION</u>.
2) <u>NEGATIVE SLOPE</u> is <u>DECELERATION</u> (slowing down).
3) <u>FLAT SECTIONS</u> are <u>STEADY SPEED</u>.
4) <u>AREA UNDER GRAPH = DISTANCE TRAVELLED</u>.

The <u>units of acceleration</u> equal the <u>speed units per the time units</u>.

For speed in m/s and time in seconds the units of acceleration are m/s per s — this is written as <u>m/s^2</u>.

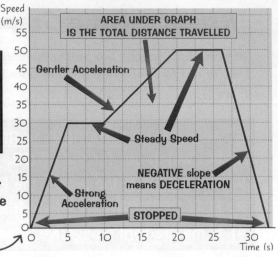

This graph is exactly the same shape as the one on page 97, but it means something completely different.

The D/T graph showed something <u>moving away</u> and then <u>back again</u> with <u>steady speeds</u> and <u>long stops</u>, rather like an ocean liner. The <u>S/T graph</u> on the other hand shows something that sets off from <u>rest</u>, <u>accelerates strongly</u>, <u>holds its speed</u>, then <u>accelerates</u> again up to a <u>maximum speed</u> which it holds for a while, and then comes to a <u>dramatic halt</u> at the end. More like a <u>Ferrari</u> than an ocean liner...

EXAMPLE:
The graph below shows the speed of a car as it travelled between two sets of traffic lights.

a) **What was the car's initial acceleration?**

The gradient of the first section of the graph gives the initial acceleration.

$$\text{gradient} = \frac{\text{change in speed}}{\text{change in time}}$$
$$= \frac{10 \text{ m/s}}{2.5 \text{ s}}$$
$$= 4 \text{ m/s}^2$$

b) **After how many seconds did the car stop accelerating?**

The horizontal part of the graph shows the car travelling at a constant speed.

7.5 s

c) **How far did the car travel at a constant speed?**

The area under the horizontal section of the graph gives the distance travelled at constant speed.

area = 2.5 × 12.5 = 31.25 m

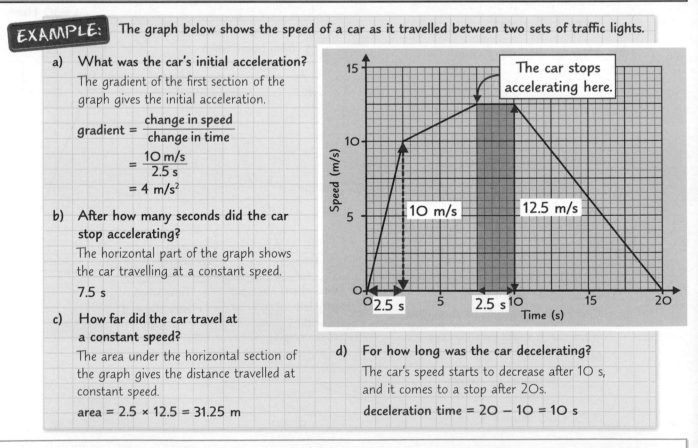

d) **For how long was the car decelerating?**

The car's speed starts to decrease after 10 s, and it comes to a stop after 20s.

deceleration time = 20 − 10 = 10 s

Moan, moan, moan is all my slope ever does — he's just so negative...

The first step for this sort of question is to double-check if it's a distance-time graph or a speed-time graph. Learn the four rules in the orange box, work through the example, then try this Exam Practice Question:

Q1   Using the second graph above, find: (4)
    a)   the acceleration at 5 s.   [2 marks]
    b)   the distance travelled during the deceleration.   [2 marks]

Unit Conversions

A nice easy page for a change — just some <u>facts</u> to learn. Oh, and you need to know how to <u>use them</u>.

Metric Units (1)

1) <u>Length</u>   mm, om, m, km
2) <u>Area</u>   mm², cm², m², km²,
3) <u>Volume</u>   mm³, cm³, m³, ml, litres
4) <u>Weight</u>   g, kg, tonnes
5) <u>Speed</u>   km/h, m/s

MEMORISE THESE KEY FACTS:

1 cm = 10 mm	1 tonne = 1000 kg
1 m = 100 cm	1 litre = 1000 ml
1 km = 1000 m	1 litre = 1000 cm³
1 kg = 1000 g	1 cm³ = 1 ml

EXAMPLE: A giant sea slug called Kevin was washed up near Grange-over-Sands.
He was 18.6 m in length. How long is this in mm?

Do this conversion in two steps — metres to cm then cm to mm.

1) Write down the <u>first conversion factor</u>.   1 m = 100 cm

2) <u>Multiply</u> the number of metres by 100.   18.6 × 100 = 1860 cm

3) Write down the <u>second conversion factor</u>.   1 cm = 10 mm

4) <u>Multiply</u> the number of cm by 10.   1860 × 10
= 18 600 mm

Always check your answer is sensible.
E.g. 1 m = 100 cm, so when you convert from
m to cm you should get a bigger number.

Currency Conversions (2)

You could get asked to convert between any two currencies, but you'll be given the conversion factor.

EXAMPLE: Using the exchange rate £1 = 8.8 Danish kroner,
convert the following amounts:

a) £75 to kroner.

£75 = 75 × 8.8 = 660 kroner

b) 1100 kroner to pounds.

1100 kroner = 1100 ÷ 8.8 = £125

Check your answers
— £1 = 8.8 kroner,
so the number of
kroner should always
be bigger than the
equivalent number
of pounds.

Convert Speeds in Two Steps (3)

Speeds are made up of <u>two measures</u> — a <u>distance</u> and a <u>time</u>. To convert from, say, km per hour to metres per second, you have to convert the distance unit and the time unit <u>separately</u>.

EXAMPLE: A rabbit's top speed is 56 km/h. How fast is this in m/s?

First convert from km/h to m/h: 56 km/h = (56 × 1000) m/h = 56 000 m/h

Now convert from m/h to m/s: 56 000 m/h = (56 000 ÷ 3600) m/s
= 15.6 m/s (1 d.p.)

1 minute = 60 seconds
and 1 hour = 60 minutes.
So 1 hour = 60 × 60
= <u>3600</u> seconds.

Welcome to The Conversion Factor — the new Maths game show...

Learn the metric conversions. Then turn over and write them down. Hmm, I don't know about you, but I quite fancy some conversion-based questions after all that. Which is convenient...

Q1   Convert 6¼ litres to cm³.   [2 marks] (1)

Q2   Given the exchange rate £1 = 165 Albanian leks, convert 350 leks to pounds.
Give your answer to the nearest penny.   [1 mark] (2)

Q3   Convert 80 cm/s to km per hour.   [2 marks] (3)

Unit Conversions

Converting areas and volumes from one unit to another is an exam disaster that you have to know how to avoid. 1 m² definitely does **NOT** equal 100 cm². Remember this and read on for why.

Converting Area and Volume Measurements (4)

$$1 \text{ m}^2 = 100 \text{ cm} \times 100 \text{ cm} = 10\,000 \text{ cm}^2$$
$$1 \text{ cm}^2 = 10 \text{ mm} \times 10 \text{ mm} = 100 \text{ mm}^2$$

1 m²

← 100 cm →

$$1 \text{ m}^3 = 100 \text{ cm} \times 100 \text{ cm} \times 100 \text{ cm} = 1\,000\,000 \text{ cm}^3$$
$$1 \text{ cm}^3 = 10 \text{ mm} \times 10 \text{ mm} \times 10 \text{ mm} = 1000 \text{ mm}^3$$

1 m³

← 100 cm →

EXAMPLES:

1. Convert 9 m² to cm².

To change area measurements from m² to cm² multiply by 100 twice.

9 × 100 × 100 = 90 000 cm²

2. Convert 60 000 mm³ to cm³.

To change volume measurements from mm³ to cm³ divide by 10 three times.

60 000 ÷ (10 × 10 × 10) = 60 cm³

Conversion Graphs (2)

Conversion graphs themselves are **easy** to use.

EXAMPLE: Lucas goes to Florida and spends $36 on a toy alligator. Use the graph to find what this is in pounds.

1) **Draw a line** from a value on **one axis**.
   Start from $36 on the horizontal axis.

2) Keep going until you **hit the LINE**.

3) Then **change direction** and go straight to **the other axis**.

4) **Read off the value** from this axis. The two values are **equivalent**.
   You end up at £22 on the vertical axis, so $36 is equivalent to **£22**.

EXAMPLE: Draw a graph to convert between pounds and Russian roubles, given that £1 = 45 roubles.

1) **Work out 3 pairs of values**.
   You're told £1 = 45 roubles. It's easy to work out that £2 = 90 roubles, and £4 = 180 roubles.

2) **Plot** these points **accurately** and **draw a line** through them.

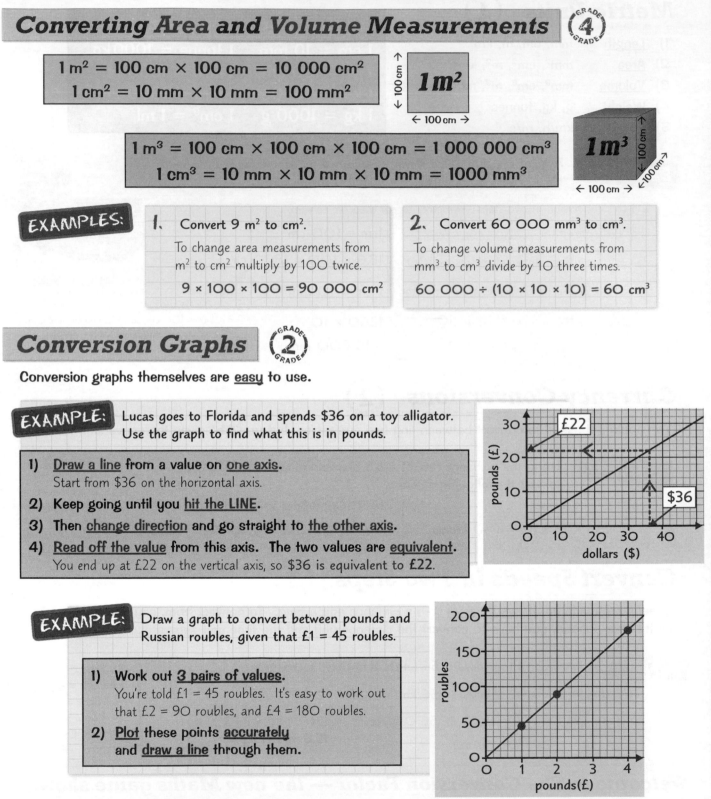

Learn how to convert areas into marks...

Conversion graphs in exams can be for all sorts of units. They all work the same way though.

Q1 Change 3 m³ to mm³. [2 marks] (4)

Q2 Use the conversion graph above to find the approximate value of £2.60 in roubles. [1 mark] (2)

Triangle Construction

How you construct a triangle depends on what <u>info you're given</u> about the triangle...

Three Sides — Use a Ruler and Compasses ③

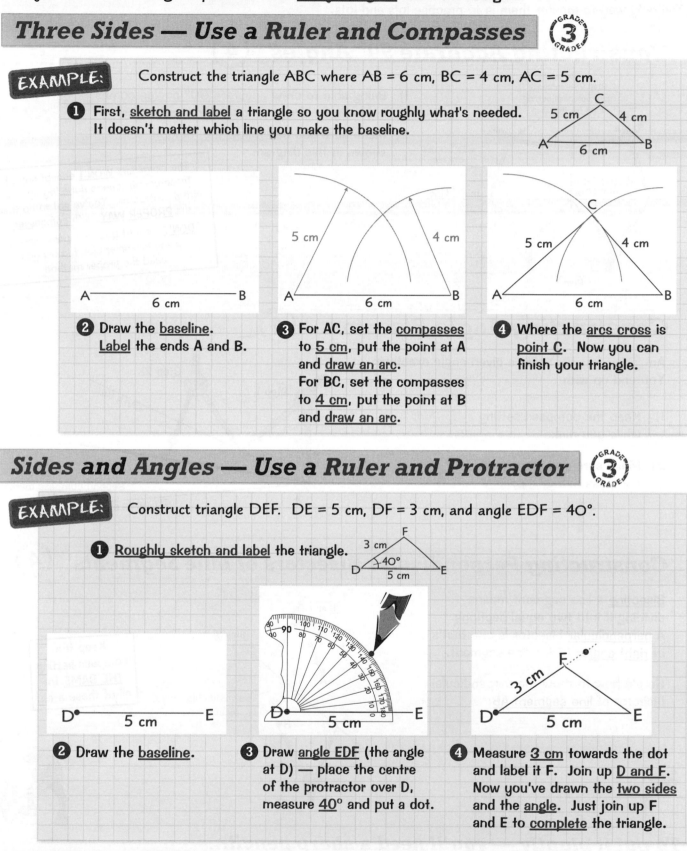

EXAMPLE: Construct the triangle ABC where AB = 6 cm, BC = 4 cm, AC = 5 cm.

1 First, <u>sketch and label</u> a triangle so you know roughly what's needed. It doesn't matter which line you make the baseline.

2 Draw the <u>baseline</u>. <u>Label</u> the ends A and B.

3 For AC, set the <u>compasses</u> to <u>5 cm</u>, put the point at A and <u>draw an arc</u>.
For BC, set the compasses to <u>4 cm</u>, put the point at B and <u>draw an arc</u>.

4 Where the <u>arcs cross</u> is <u>point C</u>. Now you can finish your triangle.

Sides and Angles — Use a Ruler and Protractor ③

EXAMPLE: Construct triangle DEF. DE = 5 cm, DF = 3 cm, and angle EDF = 40°.

1 <u>Roughly sketch and label</u> the triangle.

2 Draw the <u>baseline</u>.

3 Draw <u>angle EDF</u> (the angle at D) — place the centre of the protractor over D, measure <u>40°</u> and put a dot.

4 Measure <u>3 cm</u> towards the dot and label it F. Join up <u>D and F</u>. Now you've drawn the <u>two sides</u> and the <u>angle</u>. Just join up F and E to <u>complete</u> the triangle.

Compasses at the ready — three, two, one... Construct...

Don't forget to take a pencil, ruler and compasses into the exam. Or you'll look like a wally. ③

Q1 Construct an equilateral triangle with sides of 5 cm. Leave your construction marks visible. [2 marks]

Q2 Construct and label triangle ABC. Angle ABC = 45°, angle BCA = 40°, side BC = 7.5 cm. [2 marks]

Constructions

Don't put your compasses away just yet. There's another page on constructions coming up.
The only way to master them is to practise lots and lots.

Constructing Accurate 90° Angles

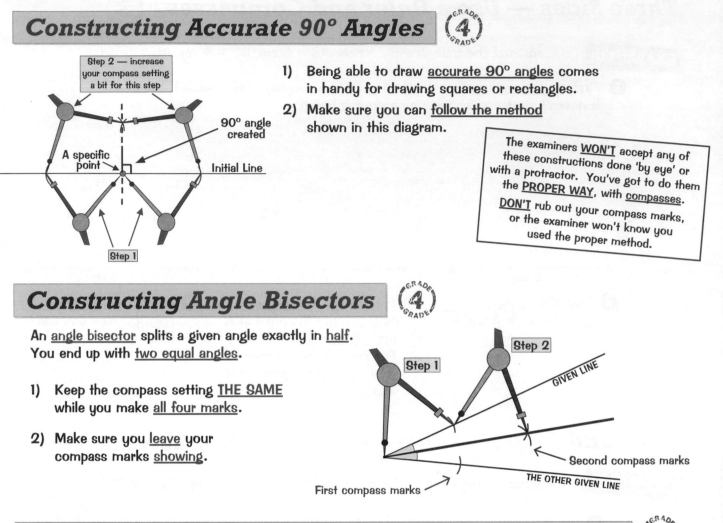

Step 2 — increase your compass setting a bit for this step

90° angle created

A specific point

Initial Line

Step 1

1) Being able to draw <u>accurate 90° angles</u> comes in handy for drawing squares or rectangles.

2) Make sure you can <u>follow the method</u> shown in this diagram.

> The examiners <u>WON'T</u> accept any of these constructions done 'by eye' or with a protractor. You've got to do them the <u>PROPER WAY</u>, with <u>compasses</u>. <u>DON'T</u> rub out your compass marks, or the examiner won't know you used the proper method.

Constructing Angle Bisectors

An <u>angle bisector</u> splits a given angle exactly in <u>half</u>. You end up with <u>two equal angles</u>.

1) Keep the compass setting <u>THE SAME</u> while you make <u>all four marks</u>.

2) Make sure you <u>leave</u> your compass marks <u>showing</u>.

Step 1

Step 2

GIVEN LINE

Second compass marks

THE OTHER GIVEN LINE

First compass marks

Constructing Perpendicular Bisectors of Line Segments

Bisecting a line segment means dividing it into <u>two equal sections</u>. A <u>perpendicular</u> bisector is one that's at <u>right angles</u> to the line segment.

Here's how to draw the perpendicular bisector of <u>line segment AB</u>:

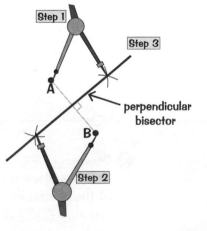

Step 1

Step 3

A

perpendicular bisector

B

Step 2

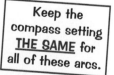

Keep the compass setting <u>THE SAME</u> for all of these arcs.

To put it bluntly — you'll need a sharp pencil...

Constructions aren't too bad really. After all, you get to draw and use compasses and stuff.
Have a go at this lovely Exam Practice Question:

Q1   Construct a triangle which has one right angle and two angles of 45°.
Leave your construction marks visible.

[3 marks]

Bearings

Bearings. They'll be useful next time you're off sailing. Or in your Maths exam.

Bearings (3)

To find or plot a bearing you must remember <u>the three key words</u>:

1) 'FROM' <u>Find the word 'FROM' in the question</u>, and put your pencil on the diagram at the point you are going '<u>from</u>'.

2) NORTHLINE At the point you are going <u>FROM</u>, <u>draw in a NORTHLINE</u>. (There'll often be one drawn for you in exam questions.)

3) CLOCKWISE Now draw in the angle <u>CLOCKWISE from the northline to the line joining the two points</u>. This angle is the required bearing.

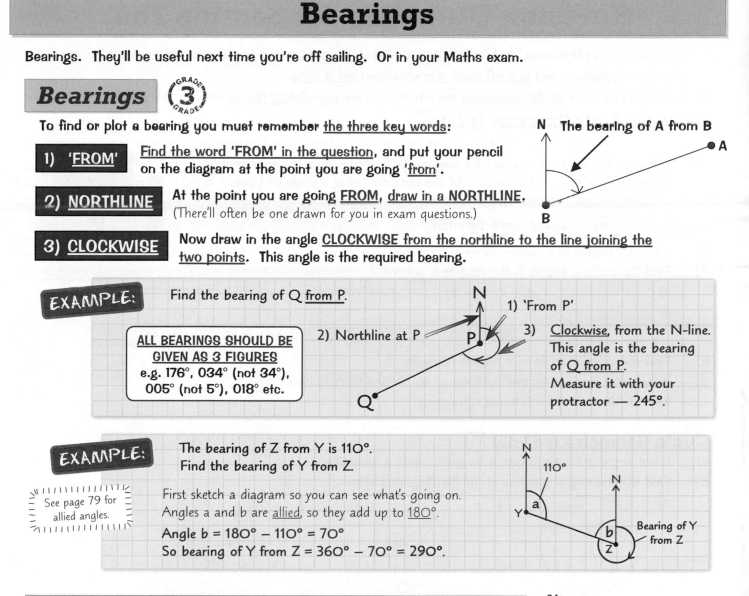

EXAMPLE: Find the bearing of Q <u>from</u> P.

ALL BEARINGS SHOULD BE GIVEN AS 3 FIGURES
e.g. 176°, 034° (not 34°), 005° (not 5°), 018° etc.

1) 'From P'
2) Northline at P
3) Clockwise, from the N-line. This angle is the bearing of Q from P. Measure it with your protractor — 245°.

EXAMPLE: The bearing of Z from Y is 110°. Find the bearing of Y from Z.

See page 79 for allied angles.

First sketch a diagram so you can see what's going on. Angles a and b are <u>allied</u>, so they add up to <u>180°</u>.

Angle b = 180° − 110° = 70°
So bearing of Y from Z = 360° − 70° = 290°.

Bearings Questions and Scale Drawings (3)

EXAMPLE: A hiker walks 2 km from point A, on a bearing of 036°. If the scale of the map below is 2 cm to 1 km, how far is the hiker now from his car?

If you are asked to <u>CALCULATE</u> a distance or an angle, you'll need to use the <u>cosine or sine rule</u> (see p.109).

First, draw a line at a <u>bearing of 036°</u> from point A. <u>1 km</u> is <u>2 cm</u> on the map and the hiker walks <u>2 km</u>, so make the line from A <u>4 cm</u> long.

You want the distance of the hiker from the car, so use a ruler to measure it on the map, then use the scale to work out the <u>real distance</u> it represents.

Distance to car on map = 3 cm. 2 cm = 1 km, so 1 cm = 0.5 km, therefore 3 cm = 1.5 km.

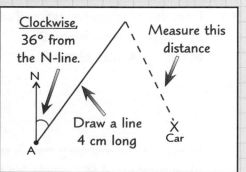

Clockwise, 36° from the N-line.
Draw a line 4 cm long
Measure this distance
Car

Please bear with me while I figure out where we are...

Learn the three key words above and scribble them out from memory. Now try these practice questions:

Q1 Measure the bearing of T from H. [1 mark] (3)

Q2 A ship sails 12 km on a bearing of 050°, then 20 km on a bearing of 100°.
It then sails directly back to its starting position. Calculate this distance to 1 d.p. [5 marks] (8)

Revision Questions for Section Four

There are lots of opportunities to show off your artistic skills here (as long as you use them to answer the questions).

- Try these questions and <u>tick off each one</u> when you <u>get it right</u>.
- When you've done <u>all the questions</u> for a topic and are <u>completely happy</u> with it, tick off the topic.

<u>Maps and Scale Drawings (p77)</u> ☑

1) How do you use a map scale to go from a real-life distance to a distance on a map, and vice versa?

2) Bobby is planning the layout of a new car park for his local supermarket, shown on the right. Draw a plan of the car park using a scale of 1 cm = 5 m.

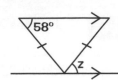

60 m, Car Park, 100 m

<u>Angles and Polygons (p78-82)</u> ☑

3) What do angles in a quadrilateral add up to?

4) Find the missing angles in the diagrams below.

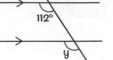

a) 83°, x, 71°   b) 112°, y   c) 58°, z

5) Find the exterior angle of a regular hexagon.

6) How many lines of symmetry does an equilateral triangle have?
What is its order of rotational symmetry?

<u>Circle Geometry (p83-85)</u> ☑

7) What angle is formed when a tangent meets a radius?

8) Find the missing angle in each of the diagrams below.

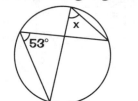

a) 53°, x   b) 21°, y   c) 57°, z

9) In the diagram, JN = 12 cm, LN = 10 cm and MN = 6 cm.
Find the length of KN.

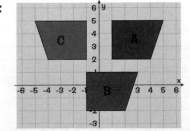

<u>Transformations (p86-88)</u> ☑

10) Describe the transformation that maps:
a) Shape A onto Shape B
b) Shape A onto shape C

11) Carry out the following transformations on the triangle **X**, which has vertices (1, 1), (4, 1) and (2, 3):
a) a rotation of 90° clockwise about (1, 1)   b) a translation by the vector $\binom{-3}{-4}$
c) an enlargement of scale factor 2, centre (1, 1)

12) A shape with area 5 cm² is enlarged by a scale factor of 4. What is the area of the enlarged shape?

<u>Congruence and Similarity (p89)</u> ☑

13) What are congruent and similar shapes?

14) The shapes on the right are similar.
What is the length of side x?

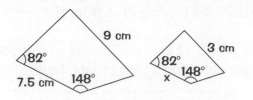

9 cm, 82°, 7.5 cm, 148°, 3 cm, 82°, x, 148°

Revision Questions for Section Four

Area, Surface Area and Volume (p90-94) ☑

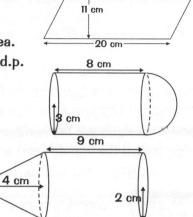

15) What is the formula for finding the area of a trapezium?
16) Find the area of the shape on the right.
17) A circle has diameter 16 cm. Find its exact circumference and area.
18) Find the area of the sector with radius 10 cm and angle 45° to 2 d.p.
19) What is the formula for finding the surface area of a sphere?
20) The shape on the right is made from a cylinder and a hemisphere. Find its exact surface area.
21) Find the volume of a hexagonal prism with a cross-sectional area of 36 cm² and a length of 11 cm.
22) Find the volume of the solid on the right (to 2 d.p.):

Time (p95) ☑

23) Write a) 4.20 pm as a 24-hour clock time,   b) 07:52 as a 12-hour clock time.
24) Using the timetable, how many minutes does the journey from Edinburgh to York last for?
25) Jane lives in Berwick and needs to be in Durham by 1.30 pm. a) What is the latest train she can catch? She lives 20 minutes' walk from the train station. b) What is the latest time she should leave the house?

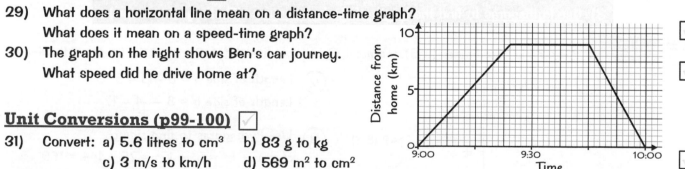

Train Timetable			
Edinburgh	11 14	11 37	12 04
Berwick	11 55	12 18	12 45
Newcastle	12 43	13 06	13 33
Durham	12 57	13 20	13 47
Darlington	13 15	13 38	14 05
York	13 45	14 08	14 35

Speed, Density and Pressure (p96) ☑

26) Find the average speed of a car if it travels 63 km in an hour and a half.
27) Find the volume of a snowman if its density is 0.4 g/cm³ and its mass is 5 kg.
28) Find the area of an object in contact with horizontal ground, if the pressure it exerts on the ground is 120 N/m² and the force acting on the object is 1320 N.

Travel Graphs (p97-98) ☑

29) What does a horizontal line mean on a distance-time graph? What does it mean on a speed-time graph?
30) The graph on the right shows Ben's car journey. What speed did he drive home at?

Unit Conversions (p99-100) ☑

31) Convert: a) 5.6 litres to cm³   b) 83 g to kg
         c) 3 m/s to km/h   d) 569 m² to cm²

Constructions (p101-102) ☑

32) Construct triangle XYZ, where XY = 5.6 cm, XZ = 7.2 cm and angle YXZ = 55°.
33) Construct an accurate 90° angle. Bisect it to form two 45° angles.
34) Draw a line 6 cm long. Construct the perpendicular bisector of the line.

Bearings (p103) ☑

35) Describe how to find a bearing from point A to point B.
36) A helicopter flies 25 km on a bearing of 210°, then 20 km on a bearing of 040°. Draw a scale diagram to show this. Use a scale of 1 cm = 5 km.

Pythagoras' Theorem

Pythagoras' theorem sounds hard but it's actually <u>dead simple</u>.
It's also dead important, so make sure you really get your teeth into it.

Pythagoras' Theorem — $a^2 + b^2 = c^2$ (4)

1) <u>PYTHAGORAS' THEOREM</u> only works for <u>RIGHT-ANGLED TRIANGLES</u>.

2) Pythagoras uses <u>two sides</u> to find the <u>third side</u>.

3) The <u>BASIC FORMULA</u> for Pythagoras is $a^2 + b^2 = c^2$

4) Make sure you get the numbers in the <u>RIGHT PLACE</u>. c is the <u>longest</u> side (called the hypotenuse) and it's always <u>opposite</u> the right angle.

5) Always <u>CHECK</u> that your answer is <u>SENSIBLE</u>.

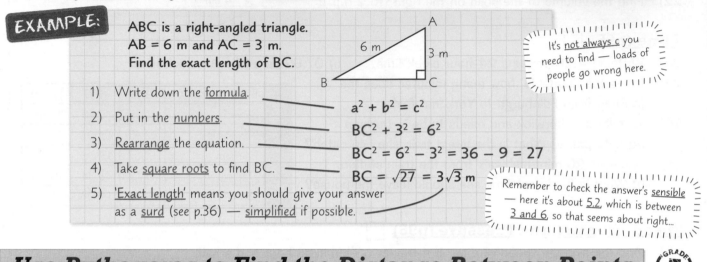

$$a^2 + b^2 = c^2$$

EXAMPLE:

ABC is a right-angled triangle.
AB = 6 m and AC = 3 m.
Find the exact length of BC.

1) Write down the <u>formula</u>. —— $a^2 + b^2 = c^2$

2) Put in the <u>numbers</u>. —— $BC^2 + 3^2 = 6^2$

3) <u>Rearrange</u> the equation. —— $BC^2 = 6^2 - 3^2 = 36 - 9 = 27$

4) Take <u>square roots</u> to find BC. —— $BC = \sqrt{27} = 3\sqrt{3}$ m

5) '<u>Exact length</u>' means you should give your answer as a <u>surd</u> (see p.36) — <u>simplified</u> if possible.

It's <u>not always c</u> you need to find — loads of people go wrong here.

Remember to check the answer's <u>sensible</u> — here it's about <u>5.2</u>, which is between <u>3 and 6</u>, so that seems about right...

Use Pythagoras to Find the Distance Between Points (5)

You need to know how to find the straight-line <u>distance</u> between <u>two points</u> on a <u>graph</u>.
If you get a question like this, follow these rules and it'll all become breathtakingly simple:

> 1) Draw a <u>sketch</u> to show the <u>right-angled triangle</u>.
> 2) Find the <u>lengths of the shorter sides</u> of the triangle.
> 3) <u>Use Pythagoras</u> to find the <u>length of the hypotenuse</u>. (That's your answer.)

EXAMPLE:

Point P has coordinates (8, 3) and point Q has coordinates (–4, 8). Find the length of the line PQ.

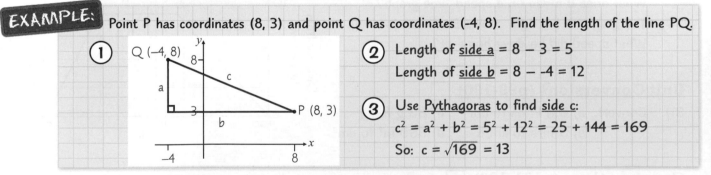

(1)

(2) Length of <u>side a</u> = 8 − 3 = 5
Length of <u>side b</u> = 8 − −4 = 12

(3) Use <u>Pythagoras</u> to find <u>side c</u>:
$c^2 = a^2 + b^2 = 5^2 + 12^2 = 25 + 144 = 169$
So: $c = \sqrt{169} = 13$

Remember, if it's not a right angle, it's a wrong angle...

Once you've learned all the Pythagoras facts on this page, try these Exam Practice Questions:

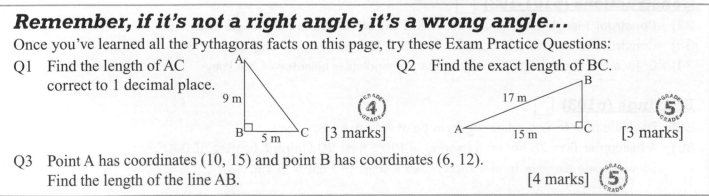

Q1   Find the length of AC correct to 1 decimal place.

9 m   5 m   (4)   [3 marks]

Q2   Find the exact length of BC.

17 m   15 m   (5)   [3 marks]

Q3   Point A has coordinates (10, 15) and point B has coordinates (6, 12).
Find the length of the line AB.   [4 marks] (5)

Trigonometry — Sin, Cos, Tan

Trigonometry — it's a big scary word. But it's not a big scary topic. An <u>important</u> topic, yes. An <u>always cropping up</u> topic, definitely. But scary? Pur-lease. Takes more than a triangle to scare me. Read on...

The 3 Trigonometry Formulas

There are three basic <u>trig formulas</u> — each one links <u>two sides and an angle</u> of a <u>right-angled triangle</u>.

$$\text{Sin } x = \frac{\text{Opposite}}{\text{Hypotenuse}}$$

$$\text{Cos } x = \frac{\text{Adjacent}}{\text{Hypotenuse}}$$

$$\text{Tan } x = \frac{\text{Opposite}}{\text{Adjacent}}$$

- The <u>Hypotenuse</u> is the <u>LONGEST SIDE</u>.
- The <u>Opposite</u> is the side <u>OPPOSITE</u> the angle <u>being used</u> (x).
- The <u>Adjacent</u> is the (other) side <u>NEXT TO</u> the angle <u>being used</u>.

Opposite (O)   Hypotenuse (H)   Adjacent (A) x

1) Whenever you come across a trig question, work out which <u>two sides</u> of the triangle are involved in that question — then <u>pick the formula</u> that involves those sides.

2) <u>To find the angle — use the inverse</u>, i.e. press SHIFT or 2ndF, followed by <u>sin</u>, <u>cos</u> or <u>tan</u> (and make sure your calculator is in DEG mode) — your calculator will display <u>sin⁻¹</u>, <u>cos⁻¹</u> or <u>tan⁻¹</u>.

3) Remember, you can only use sin, cos and tan on <u>right-angled triangles</u> — you may have to add lines to the diagram to create one.

There's more about formula triangles on p.96 if you need to jog your memory.

Formula Triangles Make Things Simple

A handy way to tackle trig questions is to convert the formulas into <u>formula triangles</u>. Then you can use the <u>same method every time</u>, no matter which side or angle is being asked for.

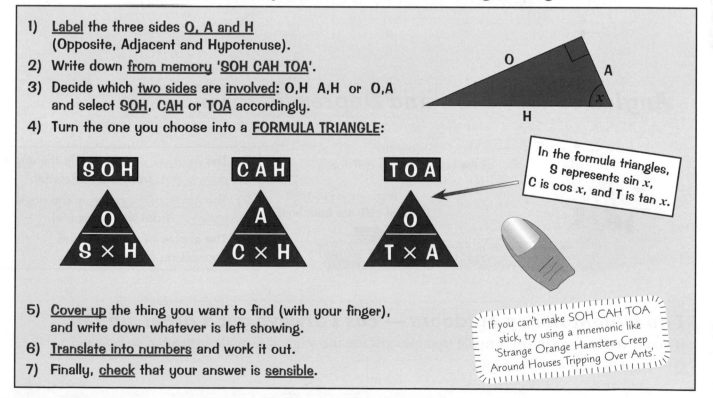

1) <u>Label</u> the three sides <u>O, A and H</u> (Opposite, Adjacent and Hypotenuse).
2) Write down <u>from memory</u> 'SOH CAH TOA'.
3) Decide which <u>two sides</u> are <u>involved</u>: O,H   A,H   or   O,A and select <u>SOH</u>, <u>CAH</u> or <u>TOA</u> accordingly.
4) Turn the one you choose into a <u>FORMULA TRIANGLE</u>:

In the formula triangles, S represents sin x, C is cos x, and T is tan x.

5) <u>Cover up</u> the thing you want to find (with your finger), and write down whatever is left showing.
6) <u>Translate into numbers</u> and work it out.
7) Finally, <u>check</u> that your answer is <u>sensible</u>.

If you can't make SOH CAH TOA stick, try using a mnemonic like 'Strange Orange Hamsters Creep Around Houses Tripping Over Ants'.

SOH CAH TOA — the not-so-secret formula for success...

You need to know this stuff off by heart — so go over this page a few times until you've got those formulas firmly lodged and all ready to reel off in the exam. All set? Time for some examples...

Trigonometry — Sin, Cos, Tan

Here are some lovely examples to help you through the trials of trig.

Examples: (GRADE 5)

1 Find the length of x in the triangle shown to 3 s.f.

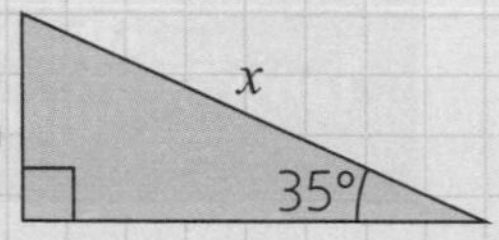

1) **Label** the sides

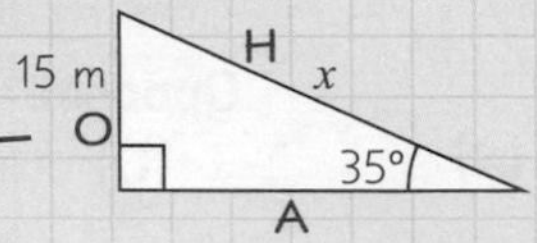

2) **Write down**

3) **O** and **H** involved

(SOH) CAH TOA

4) **Write down the formula triangle**

$$\frac{O}{S \times H}$$

5) **You want H so cover it up** to give $H = \dfrac{O}{S}$

6) **Put in the numbers**

$$x = \frac{15}{\sin 35°} = 26.1517... \, m$$

$$= 26.2 \, m \text{ (3 s.f.)}$$

Is it sensible? Yes it's about twice as big as 15, as the diagram suggests.

2 Find the angle x in this triangle to 1 d.p.

*It's an **isosceles** triangle so **split** it **down the middle** to get a **right-angled triangle**.*

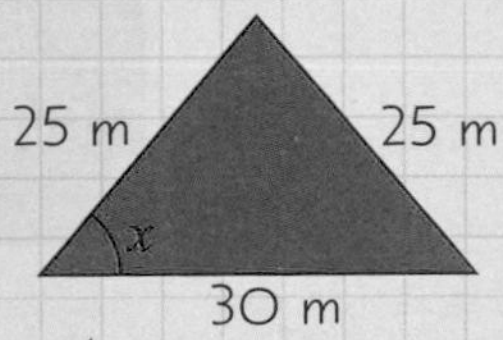

25 m   25 m   30 m

1) **Label** the sides

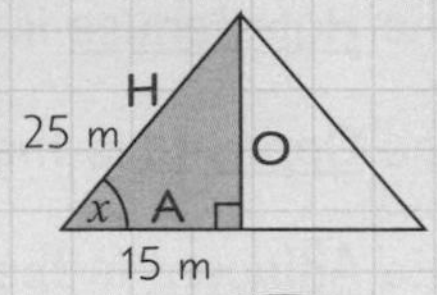

2) **Write down**

SOH (CAH) TOA

3) **A** and **H** involved

4) **Write down the formula triangle**

$$\frac{A}{C \times H}$$

5) **You want the angle** so **cover up C** to give $C = \dfrac{A}{H}$

6) **Put in the numbers** $\cos x = \dfrac{15}{25} = 0.6$

Find the inverse $\Rightarrow x = \cos^{-1}(0.6) = 53.1301...°$

$$= 53.1° \text{ (1 d.p.)}$$

Is it sensible? Yes, the angle looks about 50°.

Angles of Elevation and Depression (GRADE 6)

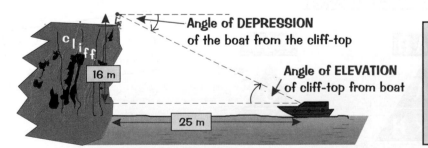

Angle of **DEPRESSION** of the boat from the cliff-top

Angle of **ELEVATION** of cliff-top from boat

16 m   25 m

1) The **Angle of Depression** is the angle **downwards** from the horizontal.

2) The **Angle of Elevation** is the angle **upwards** from the horizontal.

3) The angles of elevation and depression are **equal**.

I do trigonometry outdoors — cos I always get a great sin tan...

If you're really not a fan of formula triangles just use the original formula instead of steps 4 and 5.

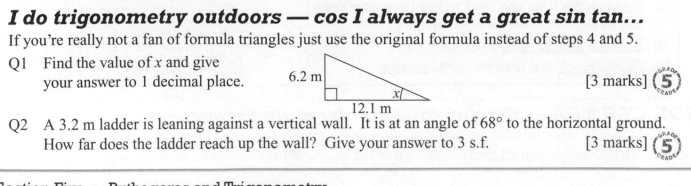

Q1   Find the value of x and give your answer to 1 decimal place.   6.2 m   12.1 m x [3 marks] (GRADE 5)

Q2   A 3.2 m ladder is leaning against a vertical wall. It is at an angle of 68° to the horizontal ground. How far does the ladder reach up the wall? Give your answer to 3 s.f.   [3 marks] (GRADE 5)

The Sine and Cosine Rules

Normal trigonometry using **SOH CAH TOA** etc. can only be applied to <u>right-angled</u> triangles. Which leaves us with the question of what to do with other-angled triangles. Step forward the <u>Sine and Cosine Rules</u>...

Labelling the Triangle

This is very important. You must label the sides and angles properly so that the letters for the sides and angles correspond with each other. Use <u>lower case letters</u> for the <u>sides</u> and <u>capitals</u> for the <u>angles</u>.

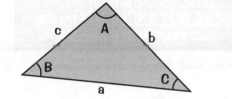

Remember, <u>side 'a' is opposite angle A</u> etc.

It doesn't matter which sides you decide to call a, b and c, just as long as the angles are then labelled properly.

Three Formulas to Learn:

The Sine Rule

$$\frac{a}{\sin A} = \frac{b}{\sin B} = \frac{c}{\sin C}$$

You don't use the whole thing with both '=' signs of course, so it's not half as bad as it looks — you just <u>choose the two bits</u> that you want:

e.g. $\frac{b}{\sin B} = \frac{c}{\sin C}$ or $\frac{a}{\sin A} = \frac{b}{\sin B}$

The Cosine Rule

The 'normal' form is...

$$a^2 = b^2 + c^2 - 2bc \cos A$$

...or this form is good for finding an angle (you get it by rearranging the 'normal' version):

or $\cos A = \dfrac{b^2+c^2-a^2}{2bc}$

Area of the Triangle

This formula comes in handy when you know <u>two sides</u> and the <u>angle between them</u>:

$$\text{Area of triangle} = \tfrac{1}{2} ab \sin C$$

Of course, you already know a <u>simple formula</u> for calculating the area using the <u>base length</u> and <u>height</u> (see p.90). The formula here is for when you don't know those values.

EXAMPLE:

Triangle XYZ has XZ = 18 cm, YZ = 13 cm and angle XZY = 58°. Find the area of the triangle, giving your answer correct to 3 significant figures.

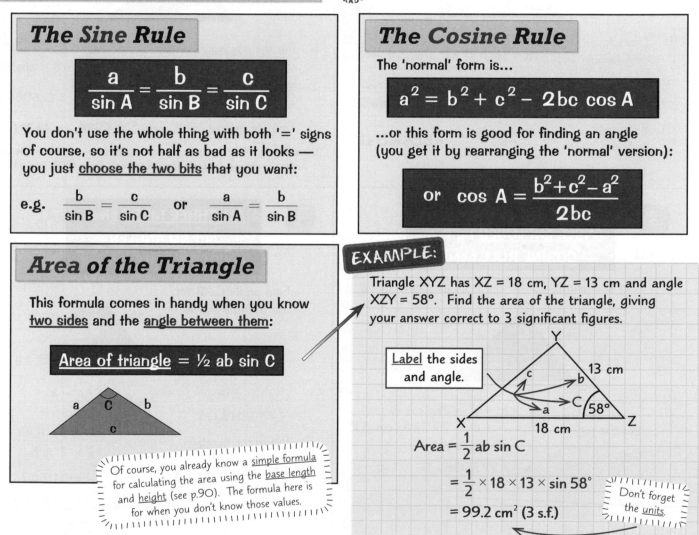

<u>Label</u> the sides and angle.

Area $= \frac{1}{2} ab \sin C$
$= \frac{1}{2} \times 18 \times 13 \times \sin 58°$
$= 99.2 \text{ cm}^2$ (3 s.f.)

Don't forget the <u>units</u>.

...and step back again. Hope you enjoyed a moment in the spotlight...

You need to learn all of these formulas off by heart and practise using them. Here's an area question to have a go at, and fear not, you'll get your chance to tackle some sine and cosine rule problems on the next page...

Q1 Triangle FGH has FG = 9 cm, FH = 12 cm and angle GFH = 37°. Find its area, giving your answer correct to 3 significant figures.

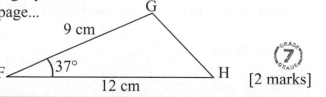

[2 marks]

The Sine and Cosine Rules

Amazingly, there are only FOUR question types where the sine and cosine rules would be applied. So learn the exact details of these four examples and you'll be laughing. WARNING: if you laugh too much people will think you're crazy.

The Four Examples

GRADE 7

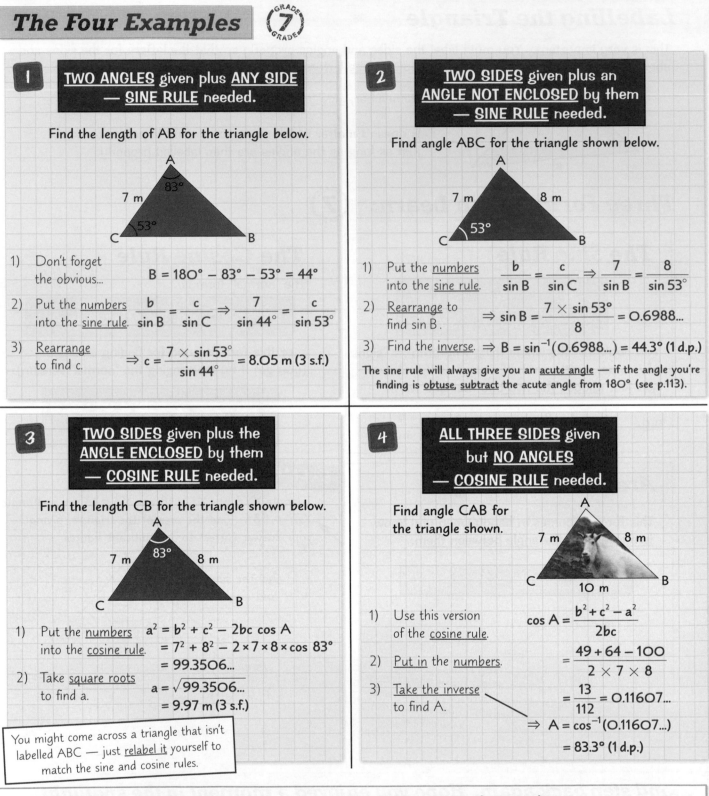

1 TWO ANGLES given plus ANY SIDE — SINE RULE needed.

Find the length of AB for the triangle below.

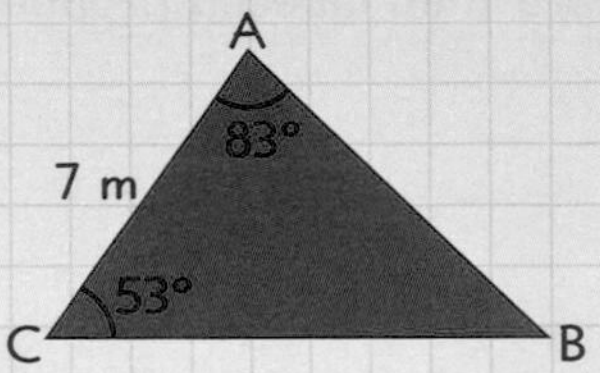

1) Don't forget the obvious... $B = 180° - 83° - 53° = 44°$

2) Put the numbers into the sine rule. $\frac{b}{\sin B} = \frac{c}{\sin C} \Rightarrow \frac{7}{\sin 44°} = \frac{c}{\sin 53°}$

3) Rearrange to find c. $\Rightarrow c = \frac{7 \times \sin 53°}{\sin 44°} = 8.05$ m (3 s.f.)

2 TWO SIDES given plus an ANGLE NOT ENCLOSED by them — SINE RULE needed.

Find angle ABC for the triangle shown below.

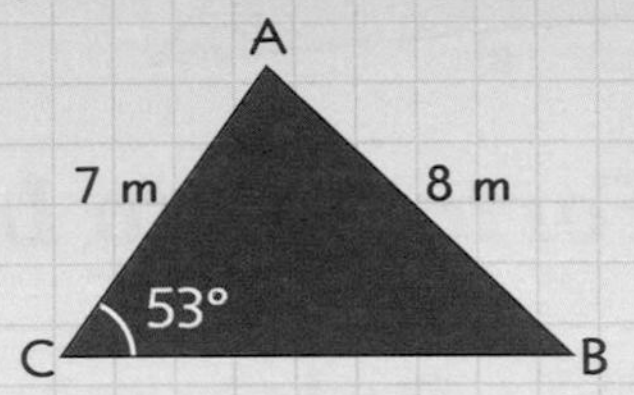

1) Put the numbers into the sine rule. $\frac{b}{\sin B} = \frac{c}{\sin C} \Rightarrow \frac{7}{\sin B} = \frac{8}{\sin 53°}$

2) Rearrange to find sin B. $\Rightarrow \sin B = \frac{7 \times \sin 53°}{8} = 0.6988...$

3) Find the inverse. $\Rightarrow B = \sin^{-1}(0.6988...) = 44.3°$ (1 d.p.)

The sine rule will always give you an acute angle — if the angle you're finding is obtuse, subtract the acute angle from 180° (see p.113).

3 TWO SIDES given plus the ANGLE ENCLOSED by them — COSINE RULE needed.

Find the length CB for the triangle shown below.

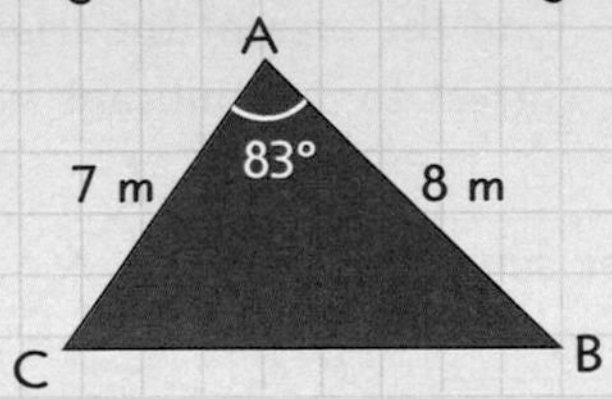

1) Put the numbers into the cosine rule. $a^2 = b^2 + c^2 - 2bc \cos A$
$= 7^2 + 8^2 - 2 \times 7 \times 8 \times \cos 83°$
$= 99.3506...$

2) Take square roots to find a. $a = \sqrt{99.3506...}$
$= 9.97$ m (3 s.f.)

You might come across a triangle that isn't labelled ABC — just relabel it yourself to match the sine and cosine rules.

4 ALL THREE SIDES given but NO ANGLES — COSINE RULE needed.

Find angle CAB for the triangle shown.

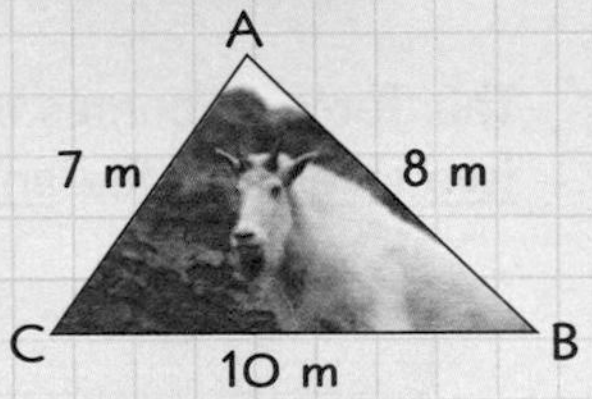

1) Use this version of the cosine rule. $\cos A = \frac{b^2 + c^2 - a^2}{2bc}$

2) Put in the numbers. $= \frac{49 + 64 - 100}{2 \times 7 \times 8}$

3) Take the inverse to find A. $= \frac{13}{112} = 0.11607...$
$\Rightarrow A = \cos^{-1}(0.11607...)$
$= 83.3°$ (1 d.p.)

4 examples + 3 formulas + 2 rules = 1 trigonometric genius...

You need to get really good at spotting which of the four methods to use, so try these practice questions.

Q1 Find the length of side AB for triangle ABC.

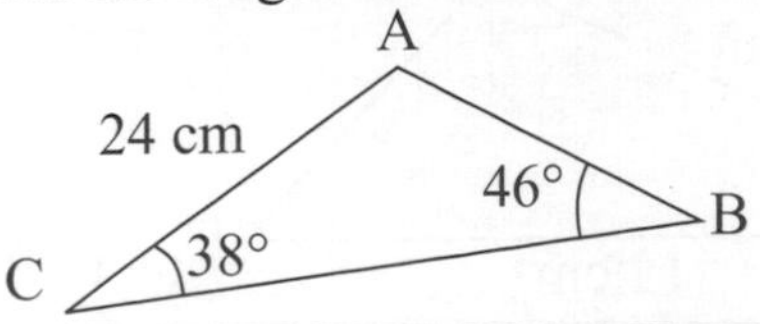

[3 marks] GRADE 7

Q2 Find the size of angle RPQ for triangle PQR.

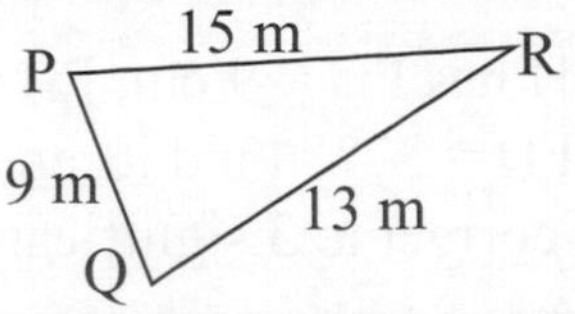

[3 marks] GRADE 7

3D Pythagoras

This is a 3D version of the 2D Pythagoras' theorem you saw on page 106.
There's just <u>one simple formula</u> — learn it and the world's your oyster...

3D Pythagoras for Cuboids — $a^2 + b^2 + c^2 = d^2$ (7)

<u>Cuboids</u> have their own formula for calculating
the length of their <u>longest diagonal</u>:

$$a^2 + b^2 + c^2 = d^2$$

In reality it's nothing you haven't seen before
— it's just <u>2D Pythagoras' theorem</u> being used <u>twice</u>:

1) <u>a, b and e</u> make a <u>right-angled triangle</u> so
    $$e^2 = a^2 + b^2$$

2) Now look at the <u>right-angled triangle</u>
    formed by <u>e, c and d</u>:
    $$d^2 = e^2 + c^2 = a^2 + b^2 + c^2$$

EXAMPLE:

Find the exact length of the diagonal BH for the cube in the diagram.

1) Write down the <u>formula</u>. $a^2 + b^2 + c^2 = d^2$

2) Put in the <u>numbers</u>. $4^2 + 4^2 + 4^2 = BH^2$

3) Take the <u>square root</u> to find BH. $\Rightarrow BH = \sqrt{48} = 4\sqrt{3}$ cm

The Cuboid Formula Can be Used in Other 3D Shapes (8)

EXAMPLE:

In the square-based pyramid shown,
M is the midpoint of the base.
Find the vertical height AM.

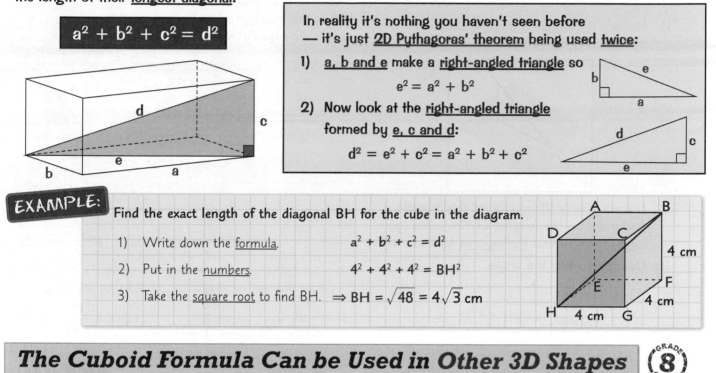

1) <u>Label N</u> as the midpoint of ED.

    Then think of <u>EN, NM and AM</u> as three <u>sides</u>
    of a <u>cuboid</u>, and <u>AE</u> as the <u>longest diagonal</u>
    in the cuboid (like d in the section above).

2) Sketch the <u>full cuboid</u>.

3) Write down the <u>3D Pythagoras formula</u>. $a^2 + b^2 + c^2 = d^2$

4) <u>Rewrite</u> it using <u>side labels</u>. $EN^2 + NM^2 + AM^2 = AE^2$

5) Put in the <u>numbers</u> and <u>solve for AM</u>. $\Rightarrow 3.5^2 + 3.5^2 + AM^2 = 9^2$

    $\Rightarrow AM = \sqrt{81 - 2 \times 12.25} = 7.52$ cm (3 s.f.)

Wow — just what can't right-angled triangles do?...

You need to be ready to tackle 3D questions in the exam,
so have a go at this Exam Practice Question:

Q1   Find the length AH in the cuboid shown to 3 s.f.

[3 marks] (7)

3D Trigonometry

3D trig may sound tricky, and in many ways it is... but it's actually just using the <u>same old rules</u>.

Angle Between Line and Plane — Use a Diagram ⑧

Learn the 3-Step Method

1) Make a <u>right-angled triangle</u> between the line and the plane.

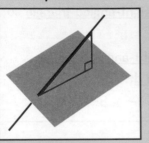

2) Draw a <u>simple 2D sketch</u> of this triangle and mark on the lengths of two sides (you might have to use <u>Pythagoras</u> to find one).

3) Use <u>trig</u> to find the angle.

Have a look at p.106-109 to jog your memory about Pythagoras and trig.

EXAMPLE:

ABCDE is a square-based pyramid with M as the midpoint of its base. Find the angle the edge AE makes with the base.

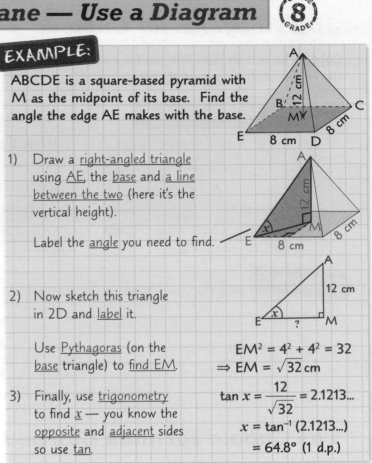

1) Draw a <u>right-angled triangle</u> using <u>AE</u>, the <u>base</u> and <u>a line between the two</u> (here it's the vertical height).

Label the <u>angle</u> you need to find.

2) Now sketch this triangle in 2D and <u>label</u> it.

Use <u>Pythagoras</u> (on the <u>base</u> triangle) to <u>find EM</u>.

$$EM^2 = 4^2 + 4^2 = 32$$
$$\Rightarrow EM = \sqrt{32} \text{ cm}$$

3) Finally, use <u>trigonometry</u> to find <u>x</u> — you know the <u>opposite</u> and <u>adjacent</u> sides so use <u>tan</u>.

$$\tan x = \frac{12}{\sqrt{32}} = 2.1213...$$
$$x = \tan^{-1}(2.1213...)$$
$$= 64.8° \text{ (1 d.p.)}$$

The Sine Rule and Cosine Rule Can Also be Used in 3D ⑨

For <u>triangles</u> inside 3D shapes that <u>aren't right-angled</u> you can use the <u>sine and cosine rules</u>. This sounds mildly terrifying but it's actually OK — just use the <u>same formulas</u> as before (see p.109-110).

EXAMPLE:

Find the size of angle AEH in the cuboid shown below.

1) <u>Draw the triangle</u> AEH and label angle AEH as x.

2) Use <u>Pythagoras'</u> theorem to find the lengths of <u>AE, AH and EH</u>.

$$AH^2 = 13^2 + 9^2 = 250 \Rightarrow AH = \sqrt{250}$$
$$AE^2 = 6^2 + 9^2 = 117 \Rightarrow AE = \sqrt{117}$$
$$EH^2 = 6^2 + 13^2 = 205 \Rightarrow EH = \sqrt{205}$$

3) <u>Find x</u> using the <u>cosine rule</u>:
Put in the <u>numbers</u>.
Rearrange and take the <u>inverse</u> to find x.

$$AH^2 = AE^2 + EH^2 - 2 \times AE \times EH \times \cos x$$
$$250 = 117 + 205 - 2\sqrt{117}\sqrt{205} \cos x$$
$$x = \cos^{-1}\left(\frac{117 + 205 - 250}{2\sqrt{117 \times 205}}\right) = 76.6° \text{ (1 d.p.)}$$

The Return of the Cosine Rule — out now in 3D...

If you need to find an angle in a 3D question, don't panic — just put those standard trig formulas to work.

Q1 Find the size of the angle between the line PV and the plane PQRS in the cuboid shown. [4 marks] ⑧

Sin, Cos and Tan for Larger Angles

You need to know about sin, cos and tan of <u>obtuse angles</u> (they're the ones between 90° and 180°).

Cosine of Obtuse Angles (7)

Values of cos x for obtuse angles are <u>negative</u>, but the cosine rule works just the same as for acute angles.

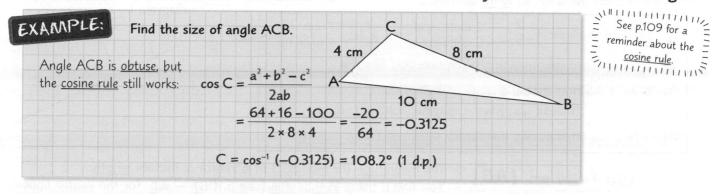

EXAMPLE: Find the size of angle ACB.

Angle ACB is <u>obtuse</u>, but the <u>cosine rule</u> still works:

$$\cos C = \frac{a^2 + b^2 - c^2}{2ab}$$

$$= \frac{64 + 16 - 100}{2 \times 8 \times 4} = \frac{-20}{64} = -0.3125$$

$$C = \cos^{-1}(-0.3125) = 108.2° \text{ (1 d.p.)}$$

See p.109 for a reminder about the cosine rule.

Sine of Obtuse Angles (7)

1) You have to be a bit more careful with sine. Each value of <u>sin x</u> between 0 and 1 corresponds to <u>2 different values</u> of x between 0° and 180°.

2) When you use your calculator's sin⁻¹ function to find the size of the angle, it gives you the answer between <u>0° and 90°</u>. If you know the angle is <u>obtuse</u>, you then have to <u>subtract</u> the calculator's answer from <u>180°</u>.

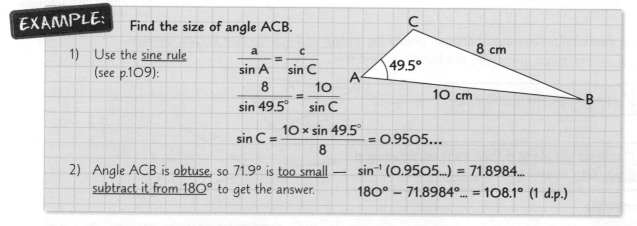

EXAMPLE: Find the size of angle ACB.

1) Use the <u>sine rule</u> (see p.109):

$$\frac{a}{\sin A} = \frac{c}{\sin C}$$

$$\frac{8}{\sin 49.5°} = \frac{10}{\sin C}$$

$$\sin C = \frac{10 \times \sin 49.5°}{8} = 0.9505...$$

2) Angle ACB is <u>obtuse</u>, so 71.9° is <u>too small</u> — <u>subtract it from 180°</u> to get the answer.

$\sin^{-1}(0.9505...) = 71.8984...$

$180° - 71.8984°... = 108.1°$ (1 d.p.)

Tan of Obtuse Angles (6)

1) When you use your calculator's tan⁻¹ function to find the size of an angle, it gives you an answer between <u>−90° and 90°</u>.

2) If you know the angle is <u>obtuse</u>, you then have to <u>add 180°</u>.

EXAMPLE: x is an obtuse angle with tan $x = -1$. Find x.

$\tan^{-1}(-1) = -45°$

It's an <u>obtuse</u> angle, so <u>add 180°</u>:

$-45° + 180° = 135°$

If you see an obtuse angle — don't ignore the warning sine...

Always make sure your answer looks sensible — don't just believe everything your calculator tells you...

Q1 Find the size of angle PQR.

9 cm   37°

P   7 cm   Q   R

[4 marks] (7)

Vectors

Vectors represent a movement of a certain <u>size</u> in a certain <u>direction</u>.
They might seem a bit weird at first, but there are really just a few facts to get to grips with...

Vector Notations (6)

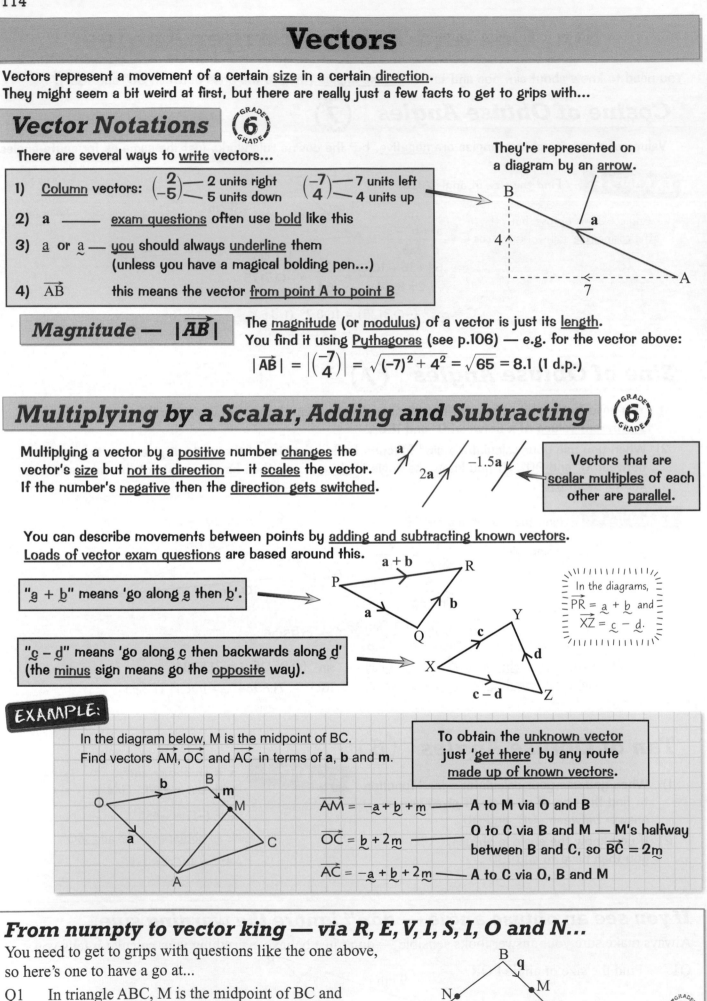

There are several ways to <u>write</u> vectors...

They're represented on a diagram by an <u>arrow</u>.

1) <u>Column</u> vectors: $\begin{pmatrix} 2 \\ -5 \end{pmatrix}$ — 2 units right, 5 units down; $\begin{pmatrix} -7 \\ 4 \end{pmatrix}$ — 7 units left, 4 units up

2) **a** ——— <u>exam questions</u> often use <u>bold</u> like this

3) <u>a</u> or a̰ — <u>you</u> should always <u>underline</u> them
(unless you have a magical bolding pen...)

4) $\overrightarrow{AB}$ this means the vector <u>from point A to point B</u>

Magnitude — $|\overrightarrow{AB}|$

The <u>magnitude</u> (or <u>modulus</u>) of a vector is just its <u>length</u>.
You find it using <u>Pythagoras</u> (see p.106) — e.g. for the vector above:

$$|\overrightarrow{AB}| = \left|\begin{pmatrix} -7 \\ 4 \end{pmatrix}\right| = \sqrt{(-7)^2 + 4^2} = \sqrt{65} = 8.1 \text{ (1 d.p.)}$$

Multiplying by a Scalar, Adding and Subtracting (6)

Multiplying a vector by a <u>positive</u> number <u>changes</u> the vector's <u>size</u> but <u>not its direction</u> — it <u>scales</u> the vector. If the number's <u>negative</u> then the <u>direction gets switched</u>.

Vectors that are <u>scalar multiples</u> of each other are <u>parallel</u>.

You can describe movements between points by <u>adding and subtracting known vectors</u>.
<u>Loads of vector exam questions</u> are based around this.

"<u>a</u> + <u>b</u>" means 'go along <u>a</u> then <u>b</u>'.

In the diagrams, $\overrightarrow{PR} = \underline{a} + \underline{b}$ and $\overrightarrow{XZ} = \underline{c} - \underline{d}$.

"<u>c</u> – <u>d</u>" means 'go along <u>c</u> then backwards along <u>d</u>' (the <u>minus</u> sign means go the <u>opposite</u> way).

EXAMPLE:

In the diagram below, M is the midpoint of BC.
Find vectors $\overrightarrow{AM}$, $\overrightarrow{OC}$ and $\overrightarrow{AC}$ in terms of **a**, **b** and **m**.

To obtain the <u>unknown vector</u> just '<u>get there</u>' by any route <u>made up of known vectors</u>.

$\overrightarrow{AM} = -\underline{a} + \underline{b} + \underline{m}$ ——— A to M via O and B

$\overrightarrow{OC} = \underline{b} + 2\underline{m}$ ——— O to C via B and M — M's halfway between B and C, so $\overrightarrow{BC} = 2\underline{m}$

$\overrightarrow{AC} = -\underline{a} + \underline{b} + 2\underline{m}$ ——— A to C via O, B and M

From numpty to vector king — via R, E, V, I, S, I, O and N...

You need to get to grips with questions like the one above, so here's one to have a go at...

Q1   In triangle ABC, M is the midpoint of BC and N is the midpoint of AB. $\overrightarrow{AC} = \mathbf{p}$ and $\overrightarrow{BM} = \mathbf{q}$.
Find $\overrightarrow{AB}$ and $\overrightarrow{NA}$ in terms of **p** and **q**.

(7)

[3 marks]

Vectors

Extra bits and pieces can crop up in vector questions — these examples will show you how to tackle them...

Vectors Along a Straight Line (8)

1) You can use vectors to show that points lie on a straight line.

2) You need to show that the vectors along each part of the line point in the same direction — i.e. they're scalar multiples of each other.

If XYZ is a straight line then $\overrightarrow{XY}$ must be a scalar multiple of $\overrightarrow{YZ}$.

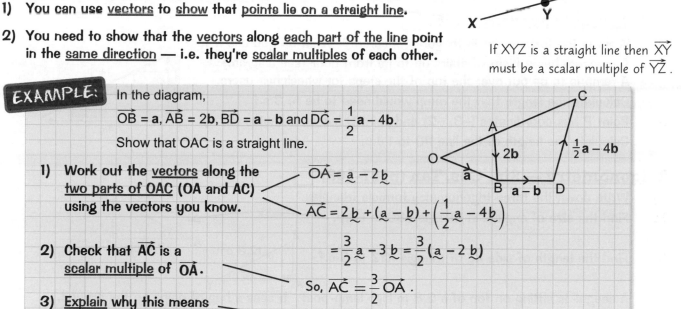

EXAMPLE:

In the diagram,
$\overrightarrow{OB} = \mathbf{a}$, $\overrightarrow{AB} = 2\mathbf{b}$, $\overrightarrow{BD} = \mathbf{a} - \mathbf{b}$ and $\overrightarrow{DC} = \frac{1}{2}\mathbf{a} - 4\mathbf{b}$.

Show that OAC is a straight line.

1) Work out the vectors along the two parts of OAC (OA and AC) using the vectors you know.

$$\overrightarrow{OA} = \underset{\sim}{a} - 2\underset{\sim}{b}$$

$$\overrightarrow{AC} = 2\underset{\sim}{b} + (\underset{\sim}{a} - \underset{\sim}{b}) + \left(\frac{1}{2}\underset{\sim}{a} - 4\underset{\sim}{b}\right)$$

2) Check that $\overrightarrow{AC}$ is a scalar multiple of $\overrightarrow{OA}$.

$$= \frac{3}{2}\underset{\sim}{a} - 3\underset{\sim}{b} = \frac{3}{2}(\underset{\sim}{a} - 2\underset{\sim}{b})$$

So, $\overrightarrow{AC} = \frac{3}{2}\overrightarrow{OA}$.

3) Explain why this means OAC is a straight line.

Therefore, $\overrightarrow{AC}$ is a scalar multiple of $\overrightarrow{OA}$, so OAC must be a straight line.

Vector Questions Can Involve Ratios (9)

Ratios are used in vector questions to tell you the lengths of different sections of a straight line. If you know the vector along part of that line, you can use this information to find other vectors along the line.

E.g. X━━━━━Y━━━━━━━Z   XY : YZ = 2 : 3 tells you that $\overrightarrow{XY} = \frac{2}{5}\overrightarrow{XZ}$ and $\overrightarrow{YZ} = \frac{3}{5}\overrightarrow{XZ}$.

EXAMPLE:

ABCD is a parallelogram, with AB parallel to DC and AD parallel to BC.
Point E lies on DC, such that DE : EC = 3 : 1.
$\overrightarrow{BC} = \mathbf{a}$ and $\overrightarrow{BA} = \mathbf{b}$.
Find $\overrightarrow{AE}$ in terms of **a** and **b**.

1) Write $\overrightarrow{AE}$ as a route along the parallelogram.

$$\overrightarrow{AE} = \overrightarrow{AD} + \overrightarrow{DE}$$

2) Use the parallel sides to find $\overrightarrow{AD}$ and $\overrightarrow{DC}$.

$$\overrightarrow{AD} = \overrightarrow{BC} = \underset{\sim}{a}$$
$$\overrightarrow{DC} = \overrightarrow{AB} = -\underset{\sim}{b}$$

3) Use the ratio to find $\overrightarrow{DE}$.

$$\overrightarrow{DE} = \frac{3}{4}\overrightarrow{DC}$$

4) Now use $\overrightarrow{AD}$ and $\overrightarrow{DE}$ to find $\overrightarrow{AE}$.

So $\overrightarrow{AE} = \overrightarrow{AD} + \overrightarrow{DE} = \underset{\sim}{a} - \frac{3}{4}\underset{\sim}{b}$

Go forth and multiply by scalars...

So remember — vectors along a straight line or on parallel lines are just scalar multiples of each other.

Q1 ABCD is a quadrilateral. $\overrightarrow{AX} = \mathbf{a}$ and $\overrightarrow{BX} = \mathbf{b}$.
AXC and BXD are straight lines, with AX : XC = BX : XD = 2 : 3.
Find $\overrightarrow{AB}$ and $\overrightarrow{DC}$ in terms of **a** and **b**.
$\overrightarrow{AD}$ and $\overrightarrow{BC}$ are not parallel. What sort of quadrilateral is ABCD? (9) [6 marks]

Revision Questions for Section Five

There are a good few facts and formulas in this section, so use this page to check you've got them all sorted.

* Try these questions and <u>tick off each one</u> when you <u>get it right</u>.
* When you've done <u>all the questions</u> for a topic and are <u>completely happy</u> with it, tick off the topic.

Pythagoras' Theorem (p106) ☑

1) What is the formula for Pythagoras' theorem? What do you use it for?
2) A museum has a flight of stairs up to its front door (see diagram). A ramp is to be put over the top of the steps for wheelchair users. Calculate the length that the ramp would need to be to 3 s.f.
3) Point P has coordinates (–3, –2) and point Q has coordinates (2, 4). Calculate the length of the line PQ to 1 d.p.

Trigonometry — Sin, Cos, Tan (p107-108) ☑

4) Write down the three trigonometry formula triangles.
5) Find the size of angle x in triangle ABC to 1 d.p.
6) Find the length of side XZ of triangle XYZ to 3 s.f.

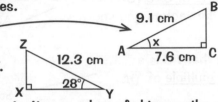

7) A seagull is sitting on top of a 2.8 m high lamp-post. It sees a bag of chips on the ground, 7.1 m away from the base of the lamp-post. Calculate the angle of depression of the chips from the top of the lamp-post, correct to 1 d.p.

The Sine and Cosine Rules (p109-110) ☑

8) Write down the sine and cosine rules and the formula (involving sin) for the area of any triangle.
9) List the 4 different types of sine/cosine rule questions and which rule you need for each.
10) In triangle FGH side FH = 8 cm, side GH = 9 cm and angle FHG = 47°. Find the length of side FG.
11) Triangle PQR has side PQ = 12 cm, side QR = 9 cm and angle PQR = 63°. Find its area.

3D Pythagoras and Trigonometry (p111-112) ☑

12) What is the formula for finding the length of the longest diagonal in a cuboid?
13) Find the length of the longest diagonal in the cuboid measuring 5 m × 6 m × 9 m.
14) Find the angle between the line BH and the plane ABCD in this cuboid.
15) Find the size of angle WPU in the cuboid shown, to the nearest degree.

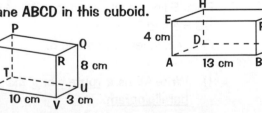

Sin, Cos and Tan for Larger Angles (p113) ☑

16) Triangle JKL has side JK = 6 cm, side JL = 11 cm and angle JLK = 28°. Find the size of the obtuse angle JKL.

Vectors (p114-115) ☑

17) What is the effect of multiplying a vector by a scalar?
18) What is the magnitude of $\binom{5}{-2}$?
19) ABCD is a quadrilateral.
   AXC is a straight line with AX : XC = 1 : 3.
   a) Find $\overrightarrow{AX}$.
   b) Find $\overrightarrow{DX}$ and $\overrightarrow{XB}$.
   c) Is DXB a straight line? Explain your answer.

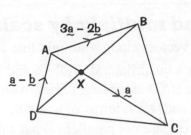

Mean, Median, Mode and Range

Mean, median, mode and range pop up all the time in statistics questions — make sure you know what they are.

The Four Definitions (3)

MODE = MOST common

MEDIAN = MIDDLE value (when values are in order of size)

MEAN = TOTAL of items ÷ NUMBER of items

RANGE = Difference between highest and lowest

> **REMEMBER:**
> Mode = most (emphasise the 'mo' in each when you say them)
> Median = mid (emphasise the m*d in each when you say them)
> Mean is just the average, but it's mean 'cos you have to work it out.

The Golden Rule

There's one vital step for finding the median that lots of people forget:

Always REARRANGE the data in ASCENDING ORDER   (and check you have the same number of entries!)

You absolutely must do this when finding the median, but it's also really useful for working out the mode too.

EXAMPLE: Find the median, mode, mean, and range of these numbers:

2, 5, 3, 2, 6, -4, 0, 9, -3, 1, 6, 3, -2, 3

> Check that you still have the same number of entries after you've rearranged them.

The **MEDIAN** is the middle value (when they're arranged in order of size) — so first, rearrange the numbers.

When there are two middle numbers, the median is halfway between the two.

-4, -3, -2, 0, 1, 2, (2, 3) 3, 3, 5, 6, 6, 9
← seven numbers this side   seven numbers this side →

Median = 2.5

> An even number of values means there will be two middle numbers.

MODE (or modal value) is the most common value. ⟶ Mode = 3

> Data sets can have more than one mode.

$$\text{MEAN} = \frac{\text{total of items}}{\text{number of items}} \longrightarrow \frac{-4-3-2+0+1+2+2+3+3+3+5+6+6+9}{14}$$

$$= 31 \div 14 = 2.214... = 2.21 \text{ (3 s.f.)}$$

RANGE = distance from lowest to highest value, i.e. from -4 up to 9. ⟶ 9 - (-4) = 13

Choose the Best Average (3)

The mean, median and mode all have their advantages and disadvantages — LEARN THEM:

	Advantages	Disadvantages
Mean	Uses all the data. Usually most representative.	Isn't always a data value. May be distorted by extreme data values.
Median	Easy to find in ordered data. Not distorted by extreme data values.	Isn't always a data value. Not always a good representation of the data.
Mode	Easy to find in tallied data. Always a data value.	Sometimes there's more than one. Not always a good representation of the data.

Strike a pose, there's nothing to it — mode...

Learn the four definitions and the extra step you have to do to find the median, then give this a go...

Q1   Find the mean, median, mode and range for the set of data below:
     1, 3, 14, -5, 6, -12, 18, 7, 23, 10, -5, -14, 0, 25, 8.   [4 marks] (3)

Quartiles and Comparing Distributions

Measures of <u>spread</u> tell you <u>how spread out</u> data is. The <u>range</u> (see the previous page) is a measure of spread over all the data values. The <u>interquartile range</u> tells you the <u>spread</u> of the <u>middle 50%</u> of values.

Quartiles Divide the Data into Four Equal Groups (6)

1) The quartiles are the <u>lower quartile Q_1</u>, the <u>median Q_2</u> and the <u>upper quartile Q_3</u>.

2) If you put the data in <u>ascending order</u>, the quartiles are <u>25%</u> (¼), <u>50%</u> (½) and <u>75%</u> (¾) of the way through the list. So if a data set has n values, you work out the <u>positions</u> of the quartiles using these <u>formulas</u>:

$$Q_1 \text{ position number} = (n + 1)/4$$
$$Q_2 \text{ position number} = 2(n + 1)/4$$
$$Q_3 \text{ position number} = 3(n + 1)/4$$

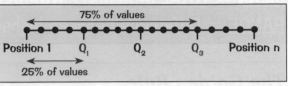

3) The <u>INTERQUARTILE RANGE</u> (IQR) is the <u>difference</u> between the <u>upper quartile</u> and the <u>lower quartile</u> and contains the <u>middle 50%</u> of values.

EXAMPLE:
a) Here are the ages, in months, of a number of fine cheeses: 7, 12, 5, 4, 3, 9, 5, 11, 7, 5, 7
Find the median and interquartile range of the ages.

1. Put the data in <u>order of size</u>. → 3, 4, 5, 5, 5, 7, 7, 7, 9, 11, 12 ← Check you've got the <u>right number</u> of values — 11 ✓

2. Find the median Q_2 — n = 11, so Q_2 is in position 2(11 + 1)/4 = 6 — i.e. Q_2 = 7 months.

3. Find Q_1 — And since n = 11, Q_1 is in position (11 + 1)/4 = 3. So Q_1 = <u>5</u>.

4. Find Q_3 — Q_3 is in position 3(11 + 1)/4 = 9. So Q_3 = <u>9</u>.

5. <u>Subtract</u> Q_1 from Q_3 — IQR = $Q_3 - Q_1$ = 9 − 5 = 4 months

Careful — the formulas tell you the <u>position</u> of the quartile, not its value.

Compare Data Using Averages and Spread (6)

To <u>compare</u> two sets of data, you should look at:

You could also compare other key values like <u>quartiles</u> or <u>min/max</u> values.

1 AVERAGES — <u>MEAN</u>, <u>MEDIAN</u> or <u>MODE</u>

Say which data set has the <u>higher/lower</u> value and <u>what that means</u> in the context of the data.

2 SPREAD — <u>RANGE</u> or <u>INTERQUARTILE RANGE</u>

Say which data set has the <u>larger/smaller</u> value. A <u>larger spread</u> means the values are <u>less consistent</u> or there is <u>more variation</u> in the data.

If the data contains <u>extreme</u> values, it's better to use the <u>IQR</u> than the range.

EXAMPLE:
b) A dealer sells fine cheeses whose median age is 9 months and whose interquartile range of ages is 2 months. Compare the ages of the cheeses sold by this dealer with the ones in part a) above.

1. You need to compare an <u>average</u> for the two distributions. → The cheeses sold by this dealer have a greater median age, so they are generally older than the cheeses in part a).

2. You need to compare a measure of <u>spread</u> for the two distributions. → The cheeses sold by this dealer have a smaller interquartile range, so there appears to be less variation in the ages of these cheeses.

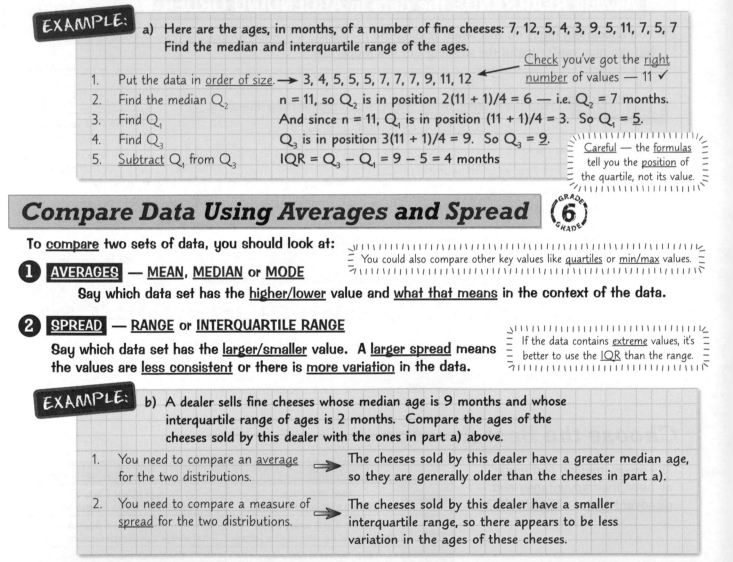

Chocolate-peanut-banana butter — not your average spread...

Learn how to find quartiles and to compare distributions. Then do this Exam Practice Question:

Q1 a) A sample of grubs has the following lengths (in cm): 3.0, 1.6, 1.4, 2.2, 0.7, 1.1, 2.6 (6)
Find the median length and the interquartile range.   [3 marks]

b) A different sample of grubs has a median length of 1.8 cm and an interquartile range of 1.9 cm. Compare the lengths of the two samples of grubs. [2 marks]

Frequency Tables — Finding Averages

The word **FREQUENCY** means **HOW MANY**, so a frequency table is just a **'How many in each category' table**.
You saw how to find <u>averages and range</u> on p.117 — it's the same ideas here, but with the data in a table.

Find Averages from Frequency Tables

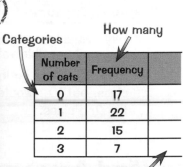

1) The <u>MODE</u> is just the <u>CATEGORY</u> with the <u>MOST ENTRIES</u>.

2) The <u>RANGE</u> is found from the <u>extremes of the first column</u>.

3) The <u>MEDIAN</u> is the <u>CATEGORY</u> of the <u>middle value in the second column</u>.

4) To find the <u>MEAN</u>, you have to <u>WORK OUT A THIRD COLUMN yourself</u>.

The <u>MEAN</u> is then: | 3rd Column Total ÷ 2nd Column Total |

Categories   How many

Number of cats	Frequency	
0	17	
1	22	
2	15	
3	7	

Mysterious 3rd column...

EXAMPLE:

Some people were asked how many sisters they have.
The table opposite shows the results.

Find the <u>mode</u>, the <u>range</u>, the <u>mean</u> and the <u>median</u> of the data.

Number of sisters	Frequency
0	7
1	15
2	12
3	8
4	4
5	0

1 The <u>MODE</u> is the <u>category</u> with the <u>most entries</u> — i.e. the one with the <u>highest frequency</u>:

The highest frequency is 15 for '1 sister', so <u>MODE</u> = 1

2 The <u>RANGE</u> is the <u>difference</u> between the highest and lowest numbers of sisters — that's 4 sisters (no one has 5 sisters) and no sisters, so:

<u>RANGE</u> = 4 − 0 = 4

3 To find the <u>MEAN</u>, <u>add a 3rd column</u> to the table showing 'number of sisters × frequency'. <u>Add up</u> these values to find the <u>total number of sisters</u> of all the people asked.

You can label the first column x and the frequency column f, then the third column is f × x.

Number of sisters (x)	Frequency (f)	No. of sisters × Frequency (f × x)
0	7	0
1	15	15
2	12	24
3	8	24
4	4	16
5	0	0
Total	46	79

$$\underline{MEAN} = \frac{\text{total number of sisters}}{\text{total number of people asked}} = \frac{79}{46} = 1.72 \text{ (3 s.f.)}$$

3rd column total

2nd column total

4 The <u>MEDIAN</u> is the <u>category</u> of the <u>middle</u> value. Work out its <u>position</u>, then <u>count through</u> the 2nd column to find it.

It helps to imagine the data set out in an ordered list:
0000000111111111111111222222222222223333333344444

median

There are 46 values, so the middle value is halfway between the 23rd and 24th values. There are a total of (7 + 15) = 22 values in the first two categories, and another 12 in the third category takes you to 34. So the 23rd and 24th values must both be in the category '2 sisters', which means the <u>MEDIAN</u> is 2.

My table has 5 columns, 6 rows and 4 legs...

Learn the four key points about averages, then try this fella:

Q1   50 people were asked how many times a week they play sport.
The table opposite shows the results.
  a) Find the median.   [2 marks]
  b) Calculate the mean.   [3 marks]

No. of times sport played	Frequency
0	8
1	15
2	17
3	6
4	4
5 or more	0

Grouped Frequency Tables

Grouped frequency tables group together the data into classes.
They look like ordinary frequency tables, but they're a slightly trickier kettle of fish...

NON-OVERLAPPING CLASSES
- Use inequality symbols to cover all possible values.
- Here, 10 would go in the 1st class, but 10.1 would go in the 2nd class.

Height (h millimetres)	Frequency
$5 < h \leq 10$	12
$10 < h \leq 15$	15

To find MID-INTERVAL VALUES:
- Add together the end values of the class and divide by 2.
- E.g. $\dfrac{5 + 10}{2} = 7.5$

Find Averages from Grouped Frequency Tables

Unlike with ordinary frequency tables, you don't know the actual data values, only the classes they're in. So you have to **ESTIMATE THE MEAN**, rather than calculate it exactly. Again, you do this by adding columns:

> 1) Add a **3RD COLUMN** and enter the **MID-INTERVAL VALUE** for each class.
>
> 2) Add a **4TH COLUMN** to show '**FREQUENCY × MID-INTERVAL VALUE**' for each class.

And you'll be asked to find the **MODAL CLASS** and the **CLASS CONTAINING THE MEDIAN**, not exact values.

EXAMPLE:

This table shows information about the weights, in kilograms, of 60 school children.

a) Write down the modal class.
b) Write down the class containing the median.
c) Calculate an estimate for the mean weight.

Weight (w kg)	Frequency
$30 < w \leq 40$	8
$40 < w \leq 50$	16
$50 < w \leq 60$	18
$60 < w \leq 70$	12
$70 < w \leq 80$	6

a) | The modal class is the one with the highest frequency. |

Modal class is $50 < w \leq 60$

b) | Work out the position of the median, then count through the 2nd column. |

There are 60 values, so the median is halfway between the 30th and 31st values.
Both these values are in the third class, so the class containing the median is $50 < w \leq 60$.

c) Add extra columns for 'mid-interval value' and 'frequency × mid-interval value'.
Add up the values in the 4th column to estimate the total weight of the 60 children.

Weight (w kg)	Frequency (f)	Mid-interval value (x)	fx
$30 < w \leq 40$	8	35	280
$40 < w \leq 50$	16	45	720
$50 < w \leq 60$	18	55	990
$60 < w \leq 70$	12	65	780
$70 < w \leq 80$	6	75	450
Total	60	—	3220

$$\text{Mean} \approx \frac{\text{total weight}}{\text{number of children}} \quad \begin{array}{l}\leftarrow \text{4th column total} \\ \leftarrow \text{2nd column total}\end{array}$$

Don't add up the mid-interval values.

$$= \frac{3220}{60}$$

$$= 53.7 \text{ kg (3 s.f.)}$$

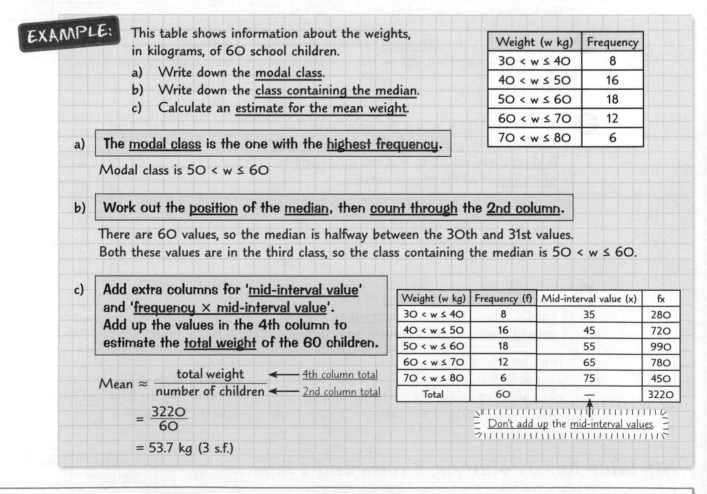

Mid-interval value — cheap ice creams...

Learn all the details on the page, then give this Exam Practice Question a go:

Q1 Estimate the mean of this data. Give your answer to 3 significant figures. **[4 marks]**

Length (l cm)	$15.5 \leq l < 16.5$	$16.5 \leq l < 17.5$	$17.5 \leq l < 18.5$	$18.5 \leq l < 19.5$
Frequency	12	18	23	8

Cumulative Frequency

Cumulative frequency just means <u>adding it up as you go along</u> — i.e. the <u>total frequency so far</u>.
A cumulative frequency <u>graph</u> shows <u>cumulative frequency</u> up the <u>side</u> and the <u>data values</u> along the <u>bottom</u>. You might be asked to draw one in the exam — here's how...

To Draw the Graph...

① <u>Add a 'CUMULATIVE FREQUENCY' COLUMN</u> to the grouped frequency table — and fill it in with the <u>RUNNING TOTAL</u> of the <u>frequency column</u>.

② <u>PLOT</u> points using the <u>HIGHEST VALUE</u> in each class and the <u>CUMULATIVE FREQUENCY</u>.

③ Plot the cumulative frequency as <u>ZERO</u> at the lowest value of the first class.

④ <u>Join</u> the points with a <u>smooth curve</u>.

EXAMPLE: The table below shows information about the heights of a group of people.

a) <u>Draw a cumulative frequency graph</u> for the data.

① Fill in the <u>cumulative frequency column</u>:

For the first class it's the same as the frequency.

For the other classes, <u>add</u> the frequency for that class to the cumulative frequency of the class above.

Height (h cm)	Frequency	Cumulative Frequency
140 < h ≤ 150	4	<u>4</u>
150 < h ≤ 160	9	4 + 9 = <u>13</u>
160 < h ≤ 170	20	13 + 20 = <u>33</u>
170 < h ≤ 180	33	33 + 33 = <u>66</u>
180 < h ≤ 190	36	66 + 36 = <u>102</u>
190 < h ≤ 200	15	102 + 15 = <u>117</u>
200 < h ≤ 210	3	117 + 3 = <u>120</u>

② <u>Plot</u> the points using the <u>highest value</u> in each class, i.e. (150, 4), (160, 13), etc.

③ Plot <u>zero</u> at the lowest value in the first class, i.e. (140, 0).

④ Join up the points with a nice <u>smooth curve</u>.

You might have to use your curve to do some other calculations (see the next page), so make sure you draw it really carefully.

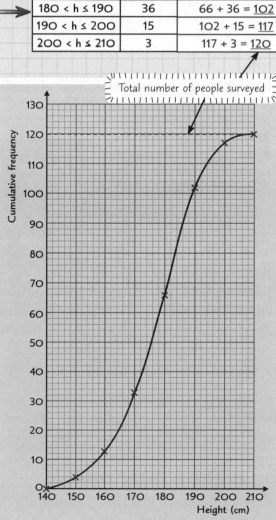

Total number of people surveyed

The fun doesn't stop here — there's so much to fit in that I've had to continue this example on the next page...

Cumulative Frequency

I'm afraid it's not enough just to be able to draw a cumulative frequency graph — you also need to be able to make estimates from them, for things like the median and the interquartile range.

GRADE 6

EXAMPLE: Continued from the previous page.... b) Use the graph drawn in part a) to estimate the median and interquartile range of the heights.

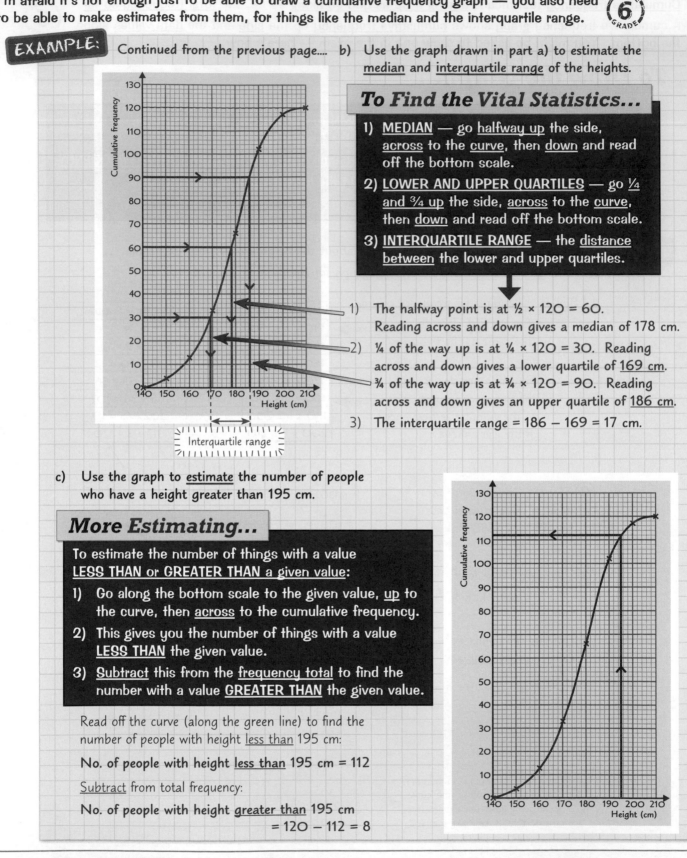

To Find the Vital Statistics...

1) **MEDIAN** — go <u>halfway up</u> the side, <u>across</u> to the <u>curve</u>, then <u>down</u> and read off the bottom scale.

2) **LOWER AND UPPER QUARTILES** — go ¼ and ¾ up the side, <u>across</u> to the <u>curve</u>, then <u>down</u> and read off the bottom scale.

3) **INTERQUARTILE RANGE** — the <u>distance</u> <u>between</u> the lower and upper quartiles.

1) The halfway point is at ½ × 120 = 60. Reading across and down gives a median of 178 cm.

2) ¼ of the way up is at ¼ × 120 = 30. Reading across and down gives a lower quartile of <u>169 cm</u>. ¾ of the way up is at ¾ × 120 = 90. Reading across and down gives an upper quartile of <u>186 cm</u>.

3) The interquartile range = 186 − 169 = 17 cm.

c) Use the graph to <u>estimate</u> the number of people who have a height greater than 195 cm.

More Estimating...

To estimate the number of things with a value **LESS THAN** or **GREATER THAN** a given value:

1) Go along the bottom scale to the given value, <u>up</u> to the curve, then <u>across</u> to the cumulative frequency.

2) This gives you the number of things with a value **LESS THAN** the given value.

3) <u>Subtract</u> this from the <u>frequency total</u> to find the number with a value **GREATER THAN** the given value.

Read off the curve (along the green line) to find the number of people with height <u>less than</u> 195 cm:

No. of people with height <u>less than</u> 195 cm = 112

<u>Subtract</u> from total frequency:

No. of people with height <u>greater than</u> 195 cm
          = 120 − 112 = 8

How do you make a total run...

Time to try another lovely Exam Practice Question.

Q1 a) Draw a cumulative frequency diagram for this data. [3 marks]
    b) Use your diagram to estimate the number of fish with a length of more than 50 mm. [2 marks]

GRADE 6

Length of fish (l mm)	Frequency
$0 < l \le 20$	4
$20 < l \le 40$	11
$40 < l \le 60$	20
$60 < l \le 80$	15
$80 < l \le 100$	6

Section Six — Statistics and Probability

Histograms and Frequency Density

A <u>histogram</u> is just a bar chart where the bars can be of <u>different widths</u>. This changes them from nice, easy-to-understand diagrams into seemingly incomprehensible monsters (and an examiner's favourite).

Histograms Show Frequency Density

1) The <u>vertical</u> axis on a histogram is always called <u>frequency density</u>. You work it out using this formula:

> **Frequency Density = Frequency ÷ Class Width**

Remember... '<u>frequency</u>' is just another way of saying 'how much' or 'how many'.

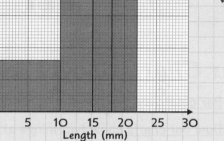

2) You can rearrange it to work out <u>how much</u> a bar represents.

> **Frequency = Frequency Density × Class Width = AREA of bar**

EXAMPLE:

This table and histogram show the lengths of beetles found in a garden.

Length (mm)	Frequency
0 < x ≤ 10	32
10 < x ≤ 15	36
15 < x ≤ 18	
18 < x ≤ 22	28
22 < x ≤ 30	16

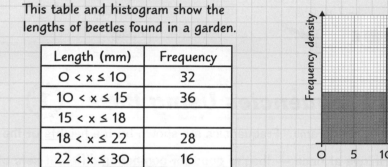

a) Use the histogram to find the missing entry in the table.

1. Add a <u>frequency density</u> column to the table and fill in what you can using the formula.

Frequency density
32 ÷ 10 = 3.2
36 ÷ 5 = 7.2
28 ÷ 4 = 7
16 ÷ 8 = 2

2. Use the frequency densities to <u>label</u> the <u>vertical axis</u> of the graph.

3. Now use the <u>3rd bar</u> to find the frequency for the class "15 < x ≤ 18".
Frequency density = 8 and class width = 3.
So frequency = frequency density × class width = 8 × 3 = 24

b) Use the table to add the bar for the class "22 < x ≤ 30 " to the histogram.

Frequency density = frequency ÷ class width = $\frac{16}{8}$ = 2

c) Estimate the number of beetles between 7.5 mm and 12.5 mm in length.

Use the formula <u>frequency = frequency density × class width</u> — multiply the frequency density of the <u>class</u> by the width of the <u>part of that class</u> you're interested in.

So the estimated number of beetles between 7.5 mm and 12.5 mm is:
3.2 × (10 − 7.5) + 7.2 × (12.5 − 10) = 3.2 × 2.5 + 7.2 × 2.5 = 8 + 18 = 26

Histograms — horrid foul creatures they are...

Although they look very like harmless bar charts, histograms are actually pretty unpleasant. Make sure you get your head around the method above...

Q1 This table shows information about the lengths of slugs in a garden. Draw a histogram to represent the information. **[4 marks]**

Length (mm)	Frequency
0 < x ≤ 40	20
40 < x ≤ 60	45
60 < x ≤ 65	15
65 < x ≤ 100	70

Section Six — Statistics and Probability

Simple Charts

These charts all show <u>frequencies</u>. (Remember... frequency = '<u>how many</u> of something'.)

Pictograms Show Frequencies Using Symbols

(GRADE 1)

Every pictogram has a <u>key</u> telling you what one symbol represents.

With pictograms, you MUST use the KEY.

EXAMPLE: This pictogram shows how many peaches were sold in a shop on different days.

a) How many peaches were sold on Tuesday?
Each circle represents <u>4 peaches</u>. There are <u>2 circles</u> for Tuesday.
$4 \times 2 = 8$ peaches

b) 10 peaches were sold on Friday.
Use this information to complete the diagram.
You need <u>2 whole circles</u> (= 8 peaches),
<u>plus</u> another <u>half a circle</u> (= 2 peaches).

Friday ● ● ◖

Key:
● represents 4 peaches

Monday	●
Tuesday	● ●
Wednesday	● ● ● ◖
Thursday	● ◖
Friday	

Bar Charts Show Frequencies Using Bars

(GRADE 1)

1) <u>Bar charts</u> are very similar to pictograms. Frequencies are shown by the <u>heights</u> of the different bars.

2) <u>Dual bar charts</u> show two things at once — they're good for <u>comparing</u> different sets of data.

EXAMPLE: This dual bar chart shows the number of men and women visiting a coffee shop on different days.

a) How many men visited the coffee shop altogether?
Men are shown by the <u>purple bars</u>.
Add up the numbers shown by the heights.
$$4 + 3 + 6 + 2 = 15 \text{ men}$$

b) On which day did the most women visit the coffee shop?
Find the <u>tallest</u> yellow bar.   Tuesday

<u>Both</u> axes on a bar chart <u>must</u> be <u>labelled</u>.

Bars representing <u>different</u> <u>categories</u> are separated by gaps.

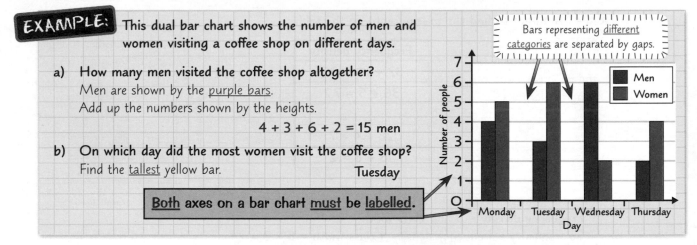

■ Men
■ Women

Two-Way Tables Show How Many in each Category

(GRADE 2)

EXAMPLE: This two-way table shows the number of cakes and loaves of bread a bakery sells on Friday and Saturday one week.

a) How many loaves of bread were sold on Saturday?
Read across to '<u>Loaves of bread</u>'
and down to '<u>Saturday</u>'.   14 loaves of bread

b) How many items were sold in total on Friday?
<u>Add</u> the number of <u>cakes</u> for <u>Friday</u>
to the number of <u>loaves of bread</u>.   12 + 10 = 22

	Cakes	Loaves of bread	Total
Friday	12	10	
Saturday	4	14	18
Total	16	24	40

	Cakes	Loaves of bread	Total
Friday	12	10	
Saturday	4	14	18
Total	16	24	40

Or you could <u>subtract</u> the <u>total</u> for Saturday from the overall total: <u>40 − 18 = 22</u>.

Pie Charts

Just like you can make the correct combination of meat and pastry into a delicious pie, examiners can make <u>pie charts</u> into tricky exam questions. Just remember the <u>Golden Pie Chart Rule</u>...

The TOTAL of Everything = 360°

1) Fraction of the Total = Angle ÷ 360° (2)

EXAMPLE:

This pie chart shows the colour of all the cars sold by a dealer.
What fraction of the cars were red?

Just remember that 'everything = 360°'.

$$\text{Fraction of red cars} = \frac{\text{angle of red cars}}{\text{angle of everything}} = \frac{72°}{360°} = \frac{1}{5}$$

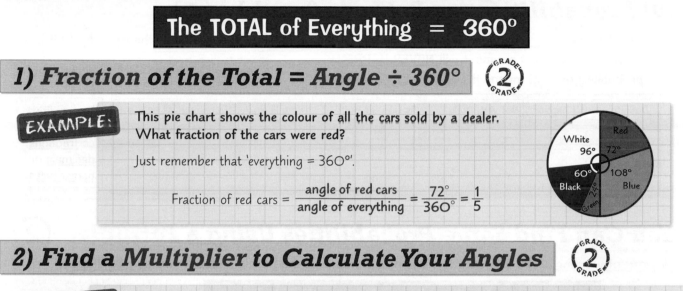

2) Find a Multiplier to Calculate Your Angles (2)

EXAMPLE:

Draw a pie chart to show this information about the types of animal in a petting zoo.

Animal	Geese	Hamsters	Guinea pigs	Rabbits	Ducks
Number	12	20	17	15	26

1. Find the <u>total</u> by <u>adding</u>.   12 + 20 + 17 + 15 + 26 = 90

2. 'Everything = 360°' — so find the <u>multiplier</u> (or <u>divider</u>) that turns your total into 360°.   Multiplier = 360 ÷ 90 = 4

3. Now <u>multiply every number</u> by 4 to get the <u>angle</u> for each sector.

Angle	12 × 4 = 48°	20 × 4 = 80°	17 × 4 = 68°	15 × 4 = 60°	26 × 4 = 104°	Total = 360°

4. Draw your pie chart accurately using a <u>protractor</u>.

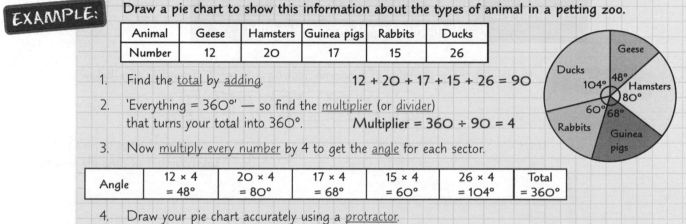

3) Find How Many by Using the Angle for 1 Thing (3)

EXAMPLE:

The pie chart on the right shows information about the types of animals liked most by different students. There were 9 students altogether.

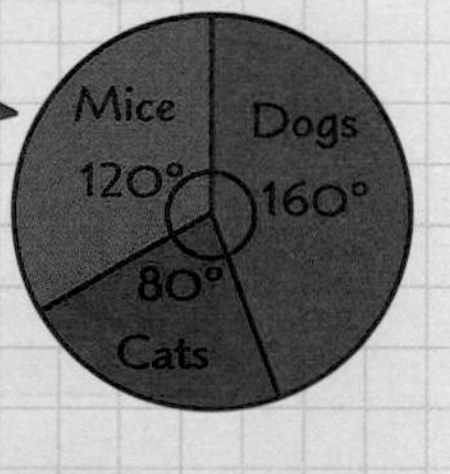

a) Work out the number of students who liked dogs most.

1. 'Everything = 360°', so...   ⟹   9 students = 360°
2. <u>Divide by 9</u> to find...   ⟹   1 student = 40°
3. The <u>angle</u> for dogs is 160°, and <u>160° ÷ 40° = 4</u>:   ⟹   4 students = 160° — 4 students liked dogs most

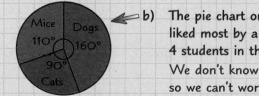

b) The pie chart on the left shows information about the types of animals liked most by a different group of students. Dave says, "This means that 4 students in this group like dogs most." Explain why Dave is not correct.
We don't know how many students in total the pie chart represents, so we can't work out how many students liked dogs most.

I like my pie charts with gravy and mushy peas...

Pie chart questions need a lot of practice. Make a start with this...

Q1   Draw an accurate pie chart to show the information about Rahul's DVD collection in this table.   [3 marks]   (2)

Type of DVD	Number
Rom Com	23
Western	25
Action	12

Section Six — Statistics and Probability

Probability Basics

A lot of people reckon <u>probability</u> is pretty tough. But learn the <u>basics</u> well, and it'll all make sense.

All Probabilities are Between 0 and 1 (1)

Probabilities are <u>always</u> between 0 and 1. The <u>higher</u> the probability of something, the <u>more likely</u> it is.
- A probability of <u>ZERO</u> means it will <u>NEVER HAPPEN</u>.
- A probability of <u>ONE</u> means it <u>DEFINITELY WILL</u>. ← You <u>can't</u> have a probability <u>bigger than 1</u>.

Definitely won't happen	Not very likely	As likely as not	Very likely	Definitely will happen
0	¼	½	¾	1
0	0.25	0.5	0.75	1
0%	25%	50%	75%	100%

Probabilities can be given as <u>fractions</u>, <u>decimals</u> or <u>percentages</u>.

You Can Find Some Probabilities Using a Formula (2)

A <u>word of warning</u>... the following formula only works if <u>all</u> the possible results are <u>equally likely</u>.

$$\text{Probability} = \frac{\text{Number of ways for something to happen}}{\text{Total number of possible results}}$$

Words like '<u>fair</u>' and '<u>at random</u>' show possible results are all equally likely. '<u>Biased</u>' and '<u>unfair</u>' mean the opposite.

EXAMPLE: Work out the probability of randomly picking a letter 'P' from the tiles below.

A P P L E   P I E

1. There are <u>3 P's</u> — so there are <u>3 different ways</u> to 'pick a letter P'.
2. And there are <u>8 tiles</u> altogether — each of these is a <u>possible result</u>.

$$\text{Probability} = \frac{\text{number of ways to pick a P}}{\text{total number of possible results}}$$

$$= \frac{3}{8} \text{ (or 0.375)}$$

Probabilities Add Up to 1 (3)

1) If <u>only one</u> possible result can happen at a time, then the probabilities of <u>all</u> the results <u>add up to 1</u>.

Probabilities always ADD UP to 1.

2) So since something must either <u>happen</u> or <u>not happen</u> (i.e. <u>only one</u> of these can happen at a time):

P(event happens) + P(event doesn't happen) = 1

So the probability of an event <u>not happening</u> equals <u>1 minus</u> the probability of it happening.

EXAMPLE: A spinner has different numbers of red, blue, yellow and green sections. What is the probability of spinning green?

Colour	red	blue	yellow	green
Probability	0.1	0.4	0.3	

<u>Only one</u> of the results can happen at a time, so all the probabilities must <u>add up to 1</u>.

P(green) = 1 − (0.1 + 0.4 + 0.3) = 0.2

The probability of this getting you marks in the exam = 1...

You need to know the facts in the boxes above. You also need to know how to <u>use</u> them.

Q1 Calculate the probability of the fair spinner on the right landing on 4. [2 marks] (2)

Q2 If the probability of spinning red on a spinner is 0.8, find the probability of spinning any colour <u>except</u> red. [1 mark] (3)

Listing Outcomes and Expected Frequency

With a lot of probability questions, a good place to start is with a list of all the <u>things that could happen</u> (also known as <u>outcomes</u>). Once you've got a list of outcomes, the rest of the question is easy.

Listing All Outcomes: Two Coins, Dice, Spinners

A <u>sample space diagram</u> is a good way to show all the possible outcomes if there are <u>two activities</u> going on (e.g. two coins being tossed, or a dice being thrown and a spinner being spun, etc.).

EXAMPLE: The spinners on the right are spun, and the scores added together.

a) Make a sample space diagram showing all the possible outcomes.

1. All the scores from one spinner go <u>along the top</u>. All the scores from the other spinner go <u>down the side</u>.

+	3	4	5
1	4	5	6
2	5	6	7
3	6	7	8

There are <u>9 outcomes</u> — even though some of the totals are repeated.

2. <u>Add</u> the two scores together to get the different possible totals (the <u>outcomes</u>).

b) Find the probability of spinning a total of 6.

There are <u>9 possible outcomes</u> altogether, and <u>3 ways</u> to score 6.

$$P(total = 6) = \frac{\text{ways to score 6}}{\text{total number of possible outcomes}}$$

$$= \frac{3}{9} = \frac{1}{3}$$

Use Probability to Find an "Expected Frequency"

You can <u>estimate</u> how often you'd <u>expect</u> something to happen if you carry out an experiment <u>n times</u>.

Expected times outcome will happen = probability × number of trials

EXAMPLE: A game involves throwing a fair six-sided dice. The player wins if they score either a 5 or a 6. If one person plays the game 180 times, estimate the number of times they will win.

1. First calculate the probability that they win <u>each game</u>.

$$\text{Probability of winning} = \frac{\text{number of ways to win}}{\text{total number of possible results}}$$

$$= \frac{2}{6} = \frac{1}{3}$$

2. Then <u>estimate</u> the number of times they'll win in <u>180</u> separate attempts.

$$\text{Expected number of wins} = \text{probability of winning} \times \text{number of trials}$$

$$= \frac{1}{3} \times 180$$

$$= 60$$

When in doubt, make a list...

Don't be fooled by complicated statistics terms — for example, a 'sample space diagram' is basically just a list. Right then... if you're ready to put your skills to the test, try this...

Q1 Two fair 6-sided dice are thrown, and their scores added together.
a) Find the probability of throwing a total of 7. [2 marks]
b) If the pair of dice are thrown 300 times, how many times would you expect a total of 7? [1 mark]

The AND / OR Rules

This page is also about when you have <u>more than one</u> thing happening at a time.

Combined Probability — Two or More Events

> 1) Always break down a complicated-looking probability question into <u>A SEQUENCE</u> of <u>SEPARATE SINGLE EVENTS</u>.
> 2) Find the probability of <u>EACH</u> of these <u>SEPARATE SINGLE EVENTS</u>.
> 3) Apply the <u>AND/OR</u> rule.

And now for the rules. Say you have <u>two events</u> — call them A and B...

The AND Rule Gives P(Both Events Happen) (6 GRADE)

$$P(A \text{ and } B) = P(A) \times P(B)$$

This only works when the two events are <u>independent</u>, i.e. the result of one event <u>does not affect</u> the other event.

This says: The probability of <u>Event A AND Event B BOTH</u> happening is equal to the two separate probabilities <u>MULTIPLIED</u> together.

EXAMPLE: Dave picks one ball at random from each of bags X and Y.
Find the probability that he picks a yellow ball from both bags.

1. Write down the <u>probabilities</u> of the different events.

   P(Dave picks a yellow ball from bag X) = $\frac{4}{10}$ = 0.4.

   P(Dave picks a yellow ball from bag Y) = $\frac{2}{8}$ = 0.25.

2. Use the <u>formula</u>. So P(Dave picks a yellow ball from both bags) = 0.4 × 0.25 = 0.1

The OR Rule Gives P(At Least One Event Happens) (5 GRADE)

$$P(A \text{ or } B) = P(A) + P(B)$$

This only works when the two events are <u>mutually exclusive</u> — in other words, when they <u>can't both happen</u> at the same time.

This says: The probability of <u>EITHER Event A OR Event B</u> happening is equal to the two separate probabilities <u>ADDED</u> together.

EXAMPLE: A spinner with red, blue, yellow and green sections was spun — the probability of it landing on each colour is shown in the table. Find the probability of spinning either red or green.

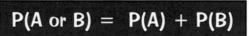

Colour	red	blue	yellow	green
Probability	0.25	0.3	0.35	0.1

1. Write down the <u>probabilities</u> of the different events. P(lands on red) = 0.25 and P(lands on green) = 0.1.
2. Use the <u>formula</u>. So P(Lands on either red or green) = 0.25 + 0.1 = 0.35

Learn AND remember this — OR you're in trouble...

The way to remember this is that it's the wrong way round — you'd want AND to go with '+' but it doesn't.
It's 'AND with ×' and 'OR with +'. Once you've got your head round that, try this Exam Practice Question:

Q1 Two fair six-sided dice are thrown.
   a) Find the probability that the first dice lands on either 3 or an even number. [2 marks] (6 GRADE)
   b) Find the probability that both dice land on 6. [2 marks]

Tree Diagrams

Learn these basic details (which apply to **ALL** tree diagrams). Then you'll be ready for the one in the exam.

Remember These Four Key Tree Diagram Facts (7)

1) On any set of branches which meet at a point, the probabilities must <u>add up to 1</u>.

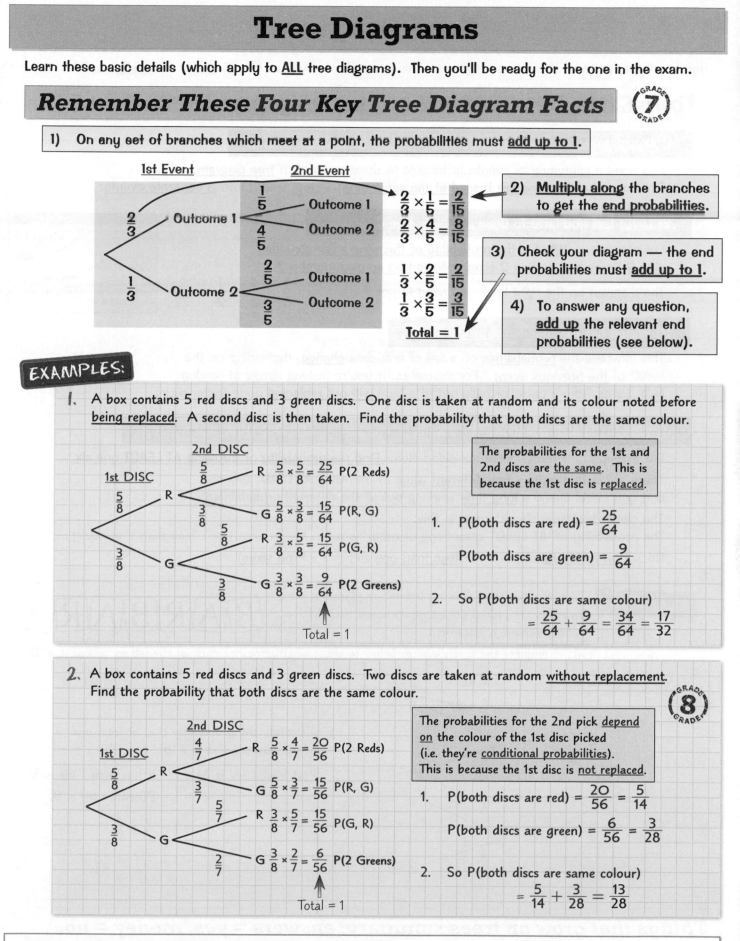

2) <u>Multiply along</u> the branches to get the <u>end probabilities</u>.

3) Check your diagram — the end probabilities must <u>add up to 1</u>.

4) To answer any question, <u>add up</u> the relevant end probabilities (see below).

EXAMPLES:

1. A box contains 5 red discs and 3 green discs. One disc is taken at random and its colour noted before <u>being replaced</u>. A second disc is then taken. Find the probability that both discs are the same colour.

The probabilities for the 1st and 2nd discs are <u>the same</u>. This is because the 1st disc is <u>replaced</u>.

1. $P(\text{both discs are red}) = \dfrac{25}{64}$

$P(\text{both discs are green}) = \dfrac{9}{64}$

2. So $P(\text{both discs are same colour})$
$= \dfrac{25}{64} + \dfrac{9}{64} = \dfrac{34}{64} = \dfrac{17}{32}$

2. A box contains 5 red discs and 3 green discs. Two discs are taken at random <u>without replacement</u>. Find the probability that both discs are the same colour. (8)

The probabilities for the 2nd pick <u>depend on</u> the colour of the 1st disc picked (i.e. they're <u>conditional probabilities</u>). This is because the 1st disc is <u>not replaced</u>.

1. $P(\text{both discs are red}) = \dfrac{20}{56} = \dfrac{5}{14}$

$P(\text{both discs are green}) = \dfrac{6}{56} = \dfrac{3}{28}$

2. So $P(\text{both discs are same colour})$
$= \dfrac{5}{14} + \dfrac{3}{28} = \dfrac{13}{28}$

Please don't make a bad tree-based joke. Oak-ay, just this once...

How convenient — answers growing on trees. Learn the routine, and then have a go at this...

Q1 A bag contains 6 red balls and 4 black ones. If two girls each pluck out a ball at random (without replacement), find the probability that they get different coloured ones. [3 marks] (8)

Tree Diagrams

Here's another page all about tree diagrams. This is excellent news, as tree diagrams are <u>really</u> useful.

Four Extra Details for the Tree Diagram Method: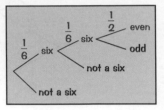

1) Always break up the question into a sequence of separate events.

You need a <u>sequence</u> of events to be able to draw any sort of <u>tree diagram</u>.
For example... '<u>3 coins are tossed at the same time</u>' — just split it into <u>3 separate events</u>.

2) Don't feel you have to draw complete tree diagrams.

For example... '<u>What is the probability of throwing a fair six-sided dice 3 times and getting 2 sixes followed by an even number?</u>'

The diagram on the right is all you need to get the answer: $\frac{1}{6} \times \frac{1}{6} \times \frac{1}{2} = \frac{1}{72}$

[Tree diagram: $\frac{1}{6}$ six, $\frac{1}{6}$ six, $\frac{1}{2}$ even, odd, not a six, not a six]

3) Watch out for conditional probabilities.

This is where the <u>probabilities</u> on a set of branches <u>change</u>, depending on the result of <u>the previous event</u>. For example... if you're picking things at random (e.g. cards from a pack, or balls out of a bag) <u>without replacing</u> your earlier picks.

> See the last example on p.129.

4) With 'AT LEAST' questions, it's always (1 – probability of 'LESS THAN that many'):

For example... '<u>I throw 3 fair six-sided dice. **Find the probability of throwing AT LEAST one six.**</u>'

There are in fact <u>quite a few different ways</u> of 'throwing AT LEAST one six', and you could spend a <u>long time</u> working out all the different probabilities.

The clever trick you should know is this:
The probability of '<u>AT LEAST</u> something or other' is just: 1 – probability of '<u>less than</u> that many'.
So... P(<u>at least one</u> six) = 1 – P(<u>less than one</u> six) = 1 – P(<u>no sixes</u>).

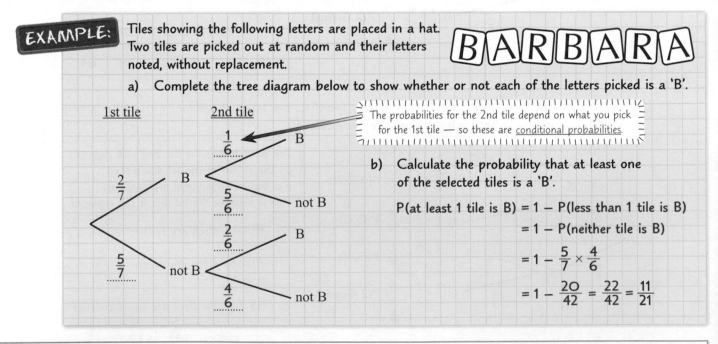

EXAMPLE: Tiles showing the following letters are placed in a hat. Two tiles are picked out at random and their letters noted, without replacement.

BARBARA

a) Complete the tree diagram below to show whether or not each of the letters picked is a 'B'.

1st tile   2nd tile

> The probabilities for the 2nd tile depend on what you pick for the 1st tile — so these are <u>conditional probabilities</u>.

[Tree diagram: $\frac{2}{7}$ B; from B: $\frac{1}{6}$ B, $\frac{5}{6}$ not B; $\frac{5}{7}$ not B; from not B: $\frac{2}{6}$ B, $\frac{4}{6}$ not B]

b) Calculate the probability that at least one of the selected tiles is a 'B'.

P(at least 1 tile is B) = 1 – P(less than 1 tile is B)

= 1 – P(neither tile is B)

= $1 - \frac{5}{7} \times \frac{4}{6}$

= $1 - \frac{20}{42} = \frac{22}{42} = \frac{11}{21}$

Things that grow on trees summary: answers = yes, money = no...

With probability questions that seem quite hard, drawing a tree diagram is usually a good place to start. Try it with the (quite hard) Exam Practice Question below...

Q1   The fair spinner on the right is spun twice. Use a tree diagram to find the probability that the score on the second spin is greater than the score on the first spin.   [3 marks]

[Spinner showing numbers 1, 2, 3, 4]

Probability from Venn Diagrams

Remember <u>Venn diagrams</u>? If you don't, head back to pages 28-29 for a crash course in all things <u>circular</u> and <u>intersecting</u>... Once you've done that, <u>read on</u> and find out how to use them to <u>calculate probabilities</u>...

Finding Probabilities from Venn Diagrams

<u>Venn diagrams</u> can be used to show the number of things in <u>different groups</u>, or with certain characteristics. You can easily work out probabilities by <u>counting up</u> the things you're interested in.

EXAMPLE: In a class of 30 pupils, 8 of them like mustard, 24 of them like ketchup and 5 of them like both mustard and ketchup.

a) Complete the Venn diagram below showing this information.

Start by filling in the <u>overlap</u>.

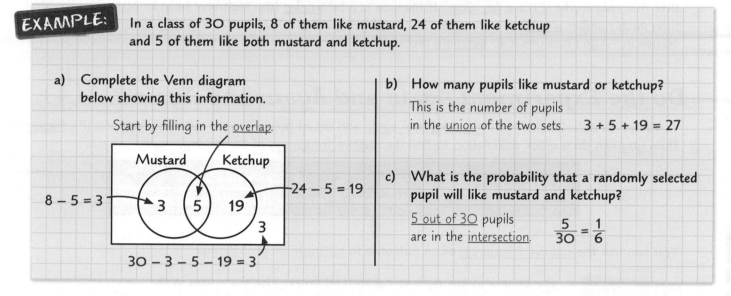

Mustard   Ketchup

8 − 5 = 3 ——→ 3   5   19 ←—— 24 − 5 = 19

3

30 − 3 − 5 − 19 = 3

b) How many pupils like mustard or ketchup?

This is the number of pupils in the <u>union</u> of the two sets.   3 + 5 + 19 = 27

c) What is the probability that a randomly selected pupil will like mustard and ketchup?

<u>5 out of 30</u> pupils are in the <u>intersection</u>. $\frac{5}{30} = \frac{1}{6}$

You could get a question in your exam about finding probabilities from a Venn diagram with <u>three</u> intersecting circles. Don't panic — it works <u>the same</u> as one with two circles, but the calculations are a bit <u>trickier</u>.

EXAMPLE: The Venn diagram below shows the number of children competing in the egg and spoon race (E), sack race (S) and crocodile wrestling (C) at a school sports day.

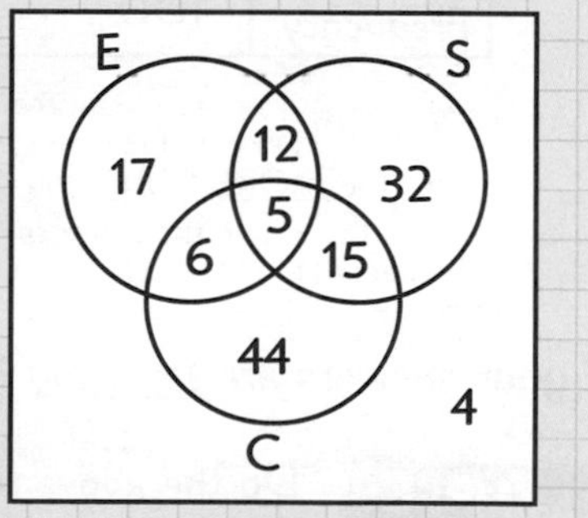

a) Find the probability that a randomly selected child is not competing in the crocodile wrestling.

n(children) = 4 + 44 + 15 + 5 + 6 + 17 + 12 + 32 = 135

n(not competing in crocodile wrestling) = 17 + 12 + 32 + 4 = 65

P(not competing in crocodile wrestling) = $\frac{65}{135} = \frac{13}{27}$

E   S
17   12   32
    5
   6   15
    44
    C   4

b) Given that a randomly selected child is competing in the egg and spoon race, find the probability that they are also competing in both the sack race and the crocodile wrestling.

n(competing in egg and spoon race) = 17 + 12 + 5 + 6 = 40

n(competing in all three events) = 5

Remember, the number in the middle is how many are in all three categories.

P(competing in all three events given they're competing in egg and spoon race) = $\frac{5}{40} = \frac{1}{8}$ = 0.125

Venn I go and spoil it all, by sayin' somethin' stupid like 'I love ∪'...

Check you can find probabilities from Venn diagrams with this Exam Practice Question...

Q1   Out of 80 customers at an ice cream van, 48 had syrup, 28 had sprinkles and 16 had both toppings on their ice cream. Use a Venn diagram to find the probability that a randomly selected customer doesn't have either topping given that they don't have sprinkles. [3 marks]

Relative Frequency

This isn't how often your granny visits. It's a way of working out <u>probabilities</u>. Since you asked, my granny visits twice a year. She'd like to visit more, but sleeping on the blow-up bed plays <u>havoc</u> with her back.

Fair or Biased?

The probability of rolling a three on a normal dice is $\frac{1}{6}$ — you know that each of the 6 numbers on the dice is <u>equally likely</u> to be rolled, and there's <u>only 1 three</u>.

BUT this only works if it's a <u>fair dice</u>. If the dice is a bit <u>wonky</u> (the technical term is '<u>biased</u>') then each number <u>won't</u> have an equal chance of being rolled. This is where <u>relative frequency</u> comes in — you can use it to <u>estimate</u> probabilities when things might be wonky.

Do the Experiment Again and Again and Again...

You need to do an experiment <u>over and over again</u> and count how often an outcome happens (its <u>frequency</u>). Then you can do a quick calculation to find the <u>relative frequency</u> of something.

$$\text{Relative frequency} = \frac{\text{Frequency}}{\text{Number of times you tried the experiment}}$$

An experiment could just mean rolling a dice.

You can use the <u>relative frequency</u> of an outcome to <u>estimate</u> its <u>probability</u>.

EXAMPLE: The spinner on the right was spun 100 times. Use the results in the table below to estimate the probability of getting each of the scores.

Score	1	2	3	4	5	6
Frequency	10	14	36	20	11	9

<u>Divide</u> each of the frequencies by 100 to find the <u>relative frequencies</u>.

Score	1	2	3	4	5	6
Relative Frequency	$\frac{10}{100} = 0.1$	$\frac{14}{100} = 0.14$	$\frac{36}{100} = 0.36$	$\frac{20}{100} = 0.2$	$\frac{11}{100} = 0.11$	$\frac{9}{100} = 0.09$

The <u>MORE TIMES</u> you do the experiment, the <u>MORE ACCURATE</u> your estimate of the probability is likely to be. If you spun the above spinner <u>1000 times</u>, chances are you'd get a <u>better</u> estimate of the probability of each score.

If your answers are <u>far away</u> from what you'd expect, then you can say that the dice/spinner/etc. is <u>biased</u>.

EXAMPLE: Do the above results suggest that the spinner is biased?

Yes, because the relative frequency of 3 is much higher than you'd expect, while the relative frequencies of 1, 5 and 6 are much lower.

For a <u>fair</u> 6-sided spinner, you'd expect all the relative frequencies to be about $1 \div 6 = 0.17$(ish).

This is a tough topic — make sure you revise it relatively frequently...

If a coin/dice/spinner is <u>fair</u>, then you can tell the probability of each result basically 'just by looking at it'. But if it's biased, then you have no option but to use relative frequencies to estimate probabilities.

Q1 Sandro threw a dice 1000 times and got the results shown in the table below.

Score	1	2	3	4	5	6
Frequency	140	137	138	259	161	165

a) Find the relative frequencies for each of the scores 1-6. [2 marks]

b) Do these results suggest that the dice is biased? Give a reason for your answer. [1 mark]

Revision Questions for Section Six

Here's the inevitable list of straight-down-the-middle questions to test how much you know.

- Have a go at each question... but <u>only tick it off</u> when you can get it right <u>without</u> cheating.
- And when you think you could handle pretty much <u>any</u> statistics question, tick off the whole topic.

Averages and Spread (p117-118) ☑

1) Write down the definitions for the mode, median, mean and range. ☑

2) a) Find the mode, median, mean and range of this data: 2, 8, 11, 15, 22, 24, 27, 30, 31, 31, 41
   b) For the above data, find the lower and upper quartiles and the interquartile range. ☑

3) Name two things you should look at when you compare two data sets. ☑

Frequency Tables and Cumulative Frequency (p119-122) ☑

4) For this grouped frequency table showing the lengths of some pet alligators:
   a) find the modal class,
   b) find the class containing the median,
   c) estimate the mean. ☑

Length (y, in m)	Frequency
$1.4 \le y < 1.5$	4
$1.5 \le y < 1.6$	8
$1.6 \le y < 1.7$	5
$1.7 \le y < 1.8$	2

5) Draw a cumulative frequency graph for the data in the above grouped frequency table. ☑

More Graphs and Charts (p123-125) ☑

6) How do you work out what frequency a bar on a histogram represents? ☑

7) As well as counting the number of symbols on a pictogram, you need to check one other thing before you can find a frequency. What's the other thing? ☑

8) The numbers of students in different years at a village school are shown in this table. Draw a bar chart to show this data. ☑

School Year	7	8	9	10	11
Number of students	40	30	40	45	25

9) Draw a pie chart to represent the data in question 8. ☑

Easy Probability (p126-127) ☑

10) What does a probability of 0 mean? What about a probability of ½? ☑

11) I pick a random number between 1 and 50. Find the probability that my number is a multiple of 6. ☑

12) What do the probabilities of all possible outcomes of an experiment add up to (if none of them can happen together)? ☑

13) I flip a fair coin twice.
   a) Complete this sample space diagram showing all the possible results.

   > HT means Heads on the first flip and Tails on the second.

	Second flip	
First flip	Heads	Tails
Heads		HT
Tails		

   b) Use your diagram to find the probability of getting 2 Heads. ☑

14) Write down the formula for estimating how many times you'd expect something to happen in n trials. ☑

Harder Probability (p128-132) ☑

15) I throw a fair six-sided dice twice. Find P(I throw a 6 and then an even number). ☑

16) I throw a fair six-sided dice. Find P(I throw either a 5 or a multiple of 3). ☑

17) I pick a card at random from a normal pack of cards. I make a note of it, but don't replace it before I then pick a second card. Use a tree diagram to find the probability of me getting two kings. ☑

18) 100 people were asked whether they like tea or coffee. Half the people said they like coffee, 34 people said they like tea, 20 people said they like both.
   a) Show this information on a Venn diagram.
   b) If one of the 100 people is randomly chosen, find the probability of them liking tea or coffee. ☑

19) When might you need to use relative frequency to find a probability? ☑

Section Six — Statistics and Probability

Answers

Section One

Page 2 — Order of Operations

Q1 a) 11   **b)** 37   **c)** 3

Q2   −4

Page 3 — Calculator Buttons

Q1   0.02530405844

(The answer will vary, depending on the number of figures displayed by the calculator.)

Page 5 — Square Roots and Cube Roots

Q1 a) 14   **b)** 8   **c)** 7.5

Q2 a) 5   **b)** 10   **c)** 21

Page 6 — Prime Numbers

Q1   61, 53, 47

Page 7 — Multiples, Factors and Prime Factors

Q1 $990 = 2 \times 3^2 \times 5 \times 11$

Q2 $160 = 2^5 \times 5$

Page 8 — LCM and HCF

Q1   84

Q2 a) 12   **b)** 30

Page 10 — Fractions

Q1 a) $\frac{17}{32}$ **b)** $\frac{2}{3}$

     c) $\frac{167}{27} = 6\frac{5}{27}$ **d)** $-\frac{43}{12} = -3\frac{7}{12}$

Q2   180

Page 11 — Fractions, Decimals and Percentages

Q1 a) $\frac{4}{10} = \frac{2}{5}$ **b)** $\frac{2}{100} = \frac{1}{50}$

     c) $\frac{77}{100}$ **d)** $\frac{555}{1000} = \frac{111}{200}$

     e) $\frac{56}{10} = \frac{28}{5}$

Q2 a) 57%   **b)** $\frac{6}{25}$ **c)** 90%

Page 13 — Fractions and Recurring Decimals

Q1 $\frac{14}{111}$

Q2   Let $r = 0.\dot{0}\dot{7}$.

Then $100r - r = 7.\dot{0}\dot{7} - 0.\dot{0}\dot{7}$

$\Rightarrow 99r = 7 \Rightarrow r = \frac{7}{99}$

Q3 $\frac{5}{111} = \frac{45}{999} = 0.\dot{0}4\dot{5}$

Page 15 — Percentages

Q1   549 ml   **Q2**   27%

Q3   £20 500   **Q4**   £209

Page 16 — Compound Interest and Depreciation

Q1   £486.20   **Q2**   £99 396.26

Page 18 — Ratios

Q1 a) 5:7   **b)** 2:3   **c)** 3:10

Q2   21 bowls of porridge

Q3   35 years old

Page 19 — Proportion

Q1   56p

Q2 a) 900 g   **b)** 180 g

Page 20 — Rounding Numbers

Q1 a) 3.57   **b)** 0.05

     c) 12.910   **d)** 3546.1

Page 21 — Rounding Numbers

Q1 a) 568   **b)** 23400

     c) 0.0456   **d)** 0.909

Q2   Answer should be either 5 (if rounded to 1 s.f.) or 6 (if rounded to nearest integer).

Page 22 — Bounds

Q1 a) x — l.b. = 2.315 m, u.b. = 2.325 m

     y — l.b. = 0.445 m, u.b. = 0.455 m

     z — l.b. = 1.145 m, u.b. = 1.155 m

     b) max = 0.92 (to 2 s.f.).

Page 24 — Standard Form

Q1 8.54×10^5; 1.8×10^{-4}

Q2   0.00456; 270 000

Q3 a) 2×10^{11} **b)** 6.47×10^{11}

Page 25 — Sets

Q1   Peter does not play badminton.

Q2   3, 5, 7 and 9

Page 26 — Sets

Q1 a) $A \cup B = \{2, 3, 4, 5, 6\}$

     b) 5

Q2   Trees that are taller than 3 m.

Page 27 — Sets

Q1 $\{1, 2, 3, 4, 6\}$

Q2 $(X' \cap Y) \subset Z$ is true.

Page 29 — Venn Diagrams

Q1 a) 22   **b)** 23

Q2

Revision Questions — Section One

Q1 a) Whole numbers — either positive or negative, or zero

     b) Numbers that can be written as fractions

     c) Numbers which will only divide by themselves or 1

Q2 a) 169   **b)** 7   **c)** 3   **d)** 125

Q3 a) $1050 = 2 \times 3 \times 5^2 \times 7$

     b) $360 = 2^3 \times 3^2 \times 5$

Q4 a) $320 = 2 \times 2 \times 2 \times 2 \times 2 \times 2 \times 5$

           $= 2^6 \times 5$

        $880 = 2 \times 2 \times 2 \times 2 \times 5 \times 11$

            $= 2^4 \times 5 \times 11$

     b) LCM $= 2^6 \times 5 \times 11 = 3520$

        HCF $= 2^4 \times 5 = 80$

Q5 a) $8\frac{2}{9}$ **b)** $\frac{33}{7}$

Q6   Multiplying: Multiply top and bottom numbers separately.

Dividing: Turn the second fraction upside down, then multiply.

Adding/subtracting: Put fractions over a common denominator, then add/subtract the numerators.

Q7 a) $\frac{14}{99}$ **b)** $\frac{22}{7} = 3\frac{1}{7}$

     c) $\frac{11}{24}$ **d)** $\frac{151}{20} = 7\frac{11}{20}$

Q8 a) Divide the top by the bottom.

     b) Put the digits after the decimal point on the top, and a power of 10 with the same number of zeros as there were decimal places on the bottom.

Q9 a) (i) $\frac{4}{100} = \frac{1}{25}$ (ii) 4%

     b) (i) $\frac{65}{100} = \frac{13}{20}$ (ii) 0.65

Q10   Let $r = 0.\dot{5}\dot{1}$.

Then $100r - r = 51.\dot{5}\dot{1} - 0.\dot{5}\dot{1}$

$\Rightarrow 99r = 51 \Rightarrow r = \frac{51}{99} = \frac{17}{33}$

Q11   To find x as a percentage of y, make sure both amounts are in the same units, then divide x by y and multiply by 100.

Q12   17.6 m

Q13   6% simple interest pays £59.62 more (to the nearest penny)

Q14   240

Answers

Q15 1. Add up the parts
2. Divide to find one part
3. Multiply to find the amounts

Q16 600, 960, 1440

Q17 £1.41

Q18 a) 427.96 **b)** 428.0
c) 430 **d)** 428.0

Q19 Estimates should be in the range 20-24

Q20 132.2425 m²

Q21 1. The front number must always be between 1 and 10.
2. The power of 10, n, is how far the decimal point moves.
3. n is positive for big numbers, and negative for small numbers.

Q22 a) 9.7×10^5 **b)** 3.56×10^9
c) 2.75×10^{-6}

Q23 a) 1.5875×10^3 **b)** 2.739×10^{12}

Q24 a) 5 and 10
b)

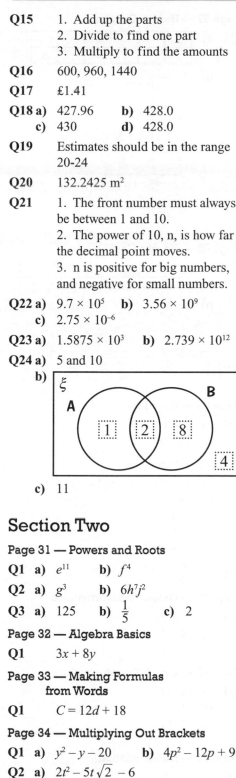

c) 11

Section Two

Page 31 — Powers and Roots

Q1 a) e^{11} **b)** f^4

Q2 a) g^3 **b)** $6h^7j^2$

Q3 a) 125 **b)** $\frac{1}{5}$ **c)** 2

Page 32 — Algebra Basics

Q1 $3x + 8y$

Page 33 — Making Formulas from Words

Q1 $C = 12d + 18$

Page 34 — Multiplying Out Brackets

Q1 a) $y^2 - y - 20$ **b)** $4p^2 - 12p + 9$

Q2 a) $2t^2 - 5t\sqrt{2} - 6$
b) $x^3 - 6x^2 + 12x - 8$

Page 35 — Factorising

Q1 $7(x - 2)$

Q2 $3y(2x + 5y)$

Q3 $2(2x + y)(2x - y)$

Q4 $\frac{6}{x + 7}$

Page 36 — Manipulating Surds

Q1 a) $2 + 3\sqrt{2}$ **b)** $9 - 4\sqrt{5}$

Q2 $4 - 2\sqrt{3}$

Page 37 — Solving Equations

Q1 $x = 2$

Q2 $y = 4$

Q3 $x = 6$

Page 38 — Solving Equations

Q1 $x = \pm 6$

Q2 $x = 8$

Page 39 — Rearranging Formulas

Q1 $q = 7(p - 2r)$ or $q = 7p - 14r$

Q2 $z = \frac{3x - y}{2}$

Page 40 — Rearranging Formulas

Q1 a) $y = \pm 2\sqrt{x}$ **b)** $y = \frac{xz}{x - 1}$

Page 41 — Factorising Quadratics

Q1 $(x + 5)(x - 3)$

Q2 $x = 4$ or $x = 5$

Page 42 — Factorising Quadratics

Q1 $(2x + 3)(x - 4)$

Q2 $x = \frac{2}{3}$ or $x = -4$

Q3 $(3x + 2)(x + 10)$

Q4 $x = -\frac{2}{5}$ or $x = 3$

Page 43 — The Quadratic Formula

Q1 $x = 0.39$ or $x = -10.39$

Q2 $x = 1.46$ or $x = -0.46$

Page 44 — Completing the Square

Q1 $(x - 6)^2 - 13$

Q2 $(x + 5)^2 - 18 = 0$, so $x = -5 \pm 3\sqrt{2}$

Page 45 — Completing the Square

Q1 a) $2(x + \frac{3}{4})^2 - \frac{49}{8}$
b) $x = 1, x = -\frac{5}{2}$
c) Minimum point $= (-\frac{3}{4}, -\frac{49}{8})$

Page 46 — Quadratic Equations — Tricky Ones

Q1 $x = \frac{1 \pm \sqrt{3}}{2}$

Page 47 — Algebraic Fractions

Q1 $\frac{3b^2}{a}$

Q2 $\frac{x(x + 3)}{4}$

Q3 $\frac{x - 11}{(x + 4)(x - 1)}$

Page 48 — Inequalities

Q1 a) $x < 4$ **b)** $x \geq 3$

Q2 $-2 \leq x \leq 4$

Page 49 — Inequalities

Q1 a) $-7 < p < 7$
b) $p \leq -8$ or $p \geq 8$

Q2 $x = 0, 1, 2, 3, 4$

Page 50 — Graphical Inequalities

Q1

Page 51 — Simultaneous Equations and Graphs

Q1 $x = 2, y = 4$

Q2 $y = 3$

Page 52 — Simultaneous Equations

Q1 $x = 5, y = 3$

Q2 $x = 3, y = -1$

Page 53 — Simultaneous Equations

Q1 $x = 0, y = 4$ and $x = 6, y = 40$

Q2 $x = 1, y = -1$ and $x = -4, y = 14$

Page 54 — Number Patterns and Sequences

Q1 Next term = 7. The rule is subtract 5 from the previous term.

Page 55 — Number Patterns and Sequences

Q1 a) $7n - 5$
b) 51
c) No, as the solution to $7n - 5 = 63$ does not give an integer value of n.

Page 56 — Number Patterns and Sequences

Q1 $S_{20} = 1110$

Page 57 — Proof

Q1 Take two consecutive even numbers, $2n$ and $2n + 2$, where n is an integer. Then $2n + (2n + 2) = 4n + 2 = 2(2n + 1)$, which is even, as $(2n + 1)$ is an integer.

Q2 $4x + 2 = 3(3a + x)$, so $x = 9a - 2$. If a is odd, then $9a$ is also odd (as odd × odd = odd). $9a - 2$ is always odd (as odd – even = odd), so x cannot be a multiple of 8 as all multiples of 8 are even.

Page 58 — Direct and Inverse Proportion

Q1 $s = 4$

Revision Questions — Section Two

Q1 a) x^9 **b)** y^2 **c)** z^{12}

Q2 $5x - 4y - 5$

Answers

Q3 $P = 7d + 5c$

Q4 **a)** $6x + 3$
 b) $x^2 - x - 6$
 c) $x^3 + 7x^2 + 7x - 15$

Q5 **a)** $7x(xy + 3z^2)$
 b) $(7 + 9pq)(7 - 9pq)$
 c) $12(x + 2y)(x - 2y)$

Q6 **a)** $3\sqrt{3}$ **b)** 5

Q7 **a)** $x = 2$ **b)** $x = \pm 3$

Q8 **a)** $p = \dfrac{qr}{q + r}$ **b)** $p = -\dfrac{4y}{3}$

Q9 **a)** $x = -3$ or $x = -6$
 b) $x = 4$ or $x = -\dfrac{3}{5}$

Q10 **a)** $x = 1.56$ or $x = -2.56$
 b) $x = 0.27$ or $x = -1.47$
 c) $x = 0.44$ or $x = -3.44$

Q11 **a)** $x = -6 \pm \sqrt{21}$
 b) $x = 3$ or $x = -\dfrac{1}{2}$

Q12 $\dfrac{3x + 1}{(x + 3)(x - 1)}$

Q13 **a)** $x \geq -2$
 b) $-1 < x \leq 6$

Q14 $x < -5$ or $x > 5$

Q15

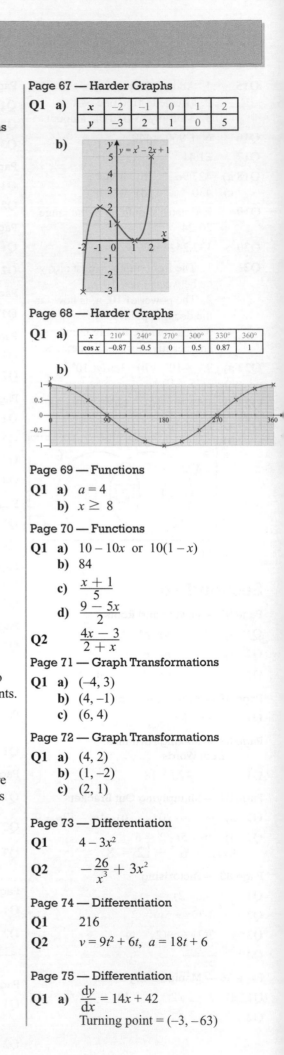

Q16 $x = 2, y = 3$

Q17 $x = -2, y = -2$ or $x = -4, y = -8$

Q18 **a)** 31, rule is add 7
 b) 256, rule is multiply by 4
 c) 19, rule is add two previous terms.

Q19 **a)** $4n + 1$
 b) $-3n + 14$

Q20 **a)** 1080
 b) 5145

Q21 Take an even number, $2p$, and an odd number, $2q + 1$.
 Their product is $2p \times (2q + 1)$
 $= 4pq + 2p = 2(2pq + p)$, which is even as $(2pq + p)$ is an integer.

Q22 $y = kx^2$

Q23 $p = 72$

Section Three

Page 60 — Coordinates

Q1 $(0.5, -1)$

Q2 $(3, 5)$

Page 61 — Straight-Line Graphs

Q1 $y = -2$

Page 62 — Plotting Straight-Line Graphs

Q1

Q2

Page 63 — Finding the Gradient

Q1 gradient $= -5$

Q2 18 (allow answers between 15 and 21)

Page 64 — "y = mx + c"

Q1

Q2 $y = \dfrac{1}{2}x + 5$

Page 65 — Parallel and Perpendicular Lines

Q1 $y = -x + 5$

Q2 Rearrange given equations into $y = mx + c$ form to find gradients.
 Gradient of line 1 $= -5$
 Gradient of line 2 $= \dfrac{1}{5}$
 $-5 \times \dfrac{1}{5} = -1$
 So $y + 5x = 2$ and $5y = x + 3$ are perpendicular as their gradients multiply together to give -1.

Page 66 — Quadratic Graphs

Q1 **a)**

 b) $x = -1.2$ (accept -1.4 to -1), $x = 5.2$ (accept 5 to 5.4).

Page 67 — Harder Graphs

Q1 **a)**

x	-2	-1	0	1	2
y	-3	2	1	0	5

 b)

Page 68 — Harder Graphs

Q1 **a)**

x	210°	240°	270°	300°	330°	360°
$\cos x$	-0.87	-0.5	0	0.5	0.87	1

 b)

Page 69 — Functions

Q1 **a)** $a = 4$
 b) $x \geq 8$

Page 70 — Functions

Q1 **a)** $10 - 10x$ or $10(1 - x)$
 b) 84
 c) $\dfrac{x + 1}{5}$
 d) $\dfrac{9 - 5x}{2}$

Q2 $\dfrac{4x - 3}{2 + x}$

Page 71 — Graph Transformations

Q1 **a)** $(-4, 3)$
 b) $(4, -1)$
 c) $(6, 4)$

Page 72 — Graph Transformations

Q1 **a)** $(4, 2)$
 b) $(1, -2)$
 c) $(2, 1)$

Page 73 — Differentiation

Q1 $4 - 3x^2$

Q2 $-\dfrac{26}{x^3} + 3x^2$

Page 74 — Differentiation

Q1 216

Q2 $v = 9t^2 + 6t$, $a = 18t + 6$

Page 75 — Differentiation

Q1 **a)** $\dfrac{dy}{dx} = 14x + 42$
 Turning point $= (-3, -63)$

b) A minimum. It is a quadratic graph with a positive coefficient of x^2, so it's a U-shaped graph.

Revision Questions — Section Three

Q1 A(5, –3), B(4, 0), C(0, 3), D(–4, 5), E(–2, –3)

Q2 (2, 1.5)

Q3 (6, 9)

Q4
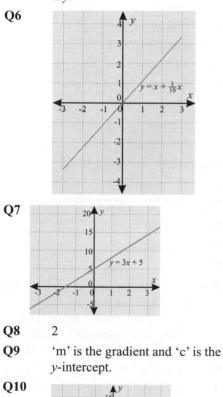

Q5 Straight-line equations just contain something x, something y and a number. They don't contain any powers of x or y, xy, $1/x$ or $1/y$.

Q6

Q7

Q8 2

Q9 'm' is the gradient and 'c' is the y-intercept.

Q10
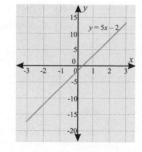

Q11 $y = 2x + 10$

Q12 The gradient of line B is 5, and the gradient of line C is $-\frac{1}{5}$.

Q13 They are both symmetrical "bucket shaped" graphs. $y = x^2 + 2x - 8$ is like a "u" whereas $y = -x^2 + 2x - 8$ is like an "n" (or an upturned bucket).

Q14
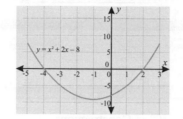

a) $x = -3.6$ (allow –3.8 to –3.5) or $x = 1.6$ (allow 1.5 to 1.8)

b) 4 (allow gradients between 3 and 5)

Q15 a) A graph with a "wiggle" in the middle. E.g.
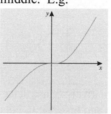

b) A graph made up of two curves in diagonally opposite quadrants. The graph is symmetrical about the lines $y = x$ and $y = -x$. E.g.
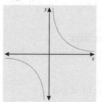

c) A graph made up of two curves in adjacent quadrants, either both above or both below the x-axis. The graph is symmetrical about the y-axis. E.g.
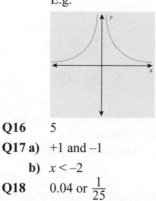

Q16 5

Q17 a) +1 and –1

b) $x < -2$

Q18 0.04 or $\frac{1}{25}$

Q19 Write out the equation $x = f(y)$, then rearrange the equation to make y the subject.

Q20 a) $y = (-x)^3 + 1$ is the original graph reflected in y-axis.

b) $y = (x + 2)^3 + 1$ is the original graph translated by 2 units in the negative x-direction.

c) $y = (3x)^2 + 1$ is the original graph stretched in the x direction by a scale factor of $\frac{1}{3}$.

d) $y = x^3 - 1$ is the original graph translated downwards by 2 units.

Q21 $15x^4 + 2$. Gradient = 1217

Q22 $v = 6$ ms^{-1}, $a = 2$ ms^{-2}

Q23 a) (1, –1) minimum

b) (–1, 1) maximum

Section Four

Page 77 — Maps and Scale Drawings
Q1 40 cm   **Q2** 4.5 cm

Page 78 — Geometry
Q1 $x = 108°$

Page 79 — Parallel Lines
Q1 $x = 116°$

Page 80 — Geometry Problems
Q1 $x = 123°$

Page 81 — Polygons
Q1 144°

Page 82 — Symmetry
Q1 a) 3 lines of symmetry, rotational symmetry order 3

b) no lines of symmetry, rotational symmetry order 2

c) 8 lines of symmetry, rotational symmetry order 8

Page 85 — Circle Geometry
Q1 angle ABD = 63° angle ACD = 63°

Q2 7.5 cm

Page 86 — The Four Transformations
Q1

Answers

Page 87 — The Four Transformations

Q1

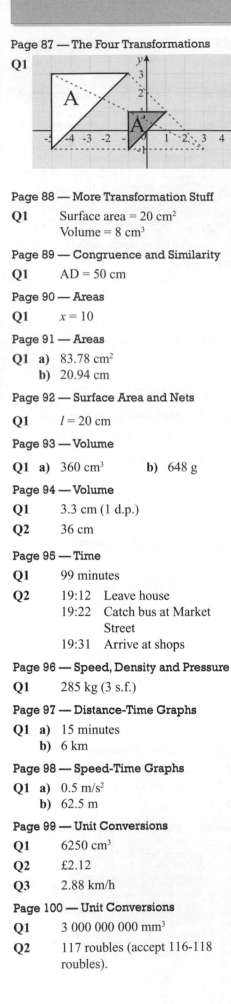

Page 88 — More Transformation Stuff

Q1 Surface area = 20 cm²
Volume = 8 cm³

Page 89 — Congruence and Similarity

Q1 AD = 50 cm

Page 90 — Areas

Q1 $x = 10$

Page 91 — Areas

Q1 a) 83.78 cm²
b) 20.94 cm

Page 92 — Surface Area and Nets

Q1 $l = 20$ cm

Page 93 — Volume

Q1 a) 360 cm³ **b)** 648 g

Page 94 — Volume

Q1 3.3 cm (1 d.p.)

Q2 36 cm

Page 95 — Time

Q1 99 minutes

Q2 19:12 Leave house
19:22 Catch bus at Market Street
19:31 Arrive at shops

Page 96 — Speed, Density and Pressure

Q1 285 kg (3 s.f.)

Page 97 — Distance-Time Graphs

Q1 a) 15 minutes
b) 6 km

Page 98 — Speed-Time Graphs

Q1 a) 0.5 m/s²
b) 62.5 m

Page 99 — Unit Conversions

Q1 6250 cm³

Q2 £2.12

Q3 2.88 km/h

Page 100 — Unit Conversions

Q1 3 000 000 000 mm³

Q2 117 roubles (accept 116-118 roubles).

Page 101 — Triangle Construction

Q1

Q2

Page 102 — Constructions

Q1 Construct a 90° angle, put your compass point on the right angle and mark a point on each line equidistant from the right angle, then join these points.

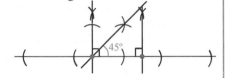

Alternatively construct a 90° angle and bisect it to get a 45° angle. Then construct a second 90° angle.

Page 103 — Bearings

Q1 297° (allow between 296° and 298°)

Q2 29.2 km (1 d.p.)

Revision Questions — Section Four

Q1 Multiply by the map scale to go from map distance to real life. Divide by the map scale to go from real life to map distance. The scale needs to be in the form 1 cm = ...

Q2 Plan should be a rectangle that's 20 cm long and 12 cm wide.

Q3 360°

Q4 a) $x = 154°$ **b)** $y = 112°$
c) $z = 58°$

Q5 60°

Q6 lines of symmetry = 3
order of rotational symmetry = 3

Q7 90°

Q8 a) $x = 53°$
b) $y = 69°$
c) $z = 33°$

Q9 5 cm

Q10 a) Translation by vector $\begin{pmatrix} -2 \\ -4 \end{pmatrix}$
b) Reflection in the y-axis

Q11

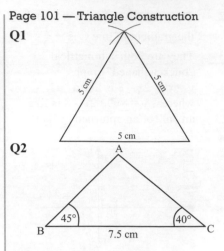

Q12 80 cm²

Q13 Congruent shapes are exactly the same size and same shape. Similar shapes are the same shape but different sizes.

Q14 $x = 2.5$ cm

Q15 $A = \frac{1}{2}(a + b) \times h_V$

Q16 220 cm²

Q17 Circumference = 16π cm, area = 64π cm²

Q18 39.27 cm²

Q19 Surface area = $4\pi r^2$

Q20 75π cm²

Q21 396 cm³

Q22 129.85 cm³

Q23 a) 16:20 **b)** 7.52 am

Q24 151 minutes

Q25 a) 12:18 **b)** 11:58

Q26 42 km/h

Q27 12 500 cm³

Q28 11 m²

Q29 On a distance-time graph it means the object has stopped. On a speed-time graph it means the object is travelling at a steady speed.

Q30 36 km/h

Q31 a) 5600 cm³ **b)** 0.083 kg
c) 10.8 km/h **d)** 5 690 000 cm²

Q32

Q33

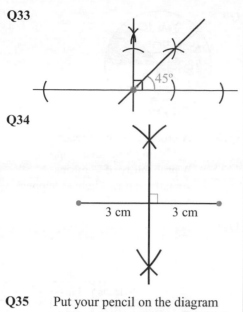

Q34

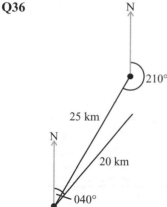

Q35 Put your pencil on the diagram at the point you're going FROM — point A. Draw a northline at this point. Measure the angle to the line AB clockwise from the northline — this is the bearing you want.

Q36

N

210°

25 km

N

20 km

040°

Section Five

Page 106 — Pythagoras' Theorem
Q1   10.3 m
Q2   8 m
Q3   5

Page 108 — Trigonometry — Sin, Cos, Tan
Q1   27.1°
Q2   2.97 m

Page 109 — The Sine and Cosine Rules
Q1   32.5 cm²

Page 110 — The Sine and Cosine Rules
Q1   20.5 cm (3 s.f.)
Q2   59.5° (3 s.f.)

Page 111 — 3D Pythagoras
Q1   14.8 cm

Page 112 — 3D Trigonometry
Q1   17.1° (3 s.f.)

Page 113 — Sin, Cos and Tan for Larger Angles
Q1   129.3° (1 d.p.)

Page 114 — Vectors
Q1 $\overrightarrow{AB} = \mathbf{p} - 2\mathbf{q}$
$\overrightarrow{NA} = \mathbf{q} - \dfrac{1}{2}\mathbf{p}$

Page 115 — Vectors
Q1 $\overrightarrow{AB} = \mathbf{a} - \mathbf{b}$
$\overrightarrow{DC} = \dfrac{3}{2}\mathbf{a} - \dfrac{3}{2}\mathbf{b} = \dfrac{3}{2}(\mathbf{a} - \mathbf{b})$
ABCD is a trapezium.

Revision Questions — Section Five
Q1 $a^2 + b^2 = c^2$
You use Pythagoras' theorem to find the missing side of a right-angled triangle.

Q2   4.72 m

Q3   7.8

Q4
$\boxed{\dfrac{O}{S \times H}}$ $\boxed{\dfrac{A}{C \times H}}$ $\boxed{\dfrac{O}{T \times A}}$

Q5   33.4°

Q6   5.77 cm

Q7   21.5°

Q8   Sine rule:
$$\dfrac{a}{\sin A} = \dfrac{b}{\sin B} = \dfrac{c}{\sin C}$$
Cosine rule:
$a^2 = b^2 + c^2 - 2bc \cos A$
Area $= \dfrac{1}{2}ab \sin C$

Q9   Two angles given plus any side — sine rule.
Two sides given plus an angle not enclosed by them — sine rule.
Two sides given plus the angle enclosed by them — cosine rule.
All three sides given but no angles — cosine rule.

Q10   6.84 cm (3 s.f.)

Q11   48.1 cm² (3 s.f.)

Q12 $a^2 + b^2 + c^2 = d^2$

Q13   11.9 m (3 s.f.)

Q14   15.2° (3 s.f.)

Q15   54°

Q16   120.6° (1 d.p.)

Q17   Multiplying by a scalar changes the size of a vector but not its direction.

Q18   5.4 (1 d.p.)

Q19 a) $\overrightarrow{AX} = \dfrac{1}{3}\mathbf{a}$

b) $\overrightarrow{DX} = \dfrac{4}{3}\mathbf{a} - \mathbf{b}$
$\overrightarrow{XB} = \dfrac{8}{3}\mathbf{a} - 2\mathbf{b}$

c) $\overrightarrow{XB} = 2\overrightarrow{DX}$, so DXB is a straight line.

Section Six

Page 117 — Mean, Median, Mode and Range
Q1   Mean = 5.27 (3 s.f.), Median = 6
Mode = –5, Range = 39

Page 118 — Quartiles and Comparing Distributions
Q1 a)   Median = 1.6 cm
Interquartile range = 1.5 cm
b)   The second set of grubs has a larger median, and so they are generally longer.
The second set of grubs has a larger interquartile range, and so there seems to be more variation in their lengths.

Page 119 — Frequency Tables — Finding Averages
Q1 a)   Median = 2
b)   Mean = 1.66

Page 120 — Grouped Frequency Tables
Q1   17.4 cm

Page 122 — Cumulative Frequency
Q1 a)

b)   Answer in the range 30–34.

Page 123 — Histograms and Frequency Density
Q1

Answers

Page 125 — Pie Charts

Q1

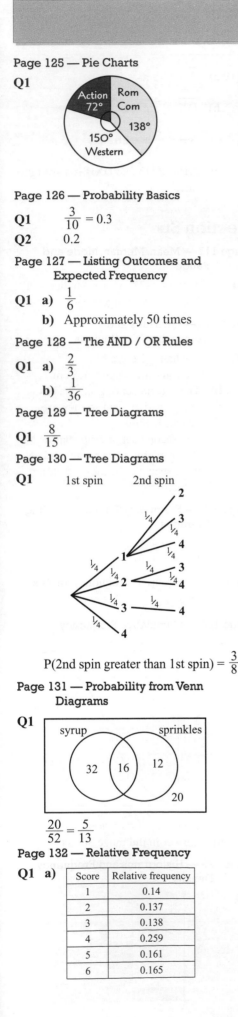

Page 126 — Probability Basics

Q1 $\frac{3}{10} = 0.3$

Q2 0.2

Page 127 — Listing Outcomes and Expected Frequency

Q1 **a)** $\frac{1}{6}$

b) Approximately 50 times

Page 128 — The AND / OR Rules

Q1 **a)** $\frac{2}{3}$

b) $\frac{1}{36}$

Page 129 — Tree Diagrams

Q1 $\frac{8}{15}$

Page 130 — Tree Diagrams

Q1

1st spin   2nd spin

P(2nd spin greater than 1st spin) $= \frac{3}{8}$

Page 131 — Probability from Venn Diagrams

Q1

$\frac{20}{52} = \frac{5}{13}$

Page 132 — Relative Frequency

Q1 **a)**

Score	Relative frequency
1	0.14
2	0.137
3	0.138
4	0.259
5	0.161
6	0.165

b) Yes, because the relative frequency for 4 is much higher than you'd expect from a fair dice (which is $1 \div 6 = 0.166...$).

Revision Questions — Section Six

Q1 The <u>mode</u> is the most common value.
The <u>median</u> is the middle value when the data has been arranged in order of size.
The <u>mean</u> is the total of the data values divided by the number of data values.
The <u>range</u> is the difference between the highest and lowest data values.

Q2 **a)** Mode = 31, Median = 24
Mean = 22, Range = 39

b) Lower quartile = 11
Upper quartile = 31
Interquartile range = 20

Q3 1. Averages (mean, median or mode)
2. Spread (range or interquartile range)

Q4 **a)** Modal class is: $1.5 \le y < 1.6$.
b) Class containing median is: $1.5 \le y < 1.6$
c) Estimated mean = 1.58 m (to 2 d.p.)

Q5

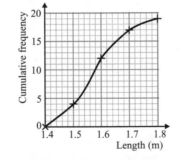

Q6 Calculate the bar's area or use the formula:
frequency = frequency density × class width.

Q7 You need to look at the key to see what each symbol represents.

Q8

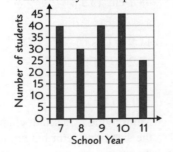

Q9

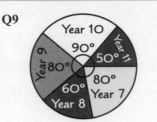

Q10 A probability of 0 means something will never happen.
A probability of ½ means something is as likely to happen as not.

Q11 $\frac{4}{25}$

Q12 1

Q13 a)

		Second flip	
		Heads	Tails
First flip	Heads	HH	HT
	Tails	TH	TT

b) $\frac{1}{4}$

Q14 Expected times outcome will happen = probability × n

Q15 $\frac{1}{12}$

Q16 $\frac{1}{2}$

Q17 $\frac{1}{221}$

Q18 a)

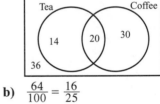

b) $\frac{64}{100} = \frac{16}{25}$

Q19 When you can't tell what the probabilities of different outcomes are 'just by looking' — e.g. when you have a biased dice/spinner etc.

Index

Index